WITHDRAWN

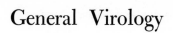

General Virology

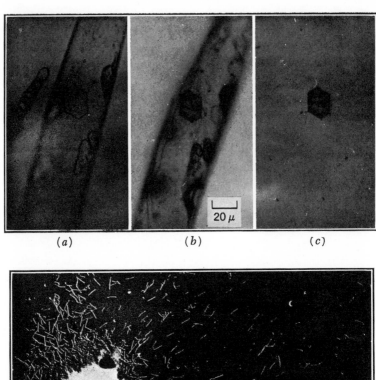

(a)　　　　　　　(b)　　　　　　　(c)

20 μ

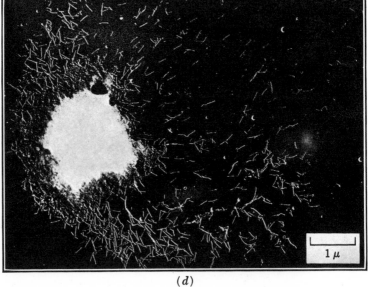

(d)

Frontispiece. A hair cell of tobacco, containing a crystal of tobacco mosaic virus, is photographed (a) before and (b) after freeze-drying. The crystal is extracted by micromanipulation in the frozen-dry state (c). Upon partial dissolution in water such crystals release characteristic virus particles (d). From: Steere and Williams (625a). Courtesy Dr. R. C. Williams, Virus Laboratory, University of California, Berkeley.

General Virology

S. E. LURIA

PROFESSOR OF BACTERIOLOGY
UNIVERSITY OF ILLINOIS
URBANA, ILLINOIS

JOHN WILEY & SONS, INC., NEW YORK

LONDON

Library of Congress Catalog Card Number: 53–11874

PRINTED IN THE UNITED STATES OF AMERICA

To
ZELLA

Preface

This book is the outgrowth of a course on viruses that I have been teaching since 1946, first at Indiana University, more recently at the University of Illinois. The problem that faced me in 1946 was planning a course in virology for graduate and advanced undergraduate students in biology and biochemistry, who had no medical orientation and no background in histopathology, in a university that was justly proud of its reputation as a center of experimental biology. I could teach either a watered-down course in virus diseases or organize a new type of course, in which virology would be presented as a biological science, like botany, zoology, or general bacteriology. My choice of the second alternative was, I think, justified. My classes in virology have been well attended and have attracted excellent students. Similar courses have since been established in other institutions.

Virology is fast becoming an important field of science, in which geneticist, cell physiologist, and biochemist find, in the ground plowed by the pathologist, a fertile soil for new approaches to fundamental problems of cell function and organization. The interest of "outsiders" in viruses has grown continuously since the middle 1930's, stimulated at first by the progress of physicochemical work on virus particles, later and more powerfully by the recognition of viruses as keys to the study of cellular integration. The eagerness with which modern bacteriophage work has been seized upon by biophysicists, geneticists, and biochemists, and the conscious efforts to create a comparative virology (whose heuristic value can be seen by perusing, for example, the proceedings of a symposium on *The Nature of Virus Multiplication* held at Oxford in 1952) are signs of the healthy growth of the new science.

In attempting to teach general virology, I was faced with the problem of the lack of a textbook. In 1946, the best books dealing with viruses were devoted to the description of virus diseases. The main exceptions were Doerr and Hallauer's *Handbuch der Virusforschung*, a bilingual treatise of vast scope, and Bawden's excellent *Plant Viruses and Virus Diseases*. Both were unsuitable as textbooks, although invaluable as reference books. In spite of many important additions to virological literature, no single volume suitable for classroom use has

ix

appeared. This book is an attempt to fulfill the need for a textbook in general virology.

My teaching of virology, and this book as a result of it, have been built around a central concept, that of the dual nature of viruses as inert particles on the one hand, and as operating constituents of functional cells on the other hand. In the light of this concept, I have tried to present the physical and chemical approach to virus particles and the biochemical and cell-physiological approach to virus-infected cells as two separate but integrated aspects of virology. In the limited space of one semester or of a book of· this size, one can hardly hope to make a biochemist or a physicochemist out of a biology student, or a biologist out of a chemist. I have covered such background information as I found useful in teaching, from the logarithms to the embryology of the chick embryo, but I have given no details of actual techniques. Any description of individual virus diseases has deliberately been omitted. The pathogenicity of a virus is, of course, less incidental to virus biology than, say, the pathogenicity of *Streptococcus pyogenes* is to bacteriology, since the virus, an integrated intracellular parasite, "lives" the life of the host as its own only life. Thus, each virus disease is potentially a different form of virus life. Yet, I feel justified, both on didactic and on conceptual grounds, in assuming a priori as much uniformity and community of mechanisms as the known facts do not contradict. This assumption stems, of course, from a belief in the intrinsic simplicity of nature and from a feeling that the ultimate contribution of science resides in the discovery of unifying and simplifying generalizations, rather than in the description of isolated situations—in the visualization of simple, overall patterns, rather than in the analysis of patchworks.

Facts about individual viruses are presented as model systems or as examples, without any attempt at extensive coverage. The choice of examples reflects my limited knowledge of many areas of virology. Being myself a specialist, I shall count on the tolerance of other specialists whose field I may have misinterpreted, and on their willingness to suggest improvements for future editions of this book. The selection of references was dictated not only by the accidents of my limited knowledge but also by an attempt to single out articles with further references, with descriptions of important methods, or with new ideas and timely syntheses.

In a science developing as fast as virology, any book is bound to be somewhat out of date by the time it appears in print. In fact, original work is proceeding at such a pace that interpretations presented in research articles must often be revised in galley proof. Yet, virology has reached the stage where we may be justified in attempting at least a provisional integration. It will be gratifying if this book contributes to such an integration.

Many friends and colleagues encouraged me to write this book; friendly periodic reminders from the publishers over a period of three years helped me fight the frequent temptation to forget about it. Special thanks go to Dr. Zella Luria, who read the whole manuscript and contributed many improvements of language, style, and reasoning, and to Mrs. Mary Delbrück, who in the summer of 1949 typed under dictation the first draft of several chapters. My friends Drs. L. M. Black, E. Caspari, M. Delbrück, G. K. Hirst, K. Maramorosch, S. M. Rose, R. W. Schlesinger, and R. Y. Stanier read some chapters at various stages of writing and made valuable suggestions. The Graduate School of Indiana University provided in 1949 a grant for secretarial help. I wish especially to thank my very good friends the students in the virology courses at Indiana University and at the University of Illinois, who stimulated and shared my enjoyment of virology and submitted themselves sympathetically to my early and recent experiments in developing an approach to this growing science.

S. E. L.

Urbana, Illinois
November, 1953

Contents

1 · Introduction—The Science of Virology 1

2 · Detection and Identification of Viruses 20

3 · Titration of Viruses 39

4 · Size and Morphology of Virus Particles 55

5 · Purification and Chemical Composition of Virus Material 85

6 · Serological Properties of Viruses 116

7 · Environmental Effects on Virus Particles 135

8 · Virus-Host Interaction—The Bacteriophage-Bacterium System 157

9 · The Bacteriophage-Bacterium System (*Continued*) 183

10 · The Interaction of Plant Viruses with Their Host Plants 209

11 · The Interaction of Animal Viruses with Their Hosts—Tissue Cultures—Intracellular Inclusions 220

12 · Growth of Viruses in the Chick Embryo 239

13 · Hemagglutination Phenomena and Virus Growth—Summary on Virus Reproduction 250

14 · Interference Phenomena in Virus Infections 273

15 · Variation in Viruses—Host Variation and Susceptibility to Viruses 290

16 · Transmission, Vectors, and Survival of Viruses 307

17 · Viruses and Tumors 321

18 · Origin and Nature of Viruses 344

19 · Appendix—The Rickettsiae 364

Bibliography-Author Index 375

Index 415

xiii

"For understanding life phenomena it is neither sufficient to know the individual elements and processes nor to interpret their order by means of machine-like structures, even less to invoke an entelechy as the organizing factor. It is not only necessary to carry out analysis in order to know as much as possible about the individual components, but it is equally necessary to know the laws of organization that unite these parts and partial processes and are just the characteristic of vital phenomena. Herein lies the essential and original object of biology."

LUDWIG VON BERTALANFFY
Problems of Life

Introduction
The Science of Virology

VIROLOGY AS A BIOLOGICAL SCIENCE

Virology has become a fundamental biological science in its own right. Just as bacteriology has emerged as a biological science out of the practically important but scientifically constricting borders of its medical applications, so has virology begun to become a body of knowledge and of generalizations, with its own perspectives and its own internal development. Having originated as a branch of pathology—human and animal pathology on the one hand, plant pathology on the other hand—the new science of virology, developed at first in response to practical needs, has reached a point where progress is dictated at least as much by the logic of its internal development as by the demands of applied areas. Analogy with other fields teaches us that the emergence of virology as a fundamental science from an applied one will actually make virology more adequate to handle those practical problems from which it arose, even though it may sometimes appear to lose sight of them. The years between 1945 and 1950 saw an increasing integration of various areas of virology, particularly under the impact of advances in the study of bacterial viruses (*172*). Nevertheless, the attempts to present virology in a coordinated way, or at least in an all-inclusive way, have been few (*187; 610*). Still today, the methodological and semantic barriers between plant, animal, and bacterial virologists are slow in yielding before the recognized need for joint efforts and for cross-fertilization of ideas.

What kind of biological science is virology? We may subdivide somewhat artificially the fundamental biological sciences (as distinct from applied sciences, like medicine, and from ancillary sciences, like biometrics) according to the nature of their subject matter, into *taxonomic, integrative,* and *interpretative* sciences. A taxonomic science

1

(for example, botany, mycology, entomology, ichthyology, mammalogy) is characterized by the fact that its subject matter is a group of organisms with a recognized taxonomic unity, that is, a common ancestry and a historical development unique to that group. Integrative sciences (physiology, ecology, genetics) analyze the common or specialized properties of living organisms in their historical dynamic relations and transformations. Interpretative sciences (biochemistry, biophysics) analyze elementary processes and functions of organisms in terms of the behavior of the pieces (molecules, atoms, electrons) that are the common material basis of all matter, living and nonliving.

A definition of viruses. Does virology fit into any of the above categories? This question has no precise answer. The subject of virology is not one immediately definable by common-sense criteria verified by taxonomic or methodological analysis. Viruses, the subject matter of virology, themselves require a definition. This, like all definitions, should be operational, that is, it should provide factual criteria for inclusion or exclusion of given objects in terms of observable properties and performable tests. Such a definition always has a certain arbitrary quality. Its value will depend on the number and size of the areas of uncertainty it leaves.

We shall adopt for viruses the following definition: *Viruses are submicroscopic entities, capable of being introduced into specific living cells and of reproducing inside such cells only.* This definition provides practical, restrictive criteria, and at the same time emphasizes the fact that virology, although it covers a group of biological entities, is not a taxonomic science in the usual sense. Indeed, there are no grounds for assuming that all objects that fulfill our definition belong to one distinctive branch of the evolutionary tree. There is not even general agreement as to whether any or all viruses can be considered as "organisms." Our definition of viruses stresses the *methodological* rather than *taxonomic* unity of the subject matter of virology. Yet it stresses the fact that viruses, although possibly not constituting a taxonomically valid group, possess the basic properties that can be validly accepted as an operational basis for defining "organisms"—the properties of individuality and of homologous reproduction. Reproduction—together with its inseparable counterpart, heritable variability—makes possible the historical continuity and perfectibility of the pattern of specificity embodied in the individual and gives it potential immortality.

We must point out, however, that the reproduction referred to in our definition is purely descriptive, stating that more virus similar to the original one is produced. No specific mechanism of reproduction is postulated in the definition.

Let us examine our definition more closely. We shall discuss the meaning of its various parts and see how the elimination of any one of them suggests possible natural relationships between viruses and other biological elements.

The requirement for ability to be introduced into host cells emphasizes the external derivation of the virus. This constitutes a requirement for the recognition of a virus as such. A virus does not need to enter every host from outside. It may be transmitted internally from generation to generation of its host, even intracellularly at cell division and in the formation of germ cells. But, to be observed, a virus must be capable at some time of entering some host organism or cell from the outside. Elimination of this requirement would identify viruses with all "self-reproducing" protoplasmic components of cells, such as genes and other units endowed with genetic continuity. As we shall see in chapter 18, the view is rather widely held that some or even most viruses may have originated by the acquisition of infectivity (that is, of external transmissibility) on the part of self-reproducing cell components. At any rate, we may emphasize from the start that, once inside the host cell, a virus appears indeed to behave as a protoplasmic element, distinct, however, from other such elements by its actual or potential transmissibility to new host cells.

The "submicroscopic" requirement is more arbitrary, but is methodologically convenient. The effective resolving power of the light microscope being around 2000 A, the definition restricts the virus field to the study of agents that at some time in their development consist of elements, recognizable in isolated form, with at least one linear dimension equal or smaller than 2000 A (43). There is, of course, no fundamental reason behind the choice of this borderline value for size. It simply turns out empirically to be an adequate point of separation. This size limit happens to be reasonably close to the limit of porosity of ordinary bacteriological filters, which can therefore be used to separate bacterial cells from virus particles without much loss of the latter (*filtrable viruses*). Several agents, however, which have dimensions greater than 2000 A are included among viruses. Our definition should really state: "submicroscopic or nearly submicroscopic entities."

Elimination of the submicroscopic size requirement would include among viruses a variety of obligate intracellular parasites, such as some bacteria (e.g., *Mycobacterium leprae*), the rickettsiae, and some algae and possibly fungi. There are sound taxonomic reasons for including such organisms with groups other than viruses. The rickettsiae (see chapter 19), according to the most accepted view, represent a special group of obligate parasitic Gram-negative bacteria. The possibility that some of the obligate parasitic microorganisms are related to viruses and the hypothesis that some viruses originated from them or from their ancestors by "regressive evolution" through parasitism are very popular among virologists (*114; 271; 395*).

The requirement for reproduction "inside living cells only" excludes all saprophytic, free-living organisms. A number of submicroscopic free-living organisms are known to exist. Many bacteria, especially in unfavorable environments, can go through submicroscopic stages or L forms, which may reproduce as such and later return to the typical bacterial morphology (*179*). Several submicroscopic free-living organisms, without known bacillary stages of development, have been described. Among them are the "pleuropneumonia organisms" originally described by Nocard and Roux (see *571*), similar in many respects to L forms of bacteria; the sewage and soil organisms of Laidlaw and Elford (*396*) and of Seiffert (*589*); and the serum organisms of Barnard (*39*). The pleuropneumonia and sewage organisms have well-defined and not too complex nutritional requirements for growth (*519*). This in itself differentiates them from viruses, whose growth, as we shall see, appears to depend on the host cells not for a supply of nutritionally required compounds or growth factors, but for the use of the integrated enzymatic machinery of the cell, which provides energy and synthetic machinery for the virus. Indeed, viruses in the free state appear to be completely inert metabolically.

The requirement for "host specificity" included in our definition of viruses, although not excluding any known group of organisms, emphasizes again the fact that the virus-host relation is one of integration rather than of supply of nutrients. If we were to encounter an intracellular parasite apparently unable to reproduce in the free state but capable of reproduction in living cells of any kind, we could reasonably suspect that growth of this parasite in the free state would be possible if we were able to isolate and supply in cell-free form some hitherto unidentified, perhaps unstable, nutrient. On the other hand, we shall see that the relation of true viruses to their host cell is so intimate and integrative that the hope for cell-free virus reproduction is about on the same level as the hope for artificially constructed, self-reproducing cells.

The relation of virology to other biological sciences. Virology's relation to bacteriology stems on the one hand from the common technical problems of handling very small biological objects (microscopy, filtration techniques, sterilization), and on the other hand from the common interest in pathogenic microbes. Both pathogenic bacteriology and applied virology belong to the wider field of pathology. The study of pathological changes in host organisms, however, is more intimately connected with the study of viruses than with that of pathogenic bacteria, because the detection, the recognition, and the titration of viruses depend almost exclusively on observations of abnormal changes produced in some host. Fundamentally, however, virology should be concerned primarily with virus properties and functions. It should ultimately be possible to interpret all pathological changes of a host, directly or indirectly, in terms of the mechanisms by which a virus alters the infected cells.

Virology has become closely allied to protein chemistry and physicochemistry and has borrowed the techniques of these sciences, because the small size of viruses places them in the colloidal range and gives them many properties in common with proteins and other macromolecular substances. Methods for purification and for determination of the size, homogeneity, and state of dispersion of particles are similar for viruses and proteins. The overlapping size ranges of viruses and proteins do not a priori imply a similarity of organization or of chemical complexity. Such a similarity can only be tested by structural analysis. Thus, the relation of virology to protein chemistry is, at least in principle, purely technological.

THE DEVELOPMENT OF OUR KNOWLEDGE OF VIRUSES

Like all sciences, virology has not developed in a straight path, but rather by a slow accumulation of empirical knowledge. Some unity and general perspectives have only emerged in the last 10 years. Some diseases now known to be caused by viruses have been recognized for thousands of years. A Chinese description of a pestilence dating from the 10th century B.C. apparently refers to smallpox. Yellow fever, known for centuries in tropical Africa and as a scourge of ships in the African trade, was probably responsible for the legends of cursed ships, such as those of the Ancient Mariner and the Flying Dutchman (*114*). Plant virus diseases, such as potato leaf roll, have been traced to records of several hundred years ago; and tulips with the ornamentally appreciated color variegation known as tulip break, caused by a virus, have been cultivated since the 16th century (43).

The transmissibility of smallpox has been known for centuries, and vaccination against smallpox by extracts containing vaccinia virus (cowpox) was introduced as a medical practice by Jenner at the end of the 18th century (Jennerian vaccination, 361). The transmissibility of tobacco mosaic by mechanical inoculation of sap of infected plants was demonstrated by Mayer in 1886.

During the last decades of the 19th century, the successes that had attended the search for bacterial agents of many diseases drew increasing attention to various diseases for which this search had remained fruitless. The idea of submicroscopic, nonbacterial pathogens, however, was slow in finding an experimental basis. In 1892 Iwanowsky reported the transmission of tobacco mosaic by means of sap filtered through bacteriological filters which were supposed to retain all bacteria. His report went unnoticed; its significance was apparently not fully clear to the author himself. In 1898–1899 Loeffler and Frosch (428) for foot-and-mouth disease and Beijerinck (58) for tobacco mosaic succeeded in proving serial transmission by bacteria-free filtrates in which no microscopic organism could be detected. Impressed by this unexpected finding, Beijerinck described the agent of tobacco mosaic as a *contagium vivum fluidum,* meaning by this an agent which reproduced, and therefore had life, but which was in a state of dispersion different from that of organisms. In reality, there is no clear-cut difference in the state of dispersion of small organisms and of large molecules. Moreover, the fact that virus reproduction and its pathological consequences can be initiated by a single virus particle make the state of dispersion of viruses irrelevant for their mode of action.

There followed an intense period of discovery of virus pathogens or "filtrable viruses," to employ a now obsolete expression. The early years of virology saw the development of methods permitting the microscopic visualization of the largest types of virus particles or elementary bodies. Following pioneer observations by Buist (106), many workers, and especially Paschen (514), greatly developed the art of virus staining. Meanwhile, rapid progress was made in the study of the cellular pathology of virus diseases, with the recognition of specific intracellular inclusions (see 217).

On the one hand, the work on the size and properties of virus particles contributed to the development of modern techniques of ultrafiltration, ultracentrifugation, and other physicochemical procedures, culminating in the successful purification, crystallization, and chemical characterization of virus particles (405; 622). On the other hand, research on cellular pathology of virus infections gave a great stimulus, first, to the study of tissue cultures, and second, to the study of chick-embryo techniques as means of investigating viruses in simplified systems. The study of tissue cultures provided direct evidence of the need for contact with living, metabolizing cells as a prerequisite for virus reproduction. Frozen, killed tissue, or tissue separated from virus by membranes impermeable to the virus would not support virus reproduction. The discovery in 1910 of a virus that produces malignant tumors in chickens (562) and the generalization of this discovery to a whole group of fowl cancers in subsequent years opened the way for the realization that viruses are a major agent of neoplastic transformations, both in animals and in plants (83).

The discovery of bacteriophages or bacterial viruses by Twort (653) and by d'Hérelle (306) and the deliberate use of bacteriophages as models 'for the study of the virus-cell relation (65) provided perhaps the most important single factor for the present integration of virology into a unified science.

The recognition of the specificity of host-virus relations, of its limitations, and of its determination by genetic and developmental factors (host specificity and tissue specificity) assumed increasing importance as a result of efforts to conquer the virus diseases of man and of economically important animals and plants (see 265). From the epidemiological standpoint, the most salient developments have been the recognition of the role of arthropod vectors in the transmission of many virus diseases of animals and plants (547), the analysis of complex host-vector-virus cycles (601), and the clarification of the role of latent infections of reservoir hosts in perpetuating pathogenic viruses. The analysis of spontaneous mutability in viruses. (310; 361a; 457) not only contributed to the epidemiological understanding of virus diseases but also established the nature of viruses as independently evolving and therefore taxonomically independent genetic systems. Similarly, the analysis of the serological properties of viruses (121) established their nature as chemically specific, host-independent structural elements, while providing a basis for a multitude of diagnostic tests for virus diseases.

PLAN OF THE BOOK

It will be our aim to study viruses as a group, in spite of the recognized uncertainty as to the extent of taxonomic kinship among what we call viruses. We shall not attempt the description of individual virus diseases nor of individual viruses, but shall rather deal with the facts and methods of virology as a whole. We shall, however, undertake whenever possible the interpretation of certain phases of applied virology in terms of fundamental virus properties. For example, a discussion of virus ecology will of necessity be closely allied to a general discussion of the epidemiology of virus diseases. We shall subdivide our subject matter as follows:

1. Survey of viruses; range of existence; nomenclature and classification (chapter 1).

2. Detection and titration of viruses (chapters 2 and 3).

3. The properties of viruses outside the host: size, structure, composition, organization of virus material; chemical and serological analysis; effect of physical and chemical agents (chapters 4–7).

4. Virus-host interaction: analysis of the simplest and most thoroughly investigated host-virus systems; study of virus reproduction; interaction among viruses in common hosts (chapters 8–14).

5. Viruses in nature: variation, ecology, survival, transmission; virus latency and relation of viruses to growth and morphogenesis; tumor viruses (chapters 15–17).

6. Origin and nature of viruses; relation to other biological systems (chapter 18).

7. Rickettsiae (chapter 19).

RANGE OF EXISTENCE OF VIRUSES

It is customary and reasonable to subdivide viruses, according to the major subdivisions of their hosts, into bacterial viruses (bacteriophages), plant viruses, and animal viruses. We must realize, however, that even such broad subdivisions may create ambiguities, as in "plant viruses" that reproduce in their insect vectors. We must remember that, because of their nature, viruses are detected and discovered as pathogens, that is, as agents causing abnormalities in some hosts. It is therefore logical to list them in terms of their "major host," that is, of the host whose manifestations are of the greatest importance to man—economical, medical, or otherwise. In general, each virus will have a variety of hosts, more or less related organisms, in which it can reproduce. Some of them, often those in which damage caused by the virus is slight or absent, are more important in assuring the survival and evolutionary success of the virus than the major host which arouses man's interest. In tables 1 and 2 we present an extensive though by no means complete list of animal and plant viruses.

There are several important aspects to be considered in taking stock of the range of organisms that have been found to be hosts for viruses. As far as bacterial viruses are concerned there is hardly a group of readily cultivable bacteria for which bacteriophages are not known. The bacteria for which no phage has been described (spirochetes; myxobacteria; iron, sulfur, and nitrifying bacteria) present major technical problems to bacteriologists. Our knowledge of them is quite inadequate. It is likely that every thoroughly investigated bacterial group will be found to be the host of some phages. It is interesting to note that the host range of phages does not cut across well-established taxonomic boundaries between bacterial groups. Phages active on micrococci will not grow on streptococci; phages of enteric bacteria do not attack *Pseudomonas*. Specificity can go far beyond the rather flimsy classification boundaries that separate genera and species. It reaches down to individual strains or "clones." The explanation for this great specificity resides in the fact that phage resistance in bacteria is acquired by discrete mutational steps, so that a strain sensitive to a phage may give rise to stable mutants resistant to that specific phage.

Among animal viruses, the only invertebrates in which virus diseases have been observed are the insects. These represent, of course, the economically most important and therefore scientifically most prominent group. The study of insect virus diseases was stimulated in France in the 19th century by the losses due to diseases of the silkworm, the protagonist of the natural silk industry. Virus diseases of insects, especially Lepidoptera and Hymenoptera, are today a most important area of virology.

Among vertebrates, virus diseases have been recognized in fish (carp pox, infectious tumors) and in amphibia (virus tumor of the kidney in the leopard frog). In birds we find virus diseases of great economic importance: Newcastle disease of fowl, laryngotracheitis and many others. The main importance of some virus diseases of birds is their occasional transmission to man (psittacosis, ornithosis). Certain neoplastic virus diseases of birds, fowl sarcomas and fowl leukemia, have a tremendous interest for the virologist because of their role in the study of the relation of viruses to tumors. They represent in some respects the most thoroughly investigated cases of tumors caused by viruses.

In mammals, virus diseases have been recognized in most domestic animals and in several wild ones, particularly in rabbits, whose virus

Table 1. Representative animal viruses

Virus	Major Host	Other Natural Hosts	Transmission	Typical Reactions in Major Host	Diagnostic Reactions
Coxsackie group	Man	—	Contact	Meningitis; myalgia	Virus neutralization
Dengue	Man	Monkeys	Mosquitoes	Fever; rash; leukopenia	Complement fixation; virus neutralization
Encephalitis group Equine encephalomyelitis (Eastern, Western, Venezuelan)	Horse	Man; fowl	Mosquitoes; mites	Meningo-encephalitis	Complement fixation; virus neutralization
Japanese (type B) encephalitis	Man	Chicken; mammals?	Mosquitoes	Meningo-encephalitis	Complement fixation; virus neutralization
Lymphocytic choriomeningitis	Man	Mouse	Contact (vectors?)	Meningitis	Complement fixation; virus neutralization
Russian (Spring-Summer) encephalitis	Man	Wild mammals and birds?	Ticks	Meningitis; encephalitis	Complement fixation; virus neutralization
St. Louis encephalitis	Man	Chicken; other birds? wild mammals?	Mites, mosquitoes	Encephalitis	Complement fixation; virus neutralization
Herpes simplex	Man	—	Contact	Cold sore (fever blister); stomatitis	Complement fixation; virus neutralization
Herpes zoster (shingles)	Man	—	? (Possibly from varicella infection)	Vesicular eruption of skin along nerves	Complement fixation; virus neutralization
Inclusion conjunctivitis	Man	—	Contact	Conjunctivitis (especially in infants)	Complement fixation; agglutination of elementary bodies
Infectious hepatitis	Man	—	Contact	Jaundice	Intracellular inclusions

Virus (disease)	Host	Related/other hosts	Transmission	Symptoms	Diagnostic methods
Influenza (A, B, C)	Man	—	Contact	Flu; pneumonia	Hemagglutination inhibition; virus isolation in egg
Lymphogranuloma venereum	Man	—	Contact (genital)	Primary blister; lymph-node swelling	Staining for elementary bodies; complement fixation; skin test
Measles	Man	—	Contact	Skin rash; Koplik spots in mouth	—
Molluscum contagiosum	Man	—	Contact	Skin nodules	Intracellular inclusions
Mumps	Man	—	Contact	Parotitis	Hemagglutination inhibition; complement fixation; skin test
Poliomyelitis (Types I, II, III)	Man	—	Contact	Motor paralysis	Virus neutralization; complement fixation; (cytotoxic effect in tissue culture)
Rubella (German measles)	Man	—	Contact	Skin rash	—
Trachoma	Man	—	Contact	Chronic conjunctivitis	Intracellular inclusions
Varicella (chicken pox)	Man	—	Contact	Skin rash	Complement fixation; agglutination of elementary bodies
Variola (smallpox, alastrim)	Man	Related to cowpox (vaccinia), horsepox, sheep pox	Contact	Skin vesicles	Complement fixation; intracellular inclusions (Guarnieri bodies)
Yellow fever	Man	Monkeys	Mosquitoes	Jaundice; liver and kidney necrosis	Isolation of virus; virus neutralization
Warts (verrucae)	Man	—	Contact	Skin, genital, and laryngeal warts	—
Cowpox (vaccinia)	Cattle	Man	Contact	Skin vesicles	Complement fixation

Table 1. Representative animal viruses (Continued)

Virus	Major Host	Other Natural Hosts	Transmission	Typical Reactions in Major Host	Diagnostic Reactions
Foot-and-mouth (aphthous fever)	Cattle	Swine; sheep; man	Contact	Vesicles on oral mucosa and skin	Complement fixation
Pseudorabies (mad itch)	Cattle	Swine; cat; dog	Contact	Skin itch; pharyngeal paralysis	—
Rinderpest (cattle plague)	Cattle	Sheep; goat; buffalo	Contact	Inflammation of digestive tract	Rabbit inoculation
Louping ill	Sheep	Man?	Ticks	Meningo-encephalitis	Complement fixation; virus neutralization
Rift valley fever	Sheep	Goat; cattle; man	Mosquitoes	Liver necrosis	Virus neutralization
Hog cholera	Swine	—	Contact	Hemorrhages; leucopenia; encephalitis	Skin test
Swine influenza	Swine	—	Contact, lungworm	Pneumonia	Hemagglutination inhibition
Swamp fever (equine infectious anemia)	Horse	—	Flies; mosquitoes; contact	Destructive anemia; hemorrhages	—
Distemper (canine and fox)	Dog	Wolf; fox	Contact	Pneumonia; meningitis	Ferret inoculation
Rabies (hydrophobia)	Dog	Cat; wolf; fox; man	Contact (bite)	Throat paralysis; encephalitis	Intracellular inclusions in brain (Negri bodies); complement fixation
Feline infectious enteritis (panleucopenia)	Cat	—	Contact	Enteritis; leucopenia	—
Fowl plague	Fowl (chicken, turkey, duck)	Wild birds	Contact	Hemorrhages; edema	Chicken inoculation

			Contact, arthropod vectors		
Fowl pox	Chicken	Turkey; pigeon	Contact, arthropod vectors	Skin vesicles on head, comb	Chicken inoculation; intracellular inclusions (Bollinger bodies)
Fowl leukosis	Chicken	Other fowl	? (Insects)	Leukemia (erythroblastosis)	Blood examination
Infectious laryngotracheitis	Chicken	Pheasant	Contact	Laryngotracheitis; bronchitis	Cultivation in egg
Newcastle disease	Chicken	Other fowl	Contact	Pneumonia; encephalitis	Hemagglutination inhibition
Psittacosis	Parrot	Pigeon; other birds; man	Contact	Diarrhea; nasal discharge; necrosis of liver; pneumonia in man	Mouse inoculation; complement fixation
Rous sarcoma *	Chicken	Other fowl (artificial transmission)	Artificial	Sarcoma	—
Rabbit fibroma *	Rabbit	—	Artificial	Fibroma	—
Myxomatosis	Rabbit	—	Contact	Conjunctivitis; gelatinous tumors	—
Rabbit papilloma	Rabbit	—	?	Horny warts, becoming cancerous	—
Virus III	Rabbit (latent virus)	—	Artificial	Latent infection	—
Granulosis viruses	Lepidoptera	Specific for single species	Contact	Granular transformation of larval tissues	Capsular inclusions
Silkworm jaundice (polyhedrosis)	Silkworm	—	Contact	Fatlike transformation of silkworm larvae	Intranuclear polyhedral inclusions
Sacbrood of bee	Honey bee	—	Contact	Saclike transformation of larvae	—

* Viruses maintained in laboratory from an original isolation.

Table 2. Representative plant viruses

Name of Virus *	Transmission
Abutilon variegation	White flies?
Aster yellows	Leafhoppers
Bean mosaic	Mechanical; seed; aphids
Cocoa swollen shoot	Mealy bugs, carried by ants
Corn streak	Leafhoppers
Corn stripe	Leafhoppers
Cucumber mosaic diseases	Mechanical; seed; aphids; cucumber beetles
Elm phloem necrosis	Leafhoppers
Pea mosaic	Aphids
Peach mosaic	Aphids
Peach rosette	?
Peach yellows; little peach	Leafhoppers
Potato leaf roll	Aphids
Potato paracrinkle	Mechanical (artificial only)
Potato virus X	Mechanical
Potato virus Y	Aphids
Potato yellow dwarf	Leafhoppers
Rice stunt disease	Leafhoppers
Sugar beet curly top	Leafhoppers
Sugar beet mosaic	Aphids
Sugar cane Fiji disease	Leafhoppers
Sugar cane mosaic	Aphids
Tobacco mosaic	Mechanical
Tobacco necrosis	Mechanical (soil to roots)
Tobacco ringspot	Mechanical
Tomato bushy stunt	Mechanical
Tomato spotted wilt	Thrips
Tristeza of citrus	Aphids
Tulip break	Aphids
Turnip yellow mosaic	Flea beetles
Wheat mosaic	Mechanical (soil to roots)
Wound tumor	Leafhoppers

* Generally includes name of major host.

tumors (papilloma, fibroma) have provided an invaluable material for the study of the relation of viruses to neoplasms. Virus diseases of man (over 40 are now known) include such major epidemiological problems as smallpox, yellow fever, poliomyelitis, measles, mumps, rabies, and various types of encephalitis.

In the plant kingdom, the absence of reports of virus diseases in lower plants (except bacteria) is notable. Only the flowering plants, or angiosperms, have yielded viruses. It is difficult to decide whether viruses for other plants do not exist or have failed to be detected because of limited knowledge. We could reasonably expect that some virus diseases of yeast, of molds, or of gymnosperms would have been observed if they were at all frequent.

Among the flowering plants we have most of the plants of economic importance. Here viruses probably rank second only to fungi as agents of diseases of practical importance. Virus diseases of such field crops as potatoes, beans, beets, tobacco, sugar cane, and of fruit crops such as peaches are among the major problems of plant pathology.

Some viruses stand out historically as particularly important in general virology, apart from any practical importance, because they have provided model cases on which general principles or methods of virology have been worked out. Thus, the study of the chemistry of virus particles has progressed mainly through work on some plant viruses and bacteriophages. The physicochemical analysis of size and shape of viruses has been furthered especially by the study of tobacco mosaic virus and tomato bushy stunt virus. The analysis of virus reproduction has been carried furthest with bacteriophages and with the viruses of the influenza group. The study of tumor causation by viruses has derived much of its impetus from the discovery of virus-induced chicken sarcomas.

Yet it is essential to keep constantly in mind in the study of virology that no conclusion based on the study of one virus can a priori be generalized as valid for any other virus. In view of the presumed heterogeneity of the objects that we call viruses, the greatest caution must be exerted in attributing to any one virus a property observed in another. This does not mean that we should consider each virus as a completely distinct entity, unrelated to any others. Indeed, we recognize certain groups of viruses (those of the psittacosis-lymphogranuloma group, for example, or certain bacteriophages) as constituting taxonomic groups as valid as any found in higher organisms. We must simply keep in mind that viruses *as a group* may include things as different in their structure, chemical composition, and biological activities as any odd collection of biological materials selected on the basis of arbitrary criteria, for example, all animals shorter than an inch or all plants with pink flowers.

CLASSIFICATION OF VIRUSES

The common nomenclature for animal and plant viruses consists in using the name of the disease produced in the major host followed by the word "virus." Bacteriophages are named by code symbols (generally letters followed by numbers, as T1, C16, S13) derived from more or less accidental laboratory customs; the symbol is sometimes preceded by the Greek letter ϕ. This system of nomenclature, which is not a system of classification and which frankly admits its own empirical, nontaxonomic basis, has worked quite adequately for animal viruses and for bacteriophages, but not for plant viruses. The need and quest for a taxonomic classification, indicating natural relationships, has been an ever-present problem for plant pathologists. The difference may be due partly to a difference in scientific training. Plant pathologists are generally trained as biologists, whereas animal pathologists are more often physicians or veterinarians. Moreover, the natural relationship among plant viruses is of some practical significance, because cross-protection between related viruses infecting the same plant provides a potentially important defense mechanism in plant virus diseases. The increasing realization of the role of reservoir hosts in the epidemiology of virus diseases, both of animals and of plants, is also increasing the requirement for a characterization of viruses independent of their host range and of the pathological reactions of the hosts.[1]

The shortcomings of all systems of classification of viruses reflect, of course, our present inadequate knowledge of the nature and origin of these entities. This makes any assessment of the degrees of relationship among the viruses highly problematic. On a strictly pragmatic basis, a provisional classification can be made using any group of virus properties that are sufficiently stable and distinctive. Most of our knowledge of viruses, however, concerns the effects they produce on their hosts, effects which may reflect the properties of the hosts more than those of the viruses.

Plant pathologists have repeatedly proposed classifications or systems of nomenclature of some practical value. In some cases, the grouping criteria were the properties of virus materials in vitro. In others, the criterion was the plant host in which a virus was first described (see 43). Clearly, the latter method is of little significance as to virus rela-

[1] The problems of virus classification were discussed from many viewpoints at a symposium held in New York in 1952 (121a).

tionship, since most viruses attack many hosts. Holmes (*341*) has proposed a Latin binomial system, similar to that used for plants and animals, and has extended it to include all viruses. These would form an order, Virales, with three suborders, Phagineae (bacteriophages), Phytophagineae (plant viruses), and Zoophagineae (animal viruses), further subdivided into families, genera, and species. The properties used in grouping and separating viruses into groups are mainly symptoms produced and mode of transmission. A major weakness of the Holmes system is the utter disregard for the morphological properties of virus particles as a criterion of classification. Thus, viruses such as the foot-and-mouth agent with its tiny particles, and the large-particled, well-characterized viruses of the vaccinia group are placed together in one genus because they attack mucous membranes.

In the minds of many virologists, attempts to set up a complete or even a detailed system of classification are not only premature but also misleading. The adoption of Latin binomials suggests, by analogy with plant and animal taxonomy, a similarity of evolutionary pattern and of taxonomic hierarchy between viruses and higher organisms, which is wholly unestablished. The attempt to classify viruses about which little is known, except a description of the disease produced in one host, leads to an unjustified feeling of knowledge and full understanding. It would seem better to admit that we know a few things about a few viruses, whereas many viruses probably exist about which we know nothing. Then we could describe the best-known viruses in terms of their own properties, compare them among themselves, and organize a few main groups having as prototypes those well-known viruses that are clearly distinct from one another. One aid in this process would be the knowledge that virus variation occurs in the form of discrete mutational steps (see chapter 15). Properties known to be changed by a single mutation, such as host range and tissue affinity, would be taxonomically less valuable than those found to be more stable, such as morphology or serological specificity.

Some plant virologists (*43*) and some bacteriophage workers (*9*) have reached similar conclusions on taxonomic questions. These investigators consider as the primary criteria of natural relationship the similarity of particle size and shape and the possession of common antigens revealed by serological cross-reactions. For example, two viruses such as the tobacco mosaic agent, with rod-shaped particles of characteristic size and composition, and the tobacco necrosis virus, with spherical particles and a tendency to form crystals, can be used as prototypes for two groups of viruses, which include strains differing from the prototype by one or a few mutational steps. At the level of larger groups these two viruses could, respectively, serve as prototypes: the first for plant viruses with rod-shaped, fairly rigid particles; the second for spherical, regularly crystallizing plant viruses.

Similarly, coli-phages T2, T4, T6, and C16, which are indistinguishable in morphology, give serological cross-reactions and are capable of genetic recombination in mixed-infected hosts (see chapter 8), form a natural group, probably equivalent to a species. The various types may be considered as varieties or incipient species (9). As for defining larger groups, there seems to be little basis on which to proceed. Although phages with very different bacterial hosts (for example, micrococci or coli-dysentery organisms) do not seem to adapt from one such host to the other, they are often morphologically more similar (although serologically unrelated) than phages with common hosts. This leaves open the question of host range versus morphology as a criterion of relationship. In plant viruses, cross-protection reactions are well correlated with serological ones and permit additional groupings.

Criteria analogous to those useful in grouping plant viruses and phages can sometimes be applied to animal viruses. For example, the viruses of the smallpox-vaccinia-ectromelia group are a morphologically homogeneous group with antigenic components and other properties in common. It has been suggested (259) that this group and other viruses, such as fowl pox and molluscum contagiosum, be placed in one genus (*Borreliota*), all the members possessing fairly large particles and giving typical intracytoplasmic inclusions.

Another homogeneous group is the so-called psittacosis-lymphogranuloma-pneumonitis group, consisting of several viruses with large particles, which give serological cross-reactions and undergo similar developmental transformations inside their host cells. The infections produced by these viruses are susceptible to therapy by antibiotics. These viruses have been named "Chlamydozoaceae" and have received rating as a family of the order Rickettsiales in the 1948 edition of *Bergey's Manual of Determinative Bacteriology* (Baltimore, Williams & Wilkins).

Another natural group may be that of the influenza-mumps-Newcastle disease viruses, which have similar particles and common enzymatic activity on some surface component of red blood cells and on other substrates. Serological cross-reactions are not present among all members of this group, however. Other groups with reasonably good taxonomic standing may, for example, be the rod-shaped insect viruses producing crystalline intranuclear inclusions containing the virus, and the equally rod-shaped viruses of insects whose particles are enclosed in characteristic ellipsoidal capsules (68a).

In summary, a wisely conservative position appears to be that the more properties of viruses we learn to analyze, the more meaningful will be the relations we are able to establish. With bacteriophages, where genetic studies have progressed quite far, we may be approaching a point where genetic facts will be used to provide a rationale for taxonomic principles (9). For example, we are sometimes able to invoke as a criterion of classification not only the possession of a common character but also the possession of common mutability, which strongly suggests the possession of similar genetic determinants. This is true of the coli-phages T2, T4, T6, and C16, which undergo similar mutations. Here, the possession of common genetic determinants has been shown by tests of genetic recombination. In viruses of the tobacco mosaic group parallel mutability has also been described.

2

Detection and Identification
of Viruses

In studying viruses, we must first consider ways of recognizing that they are present. The essential thing to look for is some abnormal host manifestation, generally macroscopic. In their extracellular, free state viruses are inert and do not act on their environment. Because of their small size they cannot easily be recognized. Although in principle it should be possible to detect and recognize a virus from its morphology, particularly when an electron microscope is used, the practical value of such a method is small. Only when the presence of a virus is suspected because of some abnormal host manifestation does the investigator have recourse to attempts to locate a virus by microscopy.

Host reaction to a virus is recognized by comparing infected and normal host. No general rule can be given. Such recognition depends on our familiarity with the symptoms of the various virus diseases. This is what we might call the "art" of virology. At the basis of any scientific construction is a whole body of information, which the individual worker can learn only by experience and by accumulation of information. This we call the "art" of the scientist. For example, the background of all chemical generalizations is the acquaintance of the investigator with large numbers of chemical facts. These permit him to devise chemical tests and provide a basis for him to interpret the properties of chemical compounds.

For the practical purpose of interpreting the virologist's detection methods we may subdivide virus manifestations into two main categories: local reactions, and generalized or systemic reactions.

LOCAL REACTIONS

These are manifestations that involve only a limited number of host cells localized in one area. The limitation in size of the affected area is due either to a localization of the virus in a few cells or to the fact that only a few cells show the effect of the virus' presence, although the virus may be present beyond the limit of the recognizable lesion. A virus may remain circumscribed in a local area because of its limited ability to spread, because of a limited number of susceptible host cells, or because of a balance between host defenses and virus invasiveness.

Bacteriophage. The local lesion of bacteriophage is called a *plaque* and is an area of *lysis* or dissolution in a bacterial layer growing on a solid medium. The plaques are often quite sharp and round, and may be surrounded by haloes of incomplete lysis. Formation of discrete plaques is due to the fact that bacteriophage reproduction can only occur in growing bacterial cells. On a nutrient medium there is a race between two processes: bacterial growth and bacteriophage growth. When bacterial growth stops, lysis by bacteriophage also stops or at least proceeds at a very slow pace, so that the area of lysis remains localized. At the same time, the bacteriophage particles also diffuse through the agar and in the liquid film at its surface. Before growth stops, they may have reached bacteria at a certain distance from the original phage localization. As a consequence, smaller phages, which diffuse more rapidly, give relatively larger plaques on a given bacterium than larger phages do.

The appearance of the plaque is characteristic for each phage-host system (figure 1), and reflects the kinetics of bacteriophage growth and of bacterial growth, and the size of the bacteriophage. Size and morphology of bacteriophage plaques also depend on the composition and consistency of the nutrient medium, which affects host growth, phage growth, or both.

Plant viruses. Local lesions are generally detectable on the surfaces of leaves. The most interesting type is the *necrotic* lesion, a black or brown spot that may vary, when fully developed, from 1 to 10 mm in diameter, and which appears at the point of entry of some viruses, for example, of tobacco mosaic virus in *Nicotiana glutinosa* and in other plants. The virus enters a cell at a point where some mechanical damage has been produced on the leaf, and then spreads from cell to cell. A necrotic lesion results from rapid death of a group of infected cells, with consequent localization of the virus in a small area. The

Detection and Identification of Viruses

necrotic reaction is generally caused by hypersensitivity; the cells die so fast that virus spread is limited. It actually represents a defense mechanism both for the individual plant, which can localize the infection and survive, and for the crop, since virus localized in necrotic lesion has fewer chances of spreading from plant to plant than a virus that gives a generalized infection.

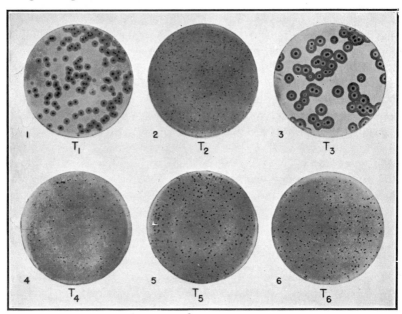

Figure 1. Plaques produced by different coli-phages on bacterial layers of a common host, *Escherichia coli,* strain B, growing on agar. Reduced to about ⅓ size. From: Demerec and Fano (*177*). Courtesy Dr. M. Demerec, Carnegie Institution, Cold Spring Harbor, New York.

Necrotic lesions have shapes and sizes characteristic for a given virus-host system (see figure 2). Necrotic lesions are particularly important (*333*) because they provide the best method for titration of those plant viruses that produce them (see chapter 3).

The presence or absence of necrotic lesions at the point of entry of the virus has been traced to specific genes of the host. The necrotic reaction to tobacco mosaic virus in species of the genus *Nicotiana* (*337*) is due to a dominant gene which determines hypersensitivity, whereas the recessive allele causes a systemic mosaic response.

A well-analyzed example is that of tobacco mosaic virus in the pepper (*339*). The type of response depends on three allelic forms of the same

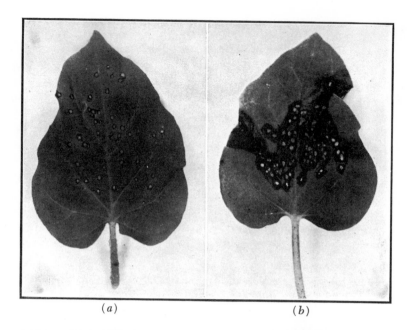

(a)   (b)

(c)   (d)

Figure 2. Local necrotic lesions produced by plant viruses on plant leaves.
(a) Tobacco mosaic virus on *Nicotiana glutinosa;* (b) tomato mosaic virus on
N. glutinosa; (c) tomato bushy stunt virus on *N. glutinosa;* (d) tobacco ringspot
virus on *N. tabacum.* Courtesy Dr. K. M. Smith, Molteno Institute, University of
Cambridge.

23

gene: one allele, L, determines a localized necrotic response; another, l', produces, when homozygous, a delayed necrotic response followed by abscission of the leaf and recovery of most plants; the third one, l, causes generalized chlorosis.

Sometimes, although the response at the point of entry is necrotic, localization does not result and the virus continues to spread. This is true, for example, of some potato viruses. Potato virus X in some varieties of potato elicits a necrotic response; in other varieties it gives generalized mottling or even symptomless infections. Even with local necrotic response, the necrotic reaction may become generalized; the localized infection, when present, may be due to virus inactivation in the plant rather than to hypersensitivity. The genetic basis of the responses of potato varieties to virus X has been partially clarified (356a; 629).

Another type of localized response is the so-called starch-iodine lesion, which consists of local areas of altered starch metabolism around the points of entry of the virus (335). To demonstrate this type of lesion, an infected leaf is treated with alcohol to remove chlorophyll and then with iodine to stain starch. The lesions appear as areas lighter than the rest of the leaf, if the leaf had recently been exposed to light, because of reduced synthesis of starch in the infected areas. Or, they may appear as darker areas, if after exposure to light the leaf had been allowed to spend several hours in darkness, presumably because the starch moves away less freely from the damaged areas, due to hindrance to food transport.

Animal viruses. Recognizable local lesions are formed either at the primary point of entry or by secondary localization of a circulating virus. They generally consist of cell destruction and cell proliferation, with the complication that inflammatory reactions are always present in animal tissues. An example of a primary localization of infection is that of infectious warts in man. A variety of warts or papillomas, flat or pointed, may result from the entry of the virus, depending on the point of entry and possibly on the virus strain. As examples of secondary localization of viruses producing recognizable local lesions we may mention the exanthemata that are the major symptoms of smallpox, measles, and chicken pox. These typical rashes are caused by the localization of the virus in the skin chorion, after which the cells of the basal layer of the epithelium are invaded and damaged and blisters are formed in the thickness of the epidermis. In some cases, for example, in the Koplik spots that appear on the oral mucosa in the early stages of measles, the localization of the virus is in the submucosal glands.

In special instances we may observe local lesions on layers of cells that are more or less uniformly susceptible. An example is the infection of the chorioallantoic membrane of the chick embryo (figure 3; see chapter 12). A virus suspension is deposited on the surface of the

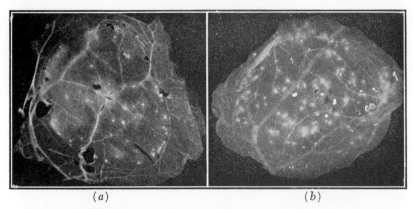

(a)   (b)

Figure 3. Chorioallantoic membrane lesions. (*a*) Myxoma virus; (*b*) Murray Valley encephalitis virus. Courtesy Dr. F. M. Burnet, Walter and Eliza Hall Institute, Melbourne.

membrane and spreads over it. Here and there, the virus gains access to a cell; this leads to the formation of a lesion. At first the lesions are discrete, but later become confluent if the infection proceeds long enough. The conditions are somewhat similar to those of a bacterial layer seeded with bacteriophage, although less well understood. Localized lesions can also be observed in layers of cells cultivated in vitro (figure 4; see chapter 11).

Sometimes, localized lesions even in deep tissues may be utilized in the diagnosis of a virus, because of either their localization or their appearance. Poliomyelitis virus produces areas of cell destruction in the anterior horns of the spinal cord, where motor cells are localized, with a resulting muscular paralysis. Rabies virus causes typical alterations in the cells of the Ammon's horn in the brain. These cells contain the characteristic intracellular inclusions of rabies (Negri bodies). Many similar examples could be cited from the pathology of animal virus diseases.

GENERALIZED REACTIONS

There is no clear-cut distinction between generalized and local reactions, since all host manifestations in a virus infection depend ultimately on the invasion of sensitive cells by virus. Nevertheless, the

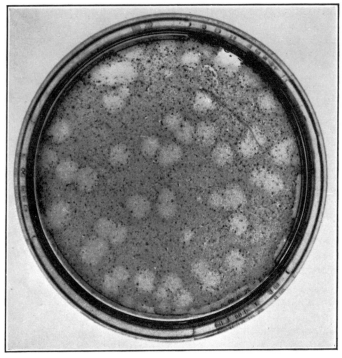

Figure 4. Plaques produced by Western equine encephalomyelitis virus on a layer of chick embryo fibroblasts in tissue culture. Courtesy Dr. R. Dulbecco, California Institute of Technology, Pasadena.

recognizable symptoms of infection are often more diffuse than the appearance of localized areas of damage. For example, we may consider the mass lysis of a bacterial culture by bacteriophage as a generalized infection, as opposed to the localized formation of plaques on a layer of bacteria. In both cases we observe lysis of large numbers of cells, but in the first there is no spatial limitation to the spread of the virus, such as is caused on a plate by the immobilization of the bacterial cells and by the limited means of dispersion of the virus.

Plant viruses. Generalized or systemic infections produce symptoms that go under a variety of names: chlorosis, mosaic, streak, yellows,

Figure 5. Aster plants. The plant on the right is normal. The plant on the left is infected with aster yellows virus. Courtesy Dr. K. Maramorosch, Rockefeller Institute, New York.

Figure 6. Leaves of *Nicotiana tabacum. Left:* normal. *Center:* infected with tobacco mosaic virus. *Right:* infected with the same virus, with a bright spot of yellow mosaic mutant. Courtesy Dr. L. O. Kunkel, Rockefeller Institute, New York.

ringspot, leaf roll, describing the type of deformation or discoloration that appears on the leaves of the infected plants (figures 5 and 6). Discoloration of leaves may be localized in ringlike areas (ringspot), in streaks, in irregular patches (mosaic), or it may appear as a uniform chlorosis or as a yellowing, often more pronounced along the

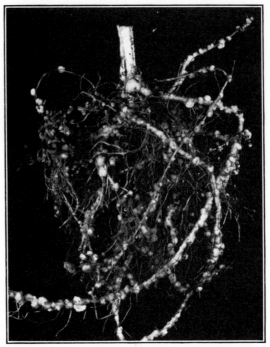

Figure 7. Tumors produced by wound tumor virus on the roots of sweet clover. Courtesy Dr. L. M. Black, University of Illinois, Urbana.

veins. Most of these changes reflect disturbances in the photosynthetic function or in the transport of food, as we have already mentioned for the starch-iodine lesions. To describe the specific alteration of the morphology or habit of a plant affected by a virus, plant pathologists have traditionally employed picturesque terms such as sugar beet curly top or potato witches' broom.

Some symptoms result from cell proliferation in virus-infected tissues, which lead to production of "enations," frilly or compact growths derived from the vein areas of the leaves. Lateral buds may proliferate to produce the symptoms of witches' broom. One virus produces multiple tumors throughout the infected plants; the tumors arise mainly in areas where the plants are wounded (*83;* figure 7).

Flowers may show symptoms of virus infection in the form of variegated colors or "breaking." Tulip break, a condition which has been known for several hundred years and which produces a highly appreciated flower appearance, is due to virus.

The symptoms of a generalized plant disease are usually visible on the new leaves formed after the infection has become systemic; old, nongrowing leaves show symptoms only if infected directly. Generally the newly growing parts of the plant show the greatest damage. On the other hand, apparent recovery occasionally occurs and the new growth is either free or almost free of symptoms, although it generally still contains virus. The type of manifestation, moreover, depends on the host. A virus may be very destructive for one host and cause a mild or latent disease in another. Different varieties of potato, for example, differ widely in their responses to potato viruses.

Animal viruses. Detection of animal viruses is even more complex than detection of plant viruses. This is due to the greater differentiation of tissues and organs, to the presence of several mechanisms of virus transport, to serological phenomena of immunity, and to secondary inflammatory processes. We may mention, as examples, the symptoms of mumps, in which the virus localizes mainly in the parotid gland, but occasionally produces an inflammation of the genital organs; and those of yellow fever, in which the virus may be widespread in many different organs and tissues. The general symptoms can always be traced to damaged and altered cell function. For example, the jaundice that accompanies yellow fever is due to the damage to the liver cells. Detailed descriptions of the manifestations of virus diseases of man and animals are found in special treatises (*414; 655*).

An interesting aspect of the general manifestation of animal virus diseases is the rather precise *incubation period* between infection and appearance of symptoms. For example, the incubation for measles is generally 10–12 days, for mumps 18–21 days, for smallpox around 12 days. This suggests that a fairly definite sequence of events must take place before the appearance of symptoms. The incubation period may include the time needed for the virus to penetrate (and possibly to reproduce at the point of entry), to circulate, to localize itself in susceptible cells, and to reproduce to the extent needed for the manifestations to appear.

We often encounter silent infections with animal viruses. The virus reproduces without giving visible symptoms. In many cases, however, the presence of the virus can be traced by the presence of circulating antibodies in the blood. This sign of infection is useful in evaluating the degree of immunity and in following the spread of a virus through a host population. The serological detection of virus infection forms an important phase of the epidemiology of virus diseases. The presence of antibody is not proof of the actual presence of the virus in the organism, because a virus disease may give rise to a lasting immunity and continuous production of antibody even after the virus has apparently disappeared from the organism. This phenomenon is relevant for the general problem of the mechanism of antibody production. It may be that the virus does not disappear completely, but only vanishes as an infectious material and remains present in some nonrecoverable form in the cells that produce antibodies.

INFLUENCE OF HOST AND ENVIRONMENT ON HOST REACTIONS

In all cases where viruses are identified from the symptoms they produce, it is important to define the situation in which we observe such symptoms. We have already mentioned several examples of the influence of the *host species* on the type of manifestation of a virus. A bacteriophage may completely dissolve the cells of a certain bacterium and may be carried without obvious manifestations within the cells of another bacterium ("lysogenic strain") (*120a; 453*). The pseudorabies virus causes a fatal disease in cattle but a mild, almost nonsymptomatic, although very contagious, infection in swine (*602*). As we shall discuss in greater detail in chapter 16, whenever a virus is very destructive for a certain host we have reason to suspect that it has some other host in which it produces a mild disease, because only such a host-virus compromise can provide a virus with opportunity for successful survival in nature. Too complete a destruction of the host cuts the ground from under the virus and tends to lead to its elimination.

The genetic basis of virus susceptibility in different hosts is emphasized in clear-cut fashion by such observations as that on a strain of mice that owes its 100% resistance to strain 17D of yellow fever to a single dominant gene. In the brain of the resistant mice the virus fails to multiply (*572*).

Another important factor is the *age* of the host. Young plants are generally more susceptible to plant viruses. In animals, the symptoms produced by a given virus in the same host often differ with the host's age. The tumor virus that produces the Rous sarcoma in adult chickens causes an inflammatory, nonproliferating disease in the newly hatched chick (198). Such differences in host reaction reflect the changes in the physiology of the host cell that take place during development and differentiation of various tissues, and also depend on the appearance or disappearance of certain specific defense mechanisms in the course of aging (for example, low antibody production in the newborn).

Symptoms also depend on the *route of entry* of a virus. For example, influenza virus entering a mouse by the usual route, through the mucosa of the upper respiratory tract, causes typical pneumonia; if injected in the brain, it may give a toxic syndrome (298). The toxic manifestations are apparently caused by an abortive reproduction of the virus in the cells of the central nervous system (582).

Other factors that influence symptomatology are the *environmental conditions* prevailing during the infection period. We have already mentioned the influence of light on the appearance of starch-iodine lesions at the points of entry of certain plant viruses. Season, soil constituents, and many other factors also affect the manifestations of plant virus diseases. Nutritional effects on the symptoms for animal viruses and also on the susceptibility to animal viruses have been noticed; greater resistance seems sometimes to be associated with some nutritional deficiencies (134). This suggests either that the shortage of an essential growth factor limits virus growth, if the requirements of virus-infected cells are greater than those of uninfected cells; or that the cells of growth-factor-deficient animals are so altered physiologically as to support less virus growth or to resist invasion.

Temperature effects on virus disease have often been observed, especially in plants. Some viruses are unable to grow at temperatures above a certain level. An infected plant may become completely sterilized by a few hours or days of immersion in a water bath at a temperature as low as 35° C. This is so for several diseases of the peach tree (388). Temperature may be the reason why such diseases are infrequent or absent in the southern part of the United States, where the summer temperature is often higher than the virus can stand. The symptoms themselves may be modified by temperature. Tobacco mosaic virus at temperatures around 35° C causes the appearance of milder symptoms, due to the selective proliferation at this higher temperature of a less virulent variant of the virus (338).

ARTIFICIAL TRANSMISSION OF VIRUSES

In studying a new virus disease and in attempting to identify its causative agent, we must meet requirements comparable to Koch's postulates for bacterial infections (555). We must prove that an agent is regularly isolated from cases of the disease, that it can be propagated in a suitable host, that it is filtrable (submicroscopic), that it reproduces only in living cells, and that, reintroduced into the original host or into a sufficiently similar one, it gives rise to the original syndrome.

The techniques for successful artificial transmission of a virus to a host are part of the art of virology. Success in a specific case depends mainly on the investigator's knowledge of the properties of the virus he is dealing with. The main problems are: the choice of the proper host and of the proper route of inoculation; a sufficient amount of virus in the inoculum; and the control of the environmental conditions. The essential requirement is to bring the virus, or to cause it to be transported, to susceptible cells where it can reproduce. In general, the outer surface of most higher plants and animals consists of virus-proof barriers, so that the virus must be introduced either through this barrier or into some openings through which it can come directly in contact with susceptible cells.

The simplest case is again that of bacteriophage. In a suitable medium, containing the necessary activating factors and ionic concentrations (see chapter 8) a phage particle infects a bacterium by simple collision, with a collision efficiency close to 100%. The presence of bacterial secretions such as capsules or slime may sometimes hinder successful contact.

Plant viruses. Several means of transmission of plant viruses may be listed. Some means apply to most viruses, others only to a few. The simplest is *mechanical transmission,* practiced by rubbing the surfaces of leaves with an applicator (a finger, or a piece of cotton or cheesecloth) soaked in the virus suspension. Rubbing causes local abrasions, through which the virus can penetrate. Some viruses have been transmitted only by such mechanical methods or by grafting. A typical example is potato virus X, for which no insect vector is known. Many plant viruses cannot be transmitted mechanically.

The number of points of virus entry produced by rubbing a leaf may vary greatly, depending on several factors difficult to control (pressure, abrasive power of the applicator). By careful standardization of technique, however, astonishingly reproducible results can be obtained. The points of entry may be broken hair cells or wounded epidermal cells.

Mechanical transmission, when it is the only method of natural transmission of a virus, requires that the virus be widespread in a plant population, so that there are frequent chances for virus to be carried mechanically from one plant to another. For example, tobacco mosaic virus is highly contagious and can be introduced into a field by a person whose hands are contaminated with virus, for example, from a cigarette containing infected tobacco leaf. Potato virus X can be transmitted from plant to plant by the rubbing of leaves blown together by wind.

Insect transmission is the natural method of transmission for a great many plant viruses. Artificially, it is utilized by causing insects to feed on infected plants within cages, then transferring them to cages with uninfected plants. In some instances the insects have been caused to feed on cell-free extracts containing virus. An ingenious method (59), suitable for the study of the leafhopper vector of curly top virus, *Circulifer tenellus,* consists of introducing the leafhoppers into a small cage consisting of a glass cylinder over one end of which a thin membrane is stretched. Droplets of the virus-containing extracts are placed on the outer side of the membrane. The insect feeds upon them by inserting its stylets through the membrane, and can be induced to feed for definite lengths of time by carefully regulating the illumination and other conditions. Thus, the leafhoppers are fed various amounts or concentrations of virus suspension, after which their ability to transmit the virus is investigated by placing them on healthy plants. It is also possible to inoculate viruses directly into the insect body (632). Many viruses that in nature are transmitted only by insects can be studied in cell-free extracts by injecting the extracts into insects, which thereby become sources of infection.

A method of transmission widely applicable to plant viruses is the *graft* method. Grafting of shoots or buds from an infected onto a healthy plant causes the passage of virus from the scion into the healthy plant, and is followed by the manifestations of systemic infection. The great majority of plant viruses can be transmitted by this method. The method has not been useful for viruses restricted to plants like corn that are difficult or impossible to graft or for viruses that produce only local lesions in most hosts, like tobacco necrosis virus. By grafting, viruses can also be transmitted to new hosts, provided of course that successful intergrafting is possible.

A refinement consists in causing a parasitic plant called dodder (*Cuscuta* sp.) to parasitize an infected plant. The special roots (haustoria) of the dodder penetrate the infected cells, and the virus spreads to the dodder. Infected dodder stems, when later allowed to parasitize healthy plants, will often transmit the virus (*61; 363*). By this method it is possible to transmit several viruses from species to species, even when these are not intergraftable (*391*).

Some theoretical problems arise with viruses·that have been transmitted only by grafting. For example, a condition known as variegation in *Abutilon,* an ornamental plant, was for a long time transmitted by graft only (although transmission by an insect vector has now been obtained; *505*). According to our definition of virus, such a condition could be considered a virus disease only because of the similarity of its symptoms with those of other virus diseases. An interesting case is that of the King Edward potato, which carries the paracrinkle virus in a completely nonsymptomatic state (*574*). Grafting of the King Edward potato onto potato plants of other varieties causes them to show a typical disease, transmissible from plant to plant by graft. The paracrinkle virus has recently been isolated and inoculated mechanically; its properties resemble those of several other potato viruses (*52*). Interesting questions have been raised, however, as to the origin of such a virus. Does it arise de novo in the King Edward potato by a change in some normal cell protein? Or does it enter this plant variety and remain latent, reproducing for innumerable generations without causing symptoms? Seed transmission of such a virus is not necessary, because potatoes are propagated from tubers. These problems will be discussed in detail in chapter 18.

Animal viruses. The simplest method of inoculation, when feasible, is the *instillation* of virus-containing material into cavities lined with susceptible cells, for example, in the extraembryonal membranes of the chick embryo or on cells growing in tissue cultures. Instillation in the respiratory tract is often successful for viruses that proliferate on the epithelium of the lung. It imitates the probable route of natural infection with viruses that are supposedly transmitted by droplet infection, such as the viruses of common cold, influenza, and probably measles and mumps. It may be possible to infect animals by feeding such viruses as that of infantile paralysis, which are supposed to proliferate in the intestine. The dropping of virus suspension on scarified skin as a method of inoculation is commonly practiced with vaccinia virus in vaccination against smallpox. A similar method is the inoculation of viruses onto the scarified cornea of rabbits and other animals.

Injection into the host's tissues is the most general method of inoculation; the virus may be injected either directly into the susceptible tissue or into a region from which it will spread to susceptible cells. Some viruses spread through the circulatory system, others along the nerve fibers. Many viruses may reach susceptible tissues if introduced intraperitoneally.

Transmission by *arthropod vectors* has been used experimentally, particularly in the study of the role of insects in the natural transmission of a disease. The experiments of Walter Reed and his collaborators in proving that yellow fever is transmitted by a mosquito have become classic in the history of virology (548). Insect transmission is seldom the only possible inoculation procedure, however, since animal virus diseases transmitted by insects can also be transmitted by direct inoculation of infectious material (for example, a patient's blood) into a susceptible animal, without need for a cycle including an obligate passage through the vector's body.

Some of the cultivation procedures for viruses represent true enrichment cultures, by which large amounts of a virus are obtained in a suitable host. Sometimes enrichment procedures are necessary as an intermediate stage between isolation of a virus and its diagnosis. This is the purpose of most "first-isolation" techniques that have been proposed. For example, in attempting the isolation of viruses from cases of influenza or other respiratory diseases in man it has been common practice to inoculate throat washings (individual or pooled) into chick embryos or into the lungs of mice. After suitable intervals of time the inoculated tissues are extracted and tested for presence of virus, either by successive reinoculations or by attempts to detect the virus through some of its properties. Another example is that of herpes virus, which produces typical intracellular inclusions in the cells of the rabbit cornea. Material taken from a patient must often be passed through the rabbit testis before sufficient amounts of virus are obtained for testing by corneal inoculation (185).

NEW HOSTS FOR VIRUSES

The importance of the correct choice of host in virus transmission has already been mentioned. It is often the key to successful work with a virus. Because of the laboratory conditions, it is seldom possible to cultivate a virus in the host from which it has been isolated. This is obvious where human diseases are concerned and is also true in many other cases. The search for new hosts or, as it has been often called, the *adaptation* of a virus to new hosts, is an important phase of virology.

With plant viruses, success is often obtained by grafting, by the use of parasitic dodder, or by choosing ·the proper insect vector. The results are often quite interesting. For example, it was suspected for a number of reasons that the virus causing witches' broom in potato and the virus of aster yellows might be identical. In the absence of intergrafting, dodder was used to transmit them to common hosts. On these hosts it was possible to show that the viruses differed in regard to their insect vectors and their host range (*391*).

Transmission of animal viruses to a new host can often be accomplished by successive transfers, often blind transfers, in the sense that the host does not show signs of the presence of the virus or that at the beginning the virus does not grow in sufficient amounts to be detected. After several transfers in the new host, adaptation often improves and the virus may then grow quite well. For example, many viruses can be made to grow in some of the cavities of the chick embryo by successive transfers.

Caution is necessary, however, since in the course of its adaptation to new hosts some of the properties of a virus may be changed. It is now generally accepted that viruses undergo mutations and that the ability to attack a new host may be present only in a few mutant individuals out of a large virus population (see chapter 15). In the new host only the mutants will proliferate, and they will establish a new virus line adapted to the new host. In the course of mutation, however, some of the properties of the original virus may be changed, even including pathogenicity for the original host. The virus worker, therefore, must be careful in drawing conclusions, for example, as to the nature of the properties of a human virus from the study of its egg-adapted (or mouse-adapted or ferret-adapted) strains.

LATENT VIRUSES

Another important caution in the artificial transmission of viruses to new hosts is the possibility of encountering latent viruses, that is, viruses which are carried without symptoms, but which may give rise to pathological manifestations after successive transfers. In attempting to isolate a virus by successive transmissions of materials through several animals or plants, virus workers have often encountered a different and completely new virus, bearing no relation to the original disease. Some examples will illustrate this point.

The parasitic dodder used to transmit certain plant viruses may itself carry the latent dodder mosaic virus, which is pathogenic for other plants (62). Virus III was discovered in rabbits (558) in the course of attempts to isolate the chicken pox virus by successive transfers of extracts from the cutaneous vesicles of human patients into rabbit testis. A virus was present in the testes of many rabbits of the colony studied, and upon unnatural transfer it revealed itself by giving typical symptoms. The virus could also be isolated from a similar series of transfers initiated without the original injection of material from chicken pox patients.

If lung extracts prepared from mice of various colonies are serially inoculated from animal to animal, after a number of transfers (from 3 to 5 or 6) the animals often respond with a typical and fatal pneumonia; a virus (pneumonia virus of mice) can be isolated (348; 486).

Another important example is the so-called Theiler's virus (mouse encephalitis; 646). This latent virus was detected in course of transfers for attempted isolation of poliomyelitis virus, and, interestingly enough, it causes in mice a syndrome very similar to poliomyelitis in man or in anthropoid apes. Theiler's virus and other related viruses are widespread in mice.

The reason for the sudden acquisition of virulence by a latent virus upon artificial transfers from one animal to another animal of the same species, even within the same colony, is obscure. It is possible that if the virus enters an animal very early in the animal's life it can establish some sort of equilibrium by which it causes only mild symptoms. If large amounts of virus are injected into an adult, the large virus inoculum, together with the damage caused by the injection, may establish conditions favorable for a sudden increase in virus reproduction leading to destruction of many host cells.

The problem of latent viruses, however, has broader connotations. Instances of latent viruses have often been cited as suggesting a possible origin of viruses from normal cell components, which become viruses upon being inoculated into other cells. The question of virus origin will be discussed more fully in chapter 18. We may mention here that virus latency is not a special situation but only an extreme one. Any virus or, more generally, any obligate parasite that is very destructive to some host must have established in nature a better modus vivendi with some other host, in order to insure its own survival. Partial latency, then, is almost a necessity for every virus in some host. The virus of herpes simplex, for example (114), is present in a very large number of individuals, in whom it reveals itself only occasionally by producing "fever blisters" or "cold sores" as a result of some disturbances of the epidermal cells, mainly around the oral cavity. This had been considered an instance of endogenous origin of a virus, until it was realized that the virus enters most individuals of a human community in early childhood, causing a mild oral inflammation called aphthous stomatitis (180). After the child recovers, the virus apparently remains localized in the neighborhood of the initial point of entry and in a state of equilibrium with the host cells, an equilibrium which may be broken by external influences.

A beautifully analyzed case (651), which shows various possible degrees of latency, is that of the lymphocytic choriomeningitis virus. This virus causes a sporadic form of meningitis in man and also produces a meningitic syndrome in apes. The virus was found present in a colony of laboratory mice. Upon successive transfer within the mouse colony the infection became widespread and nonsymptomatic. After a longer period of permanence in the colony the virus infected practically every animal, at first by entry in very early age, later even by intrauterine transmission. The virus passes through the placenta and may even be propagated through the egg. In these mouse colonies, then, it is difficult to distinguish the virus from a normal cell component, although we know when the virus first entered the colony. We also know that the virus is present in endemic form in the grey mouse, from which it is occasionally transmitted to the laboratory mouse (31).

Titration of Viruses

VIRUS TITER AND INFECTIOUS UNITS

Just as the presence of a virus is detected through the manifestations it produces in a sensitive host, so also the amount of virus activity is determined from the quantitative relations between the amount of the virus-containing material and the degree or frequency of production of specific responses in a host. The purposes of measurements of virus activity are manifold. The need for determining the amount of virus arises not only in comparing different virus suspensions but also in the course of isolation, concentration, and purification of viruses and in the study of treatments that may affect virus activity. Moreover, methods for measuring virus activity are necessary in any study of virus reproduction.

The determination of virus activity presents a number of peculiarities that distinguish it from other types of activity measurements, such as measurements of chemicals by titration. In chemical titration, what is determined is the amount of a given reagent with which an unknown amount of a chemical can react. In virus titration the conditions are somewhat different, because the virus reproduces in the sensitive host. Reproduction results in an amplification of the effects of very small amounts of virus, so that often the manifestations produced by small or large amounts of virus are indistinguishable. We have, therefore, an "all-or-none" effect. A comparison can be made with the growth of a bacterial culture, where under favorable circumstances the final result—visible growth—depends only on the presence or absence of viable bacteria in the inoculum, and not on their number.

In virus titration we determine the smallest amount of a virus suspension capable of producing a suitable manifestation in a susceptible host. This manifestation may be a generalized disease or a localized lesion, according to the virus investigated and to the purpose of the titration. The smallest amount of virus capable of producing a re-action is called an infectious unit, and the titer of the original virus suspension is given in terms of the number of infectious units per unit volume. For example, if the smallest amount of a suspension of influenza virus that causes pneumonia in mice upon nasal instillation is 0.1 ml of a dilution $1/10^6$ of an infected lung emulsion,[1] we calculate an approximate titer for the emulsion as 10^7 infectious units per ml: $1/(0.1 \times 10^{-6}) = 10^7$.

In general, titration procedures depend on methods by which inoculations can be scored as giving a positive or a negative result, as, for example, the presence or absence of lysis in a bacterial culture inoculated with bacteriophage, the presence or absence of an inflammatory reaction at the site of intradermal inoculation of vaccinia virus in rabbit, the presence or absence of paralytic symptoms in a mouse injected intracerebrally with encephalitis virus. It is sometimes possible to score the presence or absence of virus reproduction independently of the observation of host reactions. In the titration of influenza virus by inoculation in the allantoic fluid of the chick embryo, some fluid from each egg is extracted several hours or days after inoculation and is tested for presence or absence of specific hemagglutinating ability (see chapter 13).

Finally, there are cases in which the amount of activity can be measured from the number of specific responses appearing on a given surface as a result of the inoculation of a given amount of virus, as in the count of plaques for bacteriophage, in the same way as bacterial titers are estimated by colony counts.

[1] The reader should be familiar with the use of decimal notation in dealing with very large or very small numbers. For example, $1,000,000,000 = 10^9$; $1/10,000 = 10^{-4}$; $7,030,000 = 7.03 \times 10^6$; $1/250,000 = 10/2,500,000 = 4/1,000,000 = 4 \times 10^{-6}$. The exponent of 10 in the above expressions is the $\log_{10}$ of the power of 10 next below. The number 4×10^{-6} could also be expressed as $10^{(\log 4) - 6} = 10^{-5.398}$. In a series of dilutions by a factor 2, the decimal logarithms of the concentrations will differ by a constant amount $\log 2$, that is, about 0.3 (for example, $\frac{1}{2} \approx 10^{-0.3}$; $\frac{1}{4} \approx 10^{-0.6} \cdots$). In some cases, the reader will encounter the natural logarithmic notation (e^n; e^{-n}, etc.). The symbol e, the base of natural logarithms, equals $2.71828 \cdots$; $\log_e x = 2.3 \log_{10} x$; $\log_{10} x = 0.43 \log_e x$. The reader should be thoroughly conversant with the elementary theorems on powers, roots, and logarithms (for example, $10^a \times 10^b = 10^{a+b}$; $10^{-a} = 1/(10^a)$; $10^{a/b} = \sqrt[b]{10^a}$; $\log_a b = \log_c b \times \log_a c$).

TITRATION PROCEDURES

Bacteriophage titration. The simplest example is that of bacteriophages. These are generally titrated by preparing several dilutions
and plating one or more measured samples of each dilution on nutrient
medium plates with an excess of sensitive bacteria. Phage and bacteria may be introduced in a surface layer of nutrient agar (*269; 316*).
After incubation, the continuous bacterial layer is interrupted by the

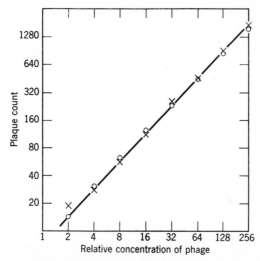

Figure 8. The proportionality between plaque count and concentration of bacteriophage. From: Ellis and Delbrück (*205*).

clear areas of lysis produced by phage. The plaque counts are analogous to colony counts for bacteria, and their values are directly proportional to the amount of phage plated (figure 8). The titer is
calculated from the plaque count, the volume of phage plated, and
the dilution. If 0.1 ml of a dilution 10^{-5} gives on the average 230
plaques, the titer will be $230/(0.1 \times 10^{-5}) = 2.3 \times 10^8$ units per ml.
In general, if y plaques are produced by a volume v (in milliliters) of
a dilution x, the titer n of infectious units per ml is $n = y/vx$.

The precision of each determination on an individual plate can be
estimated by remembering that the standard deviation, due to sampling
errors, is equal to the square root of the average number of plaques
per plate. The precision, as measured from the ratio $\sqrt{\bar{n}}/n$ between
standard deviation and count, will be greater the higher the average

number n of plaques per plate. A limitation is imposed, of course, by the fact that the plaques, if too numerous, become confluent and difficult to count.

In estimating the precision of a virus titration involving dilutions it must be remembered that, apart from sampling errors resulting from random distribution of particles, we have technical errors in the volume of the samples transferred in the dilution procedure. If, for example, a titration involves 5 dilution steps, each with a probable error of 9%, the probable error of the whole dilution series will be $(9 \times \sqrt{5})\%$.

Several technical points must be observed in carrying out any virus titration by the dilution methods. In the first place, a different pipette should be used for each successive dilution. This requirement is more strict for virus titrations than for chemical or serological procedures, because virus activity may be conditioned by the presence of single particles, and a pipette that has contained millions of virus particles cannot easily be freed of all of them by repeated rinsings. This precaution seems obvious, but has so often been neglected by beginners and others that its neglect has been christened (186) with the special name of *Pipettenfehler* (pipetting mistake). Other important precautions involve the choice of a dilution fluid in which virus activity does not rapidly deteriorate, and the control of temperature and other factors that may affect virus activity.

Animal viruses. Methods analogous to the plaque count for phage have been used, particularly the counting of discrete lesions or "pocks" produced by several viruses on the chorioallantoic membrane of the chick embryo. The maximum number of pocks countable on one membrane is about 20–100 for different viruses. Because of the rather complex manipulations involved and of the limited applicability of this technique, its use has been restricted to a few laboratories (77). Even more limited in application is the count of pustules produced on scarified areas of rabbit skin (281) or cornea (320), which have been used mainly to estimate the potency of vaccines.

A method recently introduced (196) consists of counting discrete lesions or plaques produced on monolayers of specially prepared tissue cultures. The "plaque count," exactly analogous to that used with phage, is directly proportional to the amount of inoculum. This technique should provide an ideal method of titration when it becomes applicable to a large variety of viruses.

The most common titration procedure, however, is the inoculation of equal samples of successive dilutions of a virus suspension into susceptible animals, followed by the determination of the dilution end point by scoring each inoculation as positive or negative according to the typical host responses. Titers, in infectious units per milliliter, are obtained from the concentration and the volume of the sample inoculated, assuming the last positive dilution to contain 1 unit. The factor between dilutions is usually $\frac{1}{10}$ or $\frac{1}{2}$; the smaller the denominator, the more precise is the titer obtained. In titrations of this type, there is often an "uncertain zone," in which a given dilution may give a negative result, whereas the next higher dilution gives a positive one. Such an "uncertain zone" is generally interpreted as due to the fact that an infectious unit consists of one discrete material particle.[2]

The results of a titration by dilution end point can be made more accurate by testing several samples of each dilution. For one or more dilutions there will be some positive and some negative inoculations, and it will be possible to estimate by interpolation the dilution that would give 50% positive and 50% negative results. The titers can then be expressed in multiples of the "50% infectious dose." This method can be applied to a variety of virus titrations (influenza virus in the allantoic cavity of chick embryo, neurotropic viruses in the brain of mice, etc.), whenever the response can be scored as positive or negative. The method is illustrated in table 3.

A refinement was introduced by Reed and Muench (546). The per cent of positive responses is calculated not from the actual frequencies for any one dilution but from the "accumulated sums," as illustrated in table 4. This corresponds to assuming that, if a given individual test (for example, a given egg) was positive for a certain dilution, it would have been positive if used to test any of the lower dilutions, and vice versa for a negative test. This method of calculation is only justified, however, if one assumes that the negative responses obtained at dilutions at which other inoculations are positive reflect variations in host sensitivity. We shall see that there is good reason to believe that the negative responses depend partly on the chance absence of discrete material particles (one particle constituting an infectious unit) and do not necessarily reflect variations in host sensitivity. The theoretical justification of the "accumulation method" in virus work appears doubtful, although in practice its use has many advantages.

[2] Let us suppose that a dilution 10^{-4} contains 50 infectious units per ml. A 0.1-ml sample will contain on the average 5 units and very likely will give a positive response. A 0.1-ml sample of 10^{-5} dilution will contain 0.5 unit on the average, and one such sample may or may not contain 1 unit. A 0.1 ml sample of 10^{-6} dilution will almost always give a negative response, but it may happen that the sample of 10^{-5} dilution tested contains no unit, while 1 unit has been transferred to the next dilution, with an anomalous result.

Table 3. Virus titration by the 50% end-point method

Calculation of LD_{50} (50% lethal dose). Data from Parker and Rivers (*511*).

Dilution	Amount Inoculated	Positive Responses (death)	Negative Responses (survival)	% Positive
10^{-3}	0.1 ml	4	0	100
10^{-4}	0.1 ml	4	0	100
10^{-5}	0.1 ml	3	1	75
10^{-6}	0.1 ml	1	3	25
10^{-7}	0.1 ml	0	4	0

50% end-point $= 10^{-5.5}$.
0.1 ml of a $10^{-5.5}$ dilution $= 0.1 \times 3.16 \times 10^{-6}$ ml $= 1\ LD_{50}$.
Titer in LD_{50} per ml $= 1/(0.1 \times 3.16 \times 10^{-6}) = 3.2 \times 10^{6}$.

Table 4. Virus titration by the Reed and Muench method

Dilution	Positive Responses	Negative Responses	Total Positives (sum down)	Total Negatives (sum up)	Per Cent
10^{-3}	4	0	11	0	100
10^{-4}	4	0	7	0	100
10^{-5}	2	2	3	2	60
10^{-6}	1	3	1	5	16
10^{-7}	0	4	0	9	0

The 50% end-point can be obtained by graphic interpolation (see *546*).

Several points must be kept in mind in titrating animal viruses by end-point methods. The results are bound to depend not only on the amount of virus but also on the route of inoculation, on the host animal, and on a number of other less definable factors. We must remember that a positive response is a manifestation of successful infection. This in turn depends on the proper amount of virus material reaching a susceptible cell, succeeding in infecting it, and propagating the infection to other cells. All sorts of host defenses (mechanical, humoral, and cellular) tend to reduce the chances for successful infection. The titers will then indicate the number of infectious units under the specific conditions of the test. For example, one and the same sample of influenza virus may give a titer of 10^8 units per ml if titrated in eggs and a titer of 10^6 units per ml if titrated by nasal instillation in mice. This may reflect either the greater resistance of mice or the presence of two types of virus materials in the suspension, with different abilities to attack different hosts. The situation is analogous to that of a bacterial suspension giving a higher colony count in a favorable medium than in an unfavorable one, where many cells fail to proliferate.

The incubation period method. Partly because of the large numbers of host animals needed for titration of certain viruses by the end-point method, other titration methods have been devised, none of which is of general application. The most successful type is based on the fact that for some viruses there is a fairly precise relation between the amount of inoculum and the "incubation" time between inoculation and appearance of a given symptom. For example, for rabbit papilloma virus Bryan and Beard (*103*) found that the time interval between the inoculation in the rabbit skin and the appearance of papillomas is related to the amount of inoculum C_x by the relation $t_2 - t_1 = b(\log C_1 - \log C_2)$. A plot of t versus $\log C$ gives a straight line, and unknown samples can be compared by reference to a standard plot (figure 9). Other workers found and used a similar relation between the time of death and the amount of inoculum. Gard (*248*) found for certain strains of Theiler's virus (mouse encephalitis) a relation of the type $(1/t_1) - (1/t_2) = b(\log C_1 - \log C_2)$ between the inoculum size and the time of onset of paralysis. Gard pointed out that a relation of the type $t_2 - t_1 = b(\log C_1 - \log C_2)$ can be rationalized if we postulate (a) that symptoms (or death) appear when the virus concentration in the host has reached a constant level; and (b) that virus reproduction is an approximately exponential process, similar in its overall course to the reproduction of bacterial cells in a growing culture.[3] The relation $(1/t_1) - (1/t_2) = k(\log C_2 - \log C_1)$

---

[3] Let us call Y the critical number of virus units present when symptoms appear, and let us postulate a relation between virus amount y and time t such that

$$y = e^{kt} \qquad \ln y = kt$$

Let T be the time needed to reach the amount Y of virus from an inoculum containing 1 unit. Then, for an inoculum containing C_1 units, the time t_1 needed to reach the amount Y will be shorter than T by the time that would be needed to go from 1 to C_1 units:

$$\ln Y - \ln C_1 = k[T - (T - t_1)] = kt_1 \qquad (a)$$

Similarly, for an inoculum C_2:

could reflect an accelerated logarithmic reproduction, for example, a progressively more successful overcoming of host defenses as the virus concentration increases. No direct confirmation for such a rate of virus reproduction in animals has yet been offered.

Plant viruses. Titrations are generally done by the count of necrotic or other lesions, a method introduced by Holmes in 1929 for tobacco

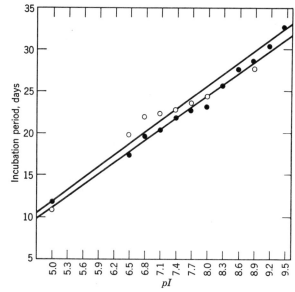

Figure 9. The inverse proportionality between the incubation period and the logarithm of the amount of papilloma virus inoculated. pI = decimal logarithm of the dilution factor (for example, pI 7.4 corresponds to a dilution $1:10^{7.4}$). From: Bryan and Beard (*103*).

mosaic virus (*333*) and extended later to many other viruses. Serial dilutions of a virus suspension are rubbed onto the surfaces of the leaves of susceptible plants. The leaves are held flat against the hand of the experimenter and rubbed with a piece of cheesecloth or some other suitable applicator previously immersed in the virus suspension. The number of lesions produced by a given dilution gives a measure of the amount of virus present (figure 10). The method requires a great deal of standardization and practice before meaningful results

$$\ln Y - \ln C_2 = k[T - (T - t_2)] = kt_2 \tag{b}$$

Subtracting a from b we obtain:

$$\ln C_1 - \ln C_2 = k(t_2 - t_1)$$

can be obtained. Even the amount of pressure exerted in rubbing
the leaf has an effect on the count of lesions, since only virus particles
that penetrate the leaf cells through local abrasions can proliferate.
Abrasive powders such as carborundum are therefore often mixed with
the virus suspension or dusted on the leaves previous to inoculations.

A number of improvements have been introduced. For example,
the half-leaf method consists in comparing the number of lesions produced by two samples rubbed on opposite halves of the same leaf or

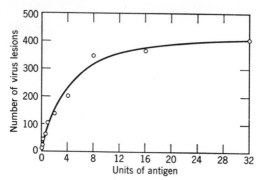

Figure 10. The relation between the count of necrotic lesions produced by
tobacco mosaic virus on *Nicotiana glutinosa* leaves and the concentration of virus
in the inoculum. The virus concentration is given in units of virus antigen as
determined by precipitin tests. From: Beale, *Contrib. Boyce Thompson Institute*
6:407, 1934.

of a series of leaves. It was found that results on opposite halves of
the same leaf are fairly consistent, whereas wide variations occur from
plant to plant and from leaf to leaf of the same plant, depending in
part on the position of the leaf on the stem. The Latin square method
(*692*) compares a series of samples by rubbing them on different leaves
of different plants in such a way that each sample is tested in various
positions on different plants. More elaborate methods are used when
only limited numbers of plants or leaves are available (*691*). It is
stated that about 50 plants are needed for a titration precise to within
10–50%. Greater precision can be obtained by the use of special experimental designs (*618a*).

In general, the number of necrotic lesions is not a linear function of
the concentration of virus, but follows the dilution curve illustrated
in figure 10. This is due in part to the fact that the maximum number
of lesions obtainable on a leaf, using a standard technique, is not
unlimited, but at most is equal to the number of wounds through which

the virus can enter. The correct measure of activity, therefore, is the ratio of the number of lesions obtained to the maximum number obtainable with the most concentrated sample. For comparison of different samples it is desirable to work in the range of concentrations in which the curve representing the dependence of the number of lesions on the virus concentration has its steepest slope, since in that range the method is most sensitive to concentration changes.

THE STATISTICAL INTERPRETATION OF THE INFECTIOUS UNIT

The infectious unit, defined as the smallest volume of a virus suspension that can elicit a positive response, must contain a certain amount of specific virus material. What does this minimum amount consist of? A priori, we can conceive of two extreme possibilities. On the one hand, a positive response may occur whenever enough virus material is inoculated to give a certain minimum concentration. This is analogous to the requirement for a minimum concentration of a chemical poison to produce toxic symptoms. On the other hand, a positive response may be conditioned by the chance that the inoculum contains at least *one individual virus particle that multiplies* and causes the specific manifestations. An obvious analogy can be drawn with bacterial growth, which is conditioned by the presence and reproduction of at least one viable bacterial cell in the inoculum. If the second hypothesis is correct, then the titers expressed in infectious units are indeed numbers of individual units, rather than multiples of minimum concentrations. The titers need not express the full numbers of virus particles, since some of the particles may fail to manifest themselves, just as some of the bacteria in an inoculum may fail to multiply.

The decision is easily reached in the case of bacteriophages. As already mentioned, the count of bacteriophage plaques is completely analogous to the colony count for bacteria. The relation between plaque numbers and amounts of phage plated is strictly linear (205; 307), as shown in figure 8. This can only be interpreted by assuming that one plaque results from the action of a single independently distributed material particle. If more than one particle had to be present in one place to produce a plaque, the plaque numbers should increase much faster than linearly with increasing amounts of phage plated (431). Similar considerations apply to plaque counts of animal viruses in tissue cultures (196).

Statistical analysis. There is an equation that expresses the distribution of independently distributed material particles in samples taken from a suspension of such particles. This is the so-called Poisson distribution (524):

$$p_r = \frac{s^r e^{-s}}{r!} \tag{1}$$

where s is the average number of particles per sample, r the actual number in a given sample, $r!$ is the product $r \times (r-1) \times (r-2) \times \cdots 3 \times 2$ ("factorial" of r), and p_r is the probability of having r particles in a given sample (and therefore also the expected frequency of samples containing r particles). For $r = 0$, $p_0 = e^{-s}$ (since $0! = 1$). This is the frequency of samples without any particles. The frequency of samples with 1 particle is $p_1 = se^{-s}$; of those with 2, $p_2 = (s^2/2)e^{-s}$, and so on.

The frequency distribution of plaques in series of plates inoculated with equal amounts of several dilutions of a phage suspension has actually been determined and found to agree with the distribution expected from equation 1 (205), as shown in table 5. This represents

Table 5. Frequency distribution of bacteriophage plaques

From Ellis and Delbrück (205)

Thirty-three 0.1-ml samples of a dilute phage preparation were plated for plaque counts. The calculated distribution corresponds to equation 1.

	p_r (Experimental)	p_r (Calculated)
0 plaques on 13 plates	0.394	0.441
1 plaque on 14 plates	0.424	0.363
2 plaques on 5 plates	0.151	0.148
3 plaques on 1 plate	0.033	0.040
4 plaques on 0 plates	0.000	0.008
	1.002	1.000

direct evidence that the number of plaques represents the number of independently distributed phage particles.

Equation 1 can also be applied where the response is of the all-or-none type, for example, presence or absence of disease in inoculated animals. The question we ask is: When a positive response occurs, does it depend on the action of a single individual particle, or does it result from the presence of a minimum number of particles (greater than 1)?

Let us write the probabilities of having more than 0, more than 1, more than 2 particles per sample:

$$P_{r>0} = 1 - p_0 = 1 - e^{-s} \tag{2}$$

$$P_{r>1} = 1 - (p_1 + p_0) = 1 - (s + 1)e^{-s} \tag{3}$$

$$P_{r>2} = 1 - (p_2 + p_1 + p_0) = 1 - [(s^2/2) + s + 1]e^{-s} \tag{4}$$

These expressions also represent the frequencies of samples that contain *at least* 1, or 2, or 3 · · · particles. The dependence of the proportion of samples with more than a given number of particles on the relative number of particles is illustrated in the plots of figure 11. The plots give the values of $Pr \geq n$ versus log s for the various values of n.

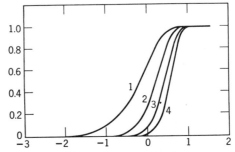

Figure 11. The theoretical dependence of the frequency of positive samples (samples with at least n particles) on the concentration of particles in an inoculum. Curves 1, 2, 3, 4 represent the expected frequencies for $n = 1$ or 2 or 3 or 4. Abscissa: logarithm of concentration (empirical scale). Ordinate: frequency of positive samples. Note the increasing steepness of the response-concentration curve for increasing values of the minimum number of particles required. From: Lauffer and Price (*404*).

The reason for the shape of the curves in the plot of P versus log s is clear: The greater the number of particles required, the steeper will be the dependence of the frequency of positive responses on amount of virus because of the faster transition from the point where all samples contain more than the minimum number of particles to the point where none does.[4]

[4] Suppose we distribute 1400 marbles at random in a series of 10 boxes, and we score as "positive" the boxes that receive at least 100 marbles. Very likely, all boxes will receive more than 100 (all "positive"). If we distribute 700 marbles at random in 10 boxes, very probably all of them will have fewer than 100 (all

To apply these curves to virus titration, let us prepare a series of virus dilutions and inoculate for each dilution a series of equal samples for infectivity test. The (unknown) average numbers of virus particles in each series will be proportional to the concentration. The frequency of positive inoculations is obtained for each series and is plotted versus the logarithm of the dilution. The dependence of this frequency of positive responses on the dilution should represent the dependence of the presence of the minimum necessary number of

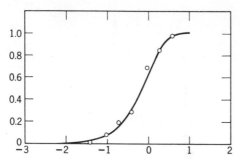

Figure 12. Experimental frequency of positive responses to inoculation of various amounts of a vaccinia virus preparation in rabbit skin. Notation as in figure 11. The solid line is curve 1 of figure 11. From: Lauffer and Price (*404*). Data from Parker (*509*).

particles on the average number of particles per sample. This can be compared with the theoretical curves of figure 11. Such comparisons, from data for various viruses, are shown in figures 12 and 13. The experimental data as a whole fit much better the curve corresponding to the requirement for at least 1 particle than those corresponding to the requirement for at least 2 or more particles.

With *bacteriophage*, the experiments consist of placing equal samples with various concentrations of phage into tubes of bacterial culture, and recording the presence or absence of lysis. The results (see figure

"negative"). Thus, dividing the *average* number of marbles per box by 2 has reduced the frequency of "positive" cases from 10/10 to 0/10.

Suppose now that we consider as "positive" the boxes with at least 1 marble. We distribute 14 marbles in 10 boxes (1.4 average per box). The expected number of boxes without marbles is 2 ($= 10 \times e^{-1.4}$). If we distribute 7 marbles only, the expected number of empty boxes becomes 4. Cutting the average number of marbles per box in half has reduced the number of "positive" boxes from 8 to 6. Thus, the smaller the number required for a "positive" score (1 instead of 100), the more gradual becomes the transition from the input that makes all scores "positive" to the one that makes them all "negative."

13) are in excellent agreement with the frequency distribution expected from equation 2 (*r* = 0; 1 particle sufficient to produce lysis) (*213; 431*). This means that 1 phage particle is sufficient to initiate mass lysis in a susceptible bacterial culture, or, in other words, that the infectious unit consists of 1 material particle.

We must realize, however, that statistical tests of this nature do not tell us that every virus particle will succeed in starting infection. It

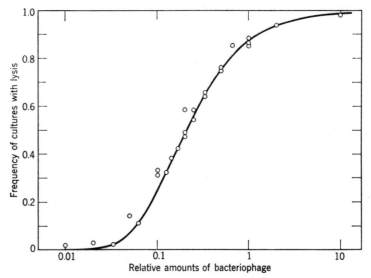

Figure 13. The frequency of positive response (lysis) in sets of bacterial cultures inoculated with various amounts of bacteriophage. Each point corresponds to a set of 160 cultures. The solid line is equivalent to curve 1 of figure 11. Modified from: Feemster and Wells (*213*).

is clear that, even though 1 particle can cause infection, not every particle will succeed in doing so, either because of intrinsic differences in the particles themselves or because of differences in the conditions of host-virus interaction, such as, for example, the presence of inhibitors that may inactivate some of the particles of the inoculum. The statistical analysis tells us only that infection can be initiated by a single particle and that it does not require the collaboration among several particles.

For bacteriophage, the plaque count titers can be compared with the actual numbers of characteristic phage particles recognizable in the electron microscope (see chapter 4). The agreement is very good, the number of actual particles being between 1 and 2.5 times the plaque counts. This means that at least 40% of the phage particles recognizable in the electron microscope, and often 100% of them, succeed in forming plaques (449).

Experiments with *animal viruses* (509; 510; 512) have given similar results. In practically all cases the results fit the curve corresponding to equation 2 (1 particle to infect). With a very virulent strain of vaccinia virus titrated in the skin of rabbits, Parker (509) found an excellent agreement with the hypothesis that the infectious unit consists of 1 particle (figure 12). Often, however, for animal viruses the frequency of positive results increases even more gradually with increasing amount of virus suspension than expected from equation 2. Deviations of this type can be explained by assuming that, although 1 particle is sufficient to start infection, other factors increase the relative chance of positive response from small inocula. For example, reversible aggregation at higher concentrations, reversible combination with inhibitors in the inoculum, or variations in host resistance could produce the observed results (see 248).

For vaccinia virus the conclusion that a single particle can initiate infection is supported in some cases by the close correspondence between infectious titers and numbers of characteristic elementary bodies in the same suspensions (about four times as many bodies as infectious units; 606). For viruses such as that of rabbit papilloma tested in rabbit's skin, however, the discrepancy is much greater, up to 10^7 or 10^8 particles per infectious unit. This in itself does not exclude the hypothesis that 1 particle is an adequate infectious unit; the other 10^7 or 10^8 may either be inactive or may have very little chance of successfully infecting a cell. Nevertheless, Bryan and Beard (104) have suggested that in papilloma the response frequency curve does not correspond to the frequency with which at least 1 virus particle is successful in producing infection, but is an expression of the distribution of sensitivity of different cells or groups of cells to the virus. They postulated a distribution of sensitivities similar to that found for response to many drugs (a normal distribution of the logarithms of the sensitivity levels, expressed as the minimum effective drug concentration; 247). On this basis an expression can be derived which fits virus titrations as well or better than equation 2. These authors have, therefore, proposed the general conclusion that variations in host sensitivity to viruses are alone responsible for the shape of the frequency distribution of positive responses as a function of the amount of virus inoculated. This conclusion is not applicable to phage titration and probably not even to vaccinia virus. The good correspondence of particle numbers and infectious unit titers (449; 606) indicates that, with inocula that give some positive and some negative inoculations, the presence or absence of particles must play the major role. For other animal viruses, the sensitivity distribution of the hosts may mask or distort the effects of the statistical distribution of the individual virus particles.

Similar considerations have been applied to the titration of *plant viruses* by necrotic lesion count. Several authors (35; 404; 693) have shown that the ratio y/N of the number y of lesions obtained with a given concentration to the maximum obtainable number N of lesions obeys the relation $y/N = 1 - e^{-s}$. This equation is analogous to equation 2 and indicates that infection results from the action of a single particle at one point of entry. Some frequently occurring deviations have been explained (35) as due to reversible aggregation of virus particles at the highest concentrations. The ratio (infectious units)/(virus particles) is generally very low, between $1/1000$ and $1/10^7$. This is not surprising, in view of the rather inefficient method of inoculation by leaf rubbing. Kleczkowski (375) has published results on tobacco mosaic virus similar to those of Bryan and Beard (104) on rabbit papilloma. The suggestion was made that the titration curve of plant viruses may reflect in part or exclusively the distribution of sensitivity of the sites of virus entry to various virus concentrations, rather than the presence or absence of individual successful virus particles.

The question is at present unsettled. As a whole, it seems likely that for most viruses 1 particle is sufficient to initiate infection. For some viruses the titration results may not be a measure of the number of successful individual particles, but simply that of the virus concentration.

Even in the most favorable cases, the titer of a virus suspension, expressed in infectious units per unit volume, corresponds to the number of particles that are successful in producing infection under the particular conditions employed in the test. The numerical relation between successful particles and actual virus particles cannot be decided by titration or by any other statistical tests, but only by actual counts or determinations of particle number. These counts, in turn, cannot distinguish between active and inactive particles, nor between particles differentially infectious for different hosts or for different routes of inoculation. At best, titration results give numbers of *statistical particles*, whose relation to the number of *actual particles* involves unknown factors of proportionality.

Size and Morphology
of Virus Particles

We have seen that virus preparations contain material particles with specific activity. The methods for the demonstration, identification, and physical study of these specific particles represent an important phase of virus research, involving the use of physical and chemical procedures which are for the most part derived from colloid chemistry and protein chemistry.

Preparation of crude virus suspensions. If the native virus material is already a fluid, for example, a phage lysate or a virus-containing body fluid, the only requirement is the elimination of bacterial contaminants by filtration through any bacteriological filter that does not retain the virus. The choice of filter is mainly a matter of experience; diatomaceous earth or sintered glass filters are generally suitable. If the virus is mostly present in intracellular form in a tissue, the tissue is minced and ground with sterile sand or ground glass or otherwise homogenized to release the virus into the surrounding fluid. The pulp is suspended in a suitable medium. Most viruses are quite stable in media of composition similar to that of host tissue, which, for animal viruses, is approximated by bacterial culture media such as meat-infusion broth. Plant viruses are generally isolated by breaking up the plant cells so that the virus is released with the plant juice. This juice should be brought near neutrality by addition of proper buffers.

Crude virus suspensions are generally stored either in a refrigerator, or by quick-freezing and storing at temperatures as low as $-70°$ C (344), or by drying in vacuo from the frozen state. Quick-freezing avoids the formation of ice crystals and minimizes protein denaturation. The fact that all known viruses are rapidly inactivated at temperatures below $100°$ C makes it possible to destroy the infectivity of viruses by the standard sterilization procedures of bacteriology.

Identification of virus particles. Once a suspension containing virus activity is available, we proceed to search it for some material to which the specific activity can be attributed. Ideally, such material should be present in infectious preparations and absent from noninfectious control preparations. Its amount should parallel the amount of virus activity, and its alteration should be accompanied by loss of activity. By a variety of methods, it has been found that virus activity is generally associated with particles characteristic for each individual virus, whose sizes vary all the way from less than the size of small bacteria (0.3 μ) to the size of medium-size protein molecules (10 mμ). Table 6 summarizes data for a number of viruses.

It will be useful to recall briefly some of the units of measure encountered in virus work. A micron (μ) is 10^{-4} cm; a millimicron (mμ), 10^{-7} cm; an angstrom (A), 10^{-8} cm. The angstrom unit is generally employed in measurements of atomic and molecular dimensions. For example, the distance between the centers of two carbon atoms in the ethane molecule is about 1.5 A; the distance between amino acids in the polypeptide chain of silk protein is 3.5 A. For large molecules or colloidal particles, we use the millimicron unit. The spherical molecule of egg albumin, containing about 350 amino acid residues, has a radius of 2.7 mμ (27 A). For a spherical particle of radius r, the volume is equal to $\frac{4}{3}\pi r^3$. If the volume and density are known, we can calculate the mass of a particle. The mass can be expressed either in standard mass units, for example, the gram and its submultiples, or in multiples of the unit of molecular weight, which is taken as $\frac{1}{16}$ of the mass of the oxygen atom, that is, 1.65×10^{-24} gram. Expressed in this way, the mass gives the molecular weight of a molecule having the same mass as our particle. A convenient unit, corresponding to 10^6 units of molecular weight, has been given the symbol Mh (*521*). As an example, a spherical virus particle, 20 mμ in diameter, consisting of material with density 1.1 grams per cm³, has a volume of $(4 \times 3.14 \times 10^3)/3$ mμ^3 = 4190 mμ^3 = 4.19×10^{-18} cm³, and a mass of $4.19 \times 10^{-18} \times 1.1$ gram = $(4.19 \times 1.1 \times 10^{-18})/(1.65 \times 10^{-24} \times 10^6)$ Mh = 2.8 Mh. The inverse of the unit of molecular weight is $N = 6.06 \times 10^{23}$, the Avogadro number. $mN/10^6$ gives the mass in Mh units, if m is the mass in grams.

VISUALIZATION OF VIRUS PARTICLES

The resolving power of the ordinary light microscope, defined as the inverse of the smallest distance at which two objects can be seen

Table 6.   The sizes of the particles of representative viruses

Virus	Shape	Electron Microscopy *	Sedimentation, Diffusion †	Ultrafiltration ‡
		Linear Dimensions, millimicrons		
Animal viruses				
Influenza (A, B, swine)	Spheres (and filaments)	100	116–124	
Fowl pox	Brick-shaped	320 × 260		
Molluscum contagiosum	Brick-shaped	330 × 260		
Chicken pox		300 × 230		
Herpes zoster	Brick-shaped	330 × 260		
Vaccinia, variola	Brick-shaped	260 × 210		
Rabbit myxoma	Brick-shaped	290 × 230		
Psittacosis, lymphogranuloma venereum, feline pneumonitis	Spheres	440–480		
Rabies	?			100–200
Rabbit fibroma	?		130	125–175
Rabbit papilloma (Shope)	Spheres	44	66	
Rous sarcoma	Spheres	70–80		
Milk factor (mammary carcinoma of mice)	Spheres	130		
Louping ill	?		22–27	15–20
Poliomyelitis	?			10–15
Mouse encephalitis	Spheres	28		
Foot-and-mouth disease	?		15–20	8–12
Equine encephalomyelitis	Spheres	42		
Japanese (type B) and St. Louis encephalitis	?			10–30
Pneumonia virus of mice	?	40		
Yellow fever	?		12–20	15–25
Polyhedrosis of silkworm	Rods	280 × 40		
Granulosis (capsule disease) of insects	Rods	270 × 40		
Plant viruses				
Tobacco mosaic	Rods	300 × 15		
Potato virus X	Filaments	16 (thickness)		
Potato yellow dwarf	Spheres (?)		110	
Tomato bushy stunt	Spheres	22	31	
Southern bean mosaic	Spheres	25	31	
Tobacco necrosis, Rothamstead strain	Spheres	17		
Turnip yellow mosaic	Spheres	20		
Bacteriophages				
Coli-phage T1	Spermlike, prismatic head	Head: 50 Tail: 150 × 10		
Coli-phage T2, T4, T6	Spermlike, prismatic head	Head: 95 × 65 Tail: 100 × 25		
Coli-phage T5	Spermlike, prismatic head	Head: 65 Tail: 170 × 10		
Coli-phage T3, T7	Prismatic (short tail)	45		
Coli-phage S13	—			10–20
Coli-phage Kottmann	Rods	100 × 35		

* Electron microscopy gives values for dry and possibly flattened particles.
† Sedimentation and diffusion methods give values for hydrated particles.
‡ Ultrafiltration data are approximate within a factor 1.5–2.

as separate and distinct, is given by: R.P. = $2(\text{N.A.})/\lambda$, in which λ is the wavelength of the light and N.A. is the numerical aperture of the objective lens. For visible light, $\lambda = 400\text{–}800$ mμ. Since the best numerical aperture obtainable is approximately 1.4, the limit of resolution is of the order of 200 mμ. This is just below the limiting porosity of ordinary bacterial filters that allow viruses to pass, and only the largest viruses can be visualized with the ordinary light microscope. The use of staining techniques improves the visibility of large virus particles both by improving contrast and by increasing the actual size of the particles through deposition of staining material.

In 1887, Buist (*106*) observed particles near the limit of visibility in smears from the contents of pustules of vaccinia and smallpox viruses after staining with the basic dye carbol fuchsin. These particles were later studied by Paschen (*514*), using either carbol fuchsin or Giemsa staining solution (methylene azur and methylene azur eosinate). The work of Paschen established the specific relation between virus activity and the presence of these bodies, which he called *elementary bodies*. This term has remained in general use to indicate particles associated with activity of certain viruses barely visible through the light microscope (figure 14). The elementary bodies of the vaccinia-smallpox virus group are often called Paschen bodies.

Generally, all techniques for staining elementary bodies employ either strongly basic dyes or metallic silver precipitated from a colloidal solution of silver hydroxide onto particles previously treated with a mordant (Morosow's method; see *655*). Elementary bodies in purified suspensions may actually be counted in stained preparations. The identification of elementary bodies in stained preparations hinges on the possibility of associating their presence with the presence of virus activity and may be complicated by the presence of foreign particles of similar size.

Dark-field microscopy is based on the visualization of particles by the light they scatter into the microscope when illuminated with an oblique beam of light which would not enter the objective. It permits visualization of particles as small as 50–100 mμ without revealing any details of size or shape. It has been found useful in the study of the evolution of animal virus infection within infected cells in the living state (figures 77, 78) (*89*).

The resolving power of the microscope can be improved by using *ultraviolet* light instead of visible light. The resolving power increases as the wavelength of the light diminishes. The main difficulty is the requirement for expensive quartz lenses or for mirror optical systems

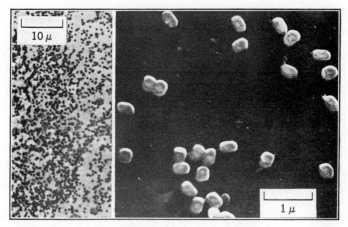

Figure 14 (left). Particles of vaccinia virus (Paschen bodies) stained by Moro-sow's method. Courtesy Dr. G. J. Buddingh, Louisiana State University, New Orleans.

Figure 16 (right). Molluscum contagiosum virus, shadowed preparation. From: Rake and Blank, *J. Invest. Dermatol.* 15:81, 1950. Courtesy Dr. G. W. Rake, Squibb Institute for Medical Research, New York.

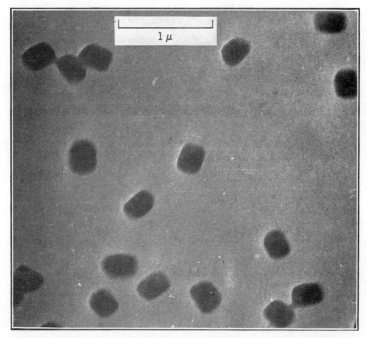

Figure 15. Vaccinia virus, unshadowed preparation. From: Green, Anderson, and Smadel (*274*). Courtesy Dr. T. F. Anderson, University of Pennsylvania, Philadelphia.

since ordinary glass is opaque to ultraviolet light. Moreover, the eye being insensitive to ultraviolet, the image must either be observed on a fluorescent screen or photographed. Ultraviolet microscopy was extensively used by Barnard (38) to observe virus particles. Recently, it has been employed by Swedish workers as a microchemical tool to measure the specific absorption of virus materials for certain wavelengths and to study quantitatively the changes in this material within infected cells (357).

Hagemann (286) introduced into virology a modification of ultraviolet microscopy, *fluorescence microscopy*. The material to be studied is stained with some dye (primulin, thioflavin) which, when illuminated with ultraviolet light, gives out a greenish-yellow fluorescent light. The requirement for quartz optics is reduced to that for a condenser and a microscope slide. Virus elementary bodies, in particular those of vaccinia and psittacosis, can be visualized and counted, but the method gives no useful information as to their size or shape. The recently introduced *phase contrast microscope* (552) has not yet yielded results of particular significance in the study of virus particles.

Electron microscopy. The electron microscope (see *153; 688*) is based on the principle that a beam of electrons can be considered as a wave system possessing a characteristic wavelength, which depends on the speed of the electrons. The faster the electrons, the shorter the wavelength. In the microscope, electrons are emitted by a hot filament, accelerated by a potential difference of 50 to 150 kv, and reach a uniform velocity at which their associated wavelength is much shorter than that of light. The electron beam is focused by electrostatic or, more commonly, by magnetic fields, much as a light beam is focused by lenses. The beam is sent through a specimen, and an enlarged electronic image of the specimen is projected onto a fluorescent screen or a photographic plate. All electrons that have passed through an area of the specimen will be focused onto a corresponding enlarged area of the image, except those that have been deflected and scattered away by interaction with the electrons contained in the atoms of the material under investigation. The probability that an electron, in passing through a unit thickness, is deflected, is proportional to the number of electrons per unit thickness. Therefore, the loss of electrons in a given region of a specimen will depend on the thickness and density of the region and on its chemical composition. Particularly important is the presence of heavy atoms, which contain more electrons per unit volume than lighter atoms. Among the elements present in substantial amounts in biological materials, phosphorus and sulfur are the most absorbent for electrons.

Since all substances, including air, can scatter electrons, the biological specimens must be examined in a high-vacuum chamber containing the electron source, the specimen, and the photographic plate. This places a severe limitation on the use of the electron microscope, since the object must be completely dry. No observation of material in the living state can be made. The specimen is supported by a thin membrane of cellulose nitrate (collodion) or other plastic material, whose thickness (less than 200 A) and lack of heavy atoms make it fairly transparent to electrons. Thin films of metals of low atomic number such as beryllium have also been employed. The average absorption of biological material for electrons is such that hardly any detail can be distinguished when an object is thicker than about 0.5 to 1 μ.

Further information can be obtained by the "shadowing" device (679). A metal is evaporated in a vacuum chamber containing the specimen, in such a way that metallic atoms hit the specimen at a small angle. The shadow effect results from the fact that the object prevents the metal from reaching the surface of the specimen in an area, which appears on a negative as a shadow of the object. The length and shape of the shadow reveal the height and surface irregularities of the object.

Another method is the use of replicas, that is, of plastic films formed by pouring a solution of plastic material on the surface of the object. The film formed by evaporation of the solvent is then stripped off the surface, and the pattern of ridges and valleys, corresponding to the depressions and reliefs on the surface of the object, can be studied with the electron microscope. This method has been particularly useful in the study of details of crystal surfaces. Pseudoreplicas, in which the stripped film carries with it a layer of the material under study, are often more useful in virus studies.

The electron microscope has made it possible to observe the detailed morphology of virus particles (figures 15–26). The Paschen bodies of vaccinia (figure 15) have a brick-shaped appearance with areas of greater opacity, corresponding either to areas of greater condensation or to less collapsible regions (274). The darker, more absorbent areas might also represent greater concentrations of nucleic acid, and, therefore, of phosphorus atoms. Treatment with alkali, which removes large amounts of nucleoproteins from the elementary bodies, leaves a less absorbent "ghost," possibly an empty membrane.

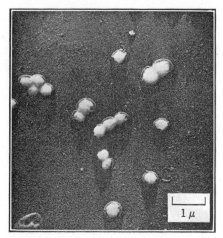

Figure 17. Feline pneumonitis virus, shadowed. From: Hamre, Rake, and Rake, *J. Exp. Med.* **86**:1, 1947. Courtesy Dr. G. W. Rake, Squibb Institute for Medical Research, New York.

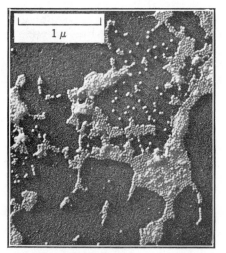

Figure 18. Spontaneous mouse encephalitis virus, strain FA, shadowed. From: Leyon, *Exp. Cell Res.* **2**:207, 1951. Courtesy Dr. H. Leyon, University of Uppsala, Sweden.

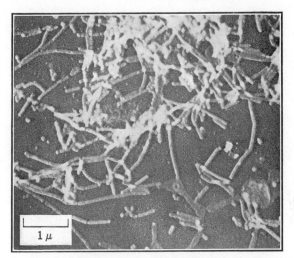

Figure 19. Influenza A, strain PR8. Virus filaments and particles in tissue cultures. From: Murphy, Kurzon, and Bang, *Proc. Soc. Exp. Biol. Med.* **73**:596, 1950. Courtesy Dr. F. B. Bang, Johns Hopkins University, Baltimore.

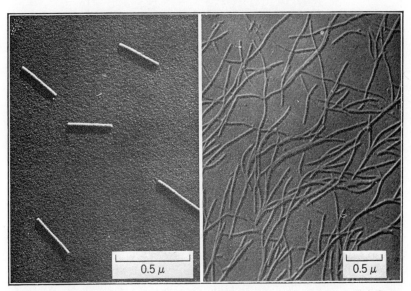

Figure 20. Tobacco mosaic virus. Courtesy Drs. C. A. Knight and R. C. Williams, Virus Laboratory, University of California, Berkeley.

Figure 21. Potato virus X. Courtesy Dr. E. van Slogteren, Laboratorium voor Bloemollenderzoek, Lisse, Holland.

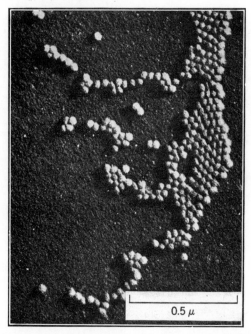

0.5 μ

Figure 22. Tomato bushy stunt virus, air dried. Note the tendency of the particles to orient in close-packed array under the influence of surface tension. Courtesy Dr. R. C. Williams, Virus Laboratory, University of California, Berkeley.

The particles of each virus are often almost perfectly homogeneous
in size. This homogeneity cannot be attributed simply to a selection
during the preparation of the suspensions, since the methods most
employed for purification, such as differential centrifugation, are not
very selective for size. The elementary bodies have a narrower size
distribution than that of bacterial cells from a growing culture, a fact
that had suggested quite early that they may reproduce by some
method other than increase in size followed by fission.

A comparison of the morphology of the various virus particles illustrates the basis for the use of morphological criteria in the classification
of viruses (568). Viruses of the smallpox-vaccinia group have similar
particles, indistinguishable from those of mouse ectromelia, which, on
the basis of biological considerations, has recently been shown to be
related to the vaccinia group (215). The viruses of the influenza
group have indistinguishable particles. The same is true of those of
the psittacosis-lymphogranuloma group.

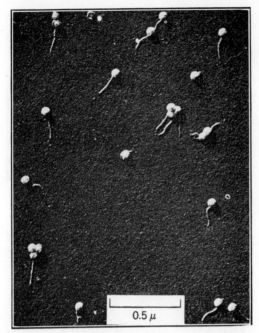

0.5 μ

Figure 23. Phage T1, air dried. Courtesy Dr. R. C. Williams, Virus Laboratory, University of California, Berkeley.

The particles of several plant viruses are shown in figures 20–22. For various bacteriophages, the morphology of the specific particles (figures 23–26) is closely correlated with criteria of genetic and serological relationship. The tadpole-like particles of many phages are among the most beautiful objects revealed by the electron microscope. Their complex morphology is an indication of their elaborate organization. Transparent ghosts with intact tails can be obtained from tailed phages by a number of treatments, including osmotic shock (*20;* figure 27). This suggests the removal of a portion of the virus materials upon lowering of the salt concentration. The "ghosts" are now known to contain most of the protein and none of the nucleic acid of the phage (*313*).

Bacteriophages illustrate the possibility of identifying and characterizing virus particles in the electron microscope through some specific manifestation of their interaction with host cells. Suspensions of different bacteriophages, derived from the same host cells, show particles characteristic for each phage. By taking "action shots" of

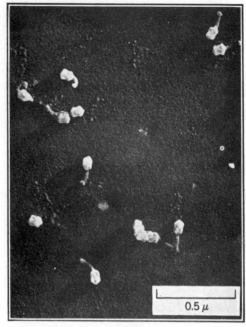

Figure 24. Phage T4, frozen-dried. Notice the geometrical features of the heads. Courtesy Dr. R. C. Williams, Virus Laboratory, University of California, Berkeley.

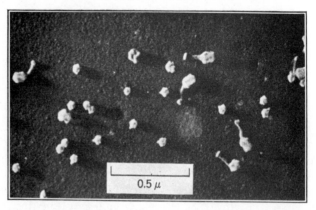

Figure 25. A mixture of phages T6 and T3, frozen-dried. Note the short appendage on the bipyramidal particles of T3. Courtesy Drs. D. Fraser and R. C. Williams, Virus Laboratory, University of California, Berkeley.

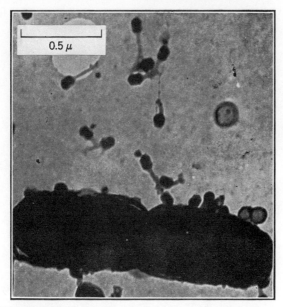

Figure 26. Phage T4, unshadowed. Courtesy Dr. T. F. Anderson, University of Pennsylvania, Philadelphia.

preparations dried at intervals after mixing phage and bacteria, it can be seen that the characteristic particles become adsorbed onto bacteria (*440;* figure 29). Upon bacterial lysis, characteristic particles are liberated in amounts corresponding to the known rise in phage activity (*448*) (figures 30, 31).

Sometimes, virus particles can be identified by the demonstration of some specific reaction, for example, adsorption of the viruses of the influenza group on the surface of specifically agglutinable red cells (figure 32). The reaction of virus particles with specific antibody has been demonstrated in the electron microscope, either as a specific conglutination of the characteristic particles or as an increase in thickness of the virus particles upon coating by antibody molecules (*22*). The thickness of the rod-shaped tobacco mosaic virus increases upon treatment with antibody by an amount supposedly corresponding to twice the length of an antibody molecule. This suggests a radial orientation of the antibody molecules perpendicular to the axis of the virus particle.

The electron microscope can be used to count the number of virus particles in a suspension (*677*). The virus suspension is mixed with a suspension of particles of polystyrene latex in known concentration.

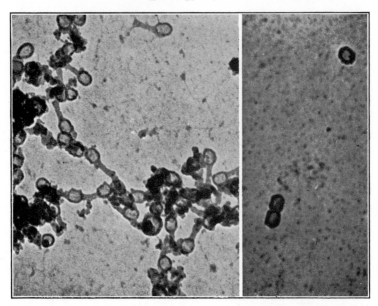

Figure 27 (left). Phage T4, unshadowed, after osmotic shock treatment. Notice the normal skin and tail and the empty head. Courtesy Dr. T. F. Anderson, University of Pennsylvania, Philadelphia.

Figure 28 (right). Immature particles of phage T2 ("doughnuts") produced under the action of proflavine. Note the resemblance with empty phage heads (see figure 27). Courtesy Dr. T. F. Anderson, University of Pennsylvania, Philadelphia.

The latex particles are spherical, extremely homogeneous in size, and easily countable. The mixed suspension is sprayed in a fine mist with a nebulizer, and droplets are collected on the specimen holder, are allowed to dry, and are examined. Whenever a droplet fits within one electron microscopic field, all the particles of either latex or virus it contains are counted (figure 33). From their relative numbers, we can then calculate the concentration of virus particles in the suspension. The estimate can be made quite accurate by increasing the numbers of particles counted. This method was used, for example, to compare the number of phage particles with that of the infectious units of phage (*449*) and to calculate the weight of the particle of tobacco mosaic virus. This was done by counting particles in accurately weighed preparations of pure virus (*680*).

The use of the electron microscope to visualize virus particles in the intracellular state is somewhat limited by the general opacity of cells

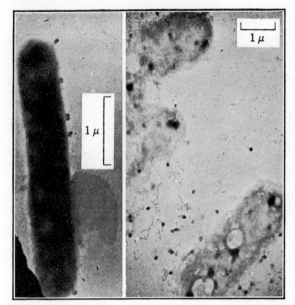

Figures 29–31. Interaction between bacteriophage and bacterium as seen in the electron microscope. *Figure 29* (left). An infected cell of *Escherichia coli* with attached particles of phage T2. *Figure 31* (right). Cell walls after lysis, surrounded by phage particles. From: Luria et al. (*448*).

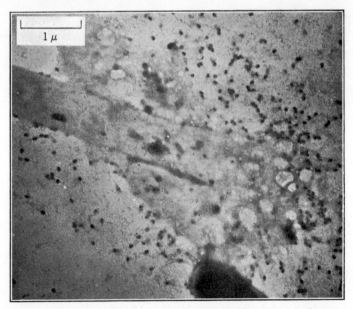

Figure 30. Two infected cells during lysis, with liberation of phage particles and protoplasmic debris. From: Luria et al. (*448*).

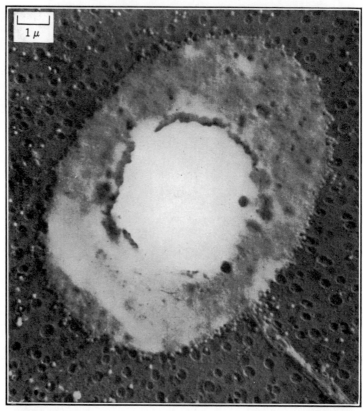

Figure 32. A chick red blood cell with particles of influenza virus B adsorbed on the cell surface. From: Heinmets (*296*). Courtesy Dr. F. Heinmets, Naval Medical Field Research Laboratory, Camp Lejeune, N. C.

to the electron beam, due to excessive thickness. Special techniques have been devised for use with tissue cultures and for observation of very thin sections of tissues (see chapter 11). The sizes of the particles associated with a number of viruses, as derived from electron microscopy, are included in table 6.

DETERMINATION OF PARTICLE SIZE BY ULTRAFILTRATION

Optical methods seldom allow direct identification of visible particles with the active virus, since the particles observed cannot be tested further. The size of active virus particles, however, can often be estimated without inactivation even on dilute, impure virus sus-

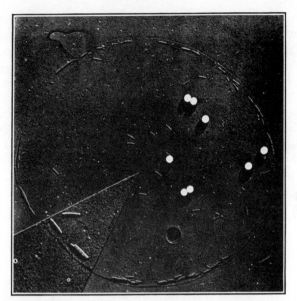

Figure 33. A droplet pattern from a mixture of tobacco mosaic virus and polystyrene latex particles. The concentration of the latex particles in the mixture is known, and the number of virus particles can be estimated from the ratio between the counts of the two types of particles. The enlarged sector shows the virus particles more clearly. Note that the rod-shaped virus particles orient themselves parallel to the edge of the droplet, due to the changes in surface tension during drying. From: *Research Today*, 8:28, 1952. Courtesy Dr. R. C. Williams, Virus Laboratory, University of California, Berkeley.

pensions by ultrafiltration, a method based on a sieve principle. Ultrafilters that retain virus are valuable not only in measuring viruses but also in obtaining virus-free preparations and in separating different viruses from a mixture.

The most useful ultrafilters are collodion membranes prepared by removing the solvent from thin layers of collodion solutions. The average pore size of the resulting collodion membrane depends on the concentration of collodion in the original solution, on the nature and the concentration of the solvent, and on the rate of solvent elimination. Early membranes prepared from solutions of collodion in acetic acid have been replaced by accurately calibrated "gradocol" membranes from ether-alcohol solution (*204*). The average pore diameter (A.P.D.) of a membrane is estimated indirectly from the pressure needed to force the first air bubbles through the membrane under water, or to force through it a given amount of water per unit time. The relation between the A.P.D. and the size of the particles that can go through the membrane is then obtained by filtering particles of known size. The correction factor, that is, the ratio between the A.P.D. and the diameter of the smallest particles that can pass, was originally given (204) as follows: A.P.D. 10–100 mμ, correction factor 3 to 2; A.P.D. 100–500 mμ, correction factor 2 to 1.3; A.P.D. 500–1000 mμ,

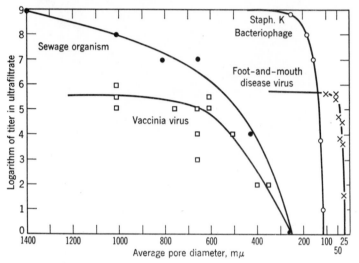

Figure 34. Filtration end-points for several viruses and other microorganisms. From: Elford (204).

correction factor 1.3 to 1. According to a more recent study (474), however, the correction factor is about 1.25 and fairly independent of A.P.D. The medium in which the material to be measured is suspended plays an important role, because it affects adsorptive phenomena that take place on the walls of the pores.

The size of virus particles is estimated from the filtration end-point, that is, from the A.P.D. of the finest filter that allows some virus to come through. For homodispersed viruses, there should be an abrupt transition from filters that allow all virus to pass, to filters that retain it all. In practice, such an abrupt change is only found for the smallest viruses (figure 34). The deviations for large particles depend more on the loss of virus particles on the walls of the pores than on inhomogeneity of virus materials.

DETERMINATION OF PARTICLE SIZE BY HYDRODYNAMIC METHODS

A number of procedures for determining the size of virus particles rest on the analysis of the motion of the particles through the suspending fluid. Since these procedures are now widely used and many properties of viruses are reported in terms based on these methods, their principles should be clearly understood by virus students. The two most important types of motion to be considered are the sedimentation of virus particles in a centrifugal field and the changes in concentration of virus particles by diffusion.

Sedimentation of spherical particles. The case of spherical particles is the simplest. A spherical particle of radius r suspended in a liquid will sediment in a gravitational or centrifugal field if its density d is greater than the density d_0 of the medium. In a gravitational field, the motor force P is equal to the gravity acceleration g multiplied by the difference between the mass of the particle and the mass of a corresponding volume of the medium: $P_g = \frac{4}{3}\pi r^3(d - d_0)g$. In a centrifugal field, the gravitational acceleration g is replaced by the centrifugal acceleration $c = (2\pi\omega)^2 x$, where ω is the number of revolutions per unit time and x is the distance of the particle from the axis of rotation of the centrifuge: $P_c = \frac{4}{3}\pi r^3(d - d_0)c$.

As a particle is accelerated in a centrifuge, its velocity v increases. This will in turn cause an increase in friction. The frictional force is measured by: $\phi = vf$. f is the "friction coefficient." Its value for spherical particles is $6\pi\eta r$, where η is the viscosity of the medium. As the velocity increases, we reach a point where the frictional force balances the centrifugal force. The particle will then continue to move at a uniform velocity, which is obtained by writing $P_c = \phi$, or

$$\frac{4}{3}\pi r^3(d - d_0)c = 6\pi\eta r v \qquad [5]$$

$$v = \frac{2}{9}\frac{(d - d_0)c}{\eta}r^2 \qquad [6]$$

These equations express Stokes' law, which describes the motion of spherical particles in a fluid under ideal conditions (that is, no interaction among the particles; the size of the particles large as compared with the size of the solvent molecules; no disturbance due to convection currents).

We see, then, that the motion of a spherical particle in a centrifugal field is determined by its size and density, by the density and viscosity of the medium, and by the centrifugal force. This force depends on the speed of rotation and on the size of the centrifugal rotor (or "head"), which determines the distance of the particle from the axis of rotation. From equation 6 we can derive the value of a magnitude $S = v/c$, called the *sedimentation constant*, which is characteristic of a given particle in a given medium at a given temperature.[1] Equation 5 can then be written in the form:

$$ S = \frac{\frac{4}{3}\pi r^3 d - \frac{4}{3}\pi r^3 d_0}{6\pi\eta r} = \frac{m[1 - (d_0/d)]}{f} \qquad [7] $$

Equations 6 and 7 can be used to determine the radius and mass of a spherical particle if we have methods to measure its density and its velocity in a centrifuge, since the centrifugal force and the density of the medium and its viscosity can all be measured without difficulty.

Diffusion of spherical particles. If a layer of a suspension of particles and a layer of the medium alone are placed in contact along a boundary plane, the random motion of the particles will make some of them pass through the boundary. The particles will move back and forth, and more will cross past the plane of the initial boundary from the side where the concentration is higher, resulting in progressive equalization of the concentrations of the two sides. If the particles are large compared with the molecules of the medium and are few

---

[1] The student should remember that all units of measure for different quantities entering an equation must be comparable. The best method is to use the so-called CGS system (centimeter, gram, second). If r is expressed in centimeters, x must also be in centimeters, and g and c in centimeters per second. This often forces a change from the units most commonly employed: for example, the diameter of a virus particle, generally given in millimicrons, must be translated into centimeters. The decimal notation (see page 40) helps in handling large or small numbers: a radius of 12 mμ corresponds to 1.2×10^{-6} cm, and the corresponding volume is $\frac{4}{3}\pi(1.2 \times 10^{-6})^3$ cm^3 = $4.2 \times 1.74 \times 10^{-18}$ cm^3 = 7.3×10^{-18} cm^3. The value of ω is often given in revolutions per minute (rpm). If ω is translated into revolutions per second (60 rpm = 1 rps), and if x is given in centimeters, an approximate comparison of centrifugal and gravitational accelerations is easily made, since the latter (980 cm per sec) can be taken as about 1000, and the ratio of the two accelerations, that is, the ratio of centrifugal force to gravity, will be about 1/1000 the value of the centrifugal force.

Densities are given in grams per cubic centimeter (or in ratios of the density to that of water at 20° C). Viscosity can also be measured as the ratio to the viscosity of water at 20° C taken as 0.01. The sedimentation constant, that is, the rate of sedimentation of the particle in water at 20° C under a unity centrifugal force, is obtained in centimeters per second. Being generally very small, it is often expressed in Svedberg units (S_{20}): 1 $S_{20} = 10^{-13}$ cm per sec. For example, the sedimentation constant of tomato bushy stunt virus is 146 $S_{20} = 1.46 \times 10^{-11}$ cm per sec.

enough not to hamper one another, their kinetic energy will depend only on the temperature, and their velocity will depend on their mass and on the temperature. The resistance of the medium depends on the frictional force, that is, on the velocity of the particles and on their frictional coefficient (see page 73). The change in concentration that takes place in 1 second across 1 cm² of a boundary between solutions differing by 1 unit concentration is defined as the *diffusion constant D.* Its value is given by

$$D = \frac{RT}{Nf} \text{ cm}^2 \text{ sec}^{-1}$$ [8]

where T is the absolute temperature, R is the so-called gas constant, N is the Avogadro number (6.02×10^{23}) and f, the friction coefficient, is given for spherical particles by $6\pi\eta r$. R and T appear in equation 8 (Einstein's equation) because of the equivalence of the motion of the molecules in an ideal gas and of spherical particles in an ideal solution. For the derivation of equation 8 the reader should consult a textbook of physical chemistry.

The diffusion constant D is obtained by measuring the concentration of particles at different times at known distances from the plane of the initial boundary.[2] The radius of the particle can then be obtained directly:

$$r = \frac{RT}{ND6\pi\eta}$$

Nonspherical particles. In the case of nonspherical particles the situation is complicated by the fact that the frictional force depends on a complex function of the linear dimensions (length, width, thickness) of the sedimenting particle. Measurements of sedimentation velocity alone or of diffusion alone do not give any direct information about the volume or mass of the particle. One way of getting around this difficulty is to measure *both* sedimentation and diffusion constants and to divide one by the other. The resulting value is independent of

[2] The actual measurements are made as follows: The suspension and the medium alone are placed in contact at time 0. At various intervals the concentration at various distances from the boundary is measured either optically or by other means. The concentration $C_{x,\,t}$ at a distance x and time t is related to x, t, and D by the expressions:

$$C_{x,\,t} = \frac{C_{x,\,0}}{2} \left(1 - \frac{2}{\sqrt{\pi}} \int_0^y e^{-v^2} \, dy \right) \qquad y^2 = \frac{x^2}{4Dt}$$

the friction coefficient and, therefore, of the shape of the particle, and is proportional to the mass only:

$$\frac{S}{D} = \frac{m[1 - (d_0/d)]N}{RT} \qquad m = \frac{S}{D} \frac{RT}{N[1 - (d_0/d)]}$$

If all units are CGS, m is obtained in grams.

An essentially equivalent way is to measure the so-called *sedimentation equilibrium*. In a relatively slow centrifugal field, the increased concentration of particles in the bottom of the tube will create an increased tendency to diffuse backward. When sedimentation and back diffusion balance each other, an equilibrium is reached, and from the concentration of particles at two given points in the centrifuge tube we can determine directly their mass.

Once the mass of an asymmetrical particle is known, we can calculate what volume, radius, and friction coefficient (f_0) it would have if it were a sphere. The ratio of the actual value of f to the value f_0 gives the "asymmetry coefficient," which indicates to what extent our particle differs from a sphere. This criterion, however, is somewhat ambiguous. The same effect produced by asymmetry could also be produced by hydration, that is, by the particle taking up water in a liquid medium. A hydrated particle diffuses more slowly because its radius is greater. The increase in volume produced by hydration causes a corresponding reduction in density. Therefore, the radius calculated from the sedimentation velocity will be too small, if the value used in equation 6 for the density of the particle is derived from measurements on dry material. For hydrated spherical particles, if the density is corrected for hydration, the radius obtained from diffusion and sedimentation measurements should be the same.

Measurement of particle density. The density of virus particles in the hydrated state can itself be measured by centrifugation. If a particle is centrifuged in a medium of the same density as its own, no sedimentation takes place. The density is measured by centrifuging the particles in a series of media of different densities. The media should be solutions of substances with low osmotic activity such as proteins, for example, serum albumin, in order not to alter the state of hydration of the particles (593). The density at which the sedimentation rate would be zero is obtained by extrapolation (figure 35). This technique attributes to different viruses densities of 1.1–1.2 as against densities of 1.3 or higher obtained for dry virus preparations. For different viruses, the amount of hydration water varies between 50 and 100% of the dry weight. These amounts of water are greater than those generally associated with purified proteins in solution (30–35%). This has been taken to suggest the existence of an osmotic membrane at the surface of some virus particles.

Sedimentation and diffusion apparatus. Some of the largest virus elementary bodies, such as those of psittacosis or vaccinia viruses, can

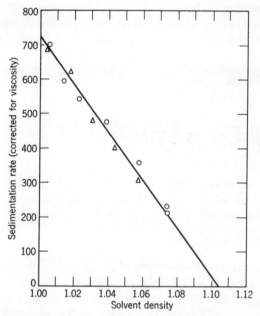

Figure 35. The sedimentation rate of influenza virus A as a function of the solvent density. The density was varied by adding bovine serum albumin, 0 to 25%. The ordinate gives the sedimentation rate. The extrapolation to rate 0 (no sedimentation) gives a density of 1.104. Data from two experiments. From: Sharp et al. (*593*).

be sedimented in fast centrifuges of the usual laboratory type. For smaller viruses, high-speed centrifuges are necessary to provide centrifugal forces sufficient to sediment them. The so-called ultracentrifuges, operated by electrical motors or by oil or air turbines, give speeds of 60,000 rpm or higher. For a particle located 6 cm from the rotational axis, 60,000 rpm correspond to a centrifugal force 250,000 times gravity. Most ultracentrifuges operate in a high vacuum, thereby reducing friction and temperature changes.

The construction and operation of ultracentrifuges present complex technical problems. For virus workers, the important problems are those connected with the measurement of the sedimentation of virus material. Ingenious methods have been developed to measure changes in concentration of virus material during centrifugation, particularly by workers possessing only centrifuges of rather simple construction. One such method consists of freezing the contents of the centrifuge tubes in the centrifuge head immediately after centrifugation, after which virus activity in various sections of the frozen columns is measured (*268*). Another method (*204*) consists of collecting a sample centrifuged in a short capillary tube immersed in a larger tube. From

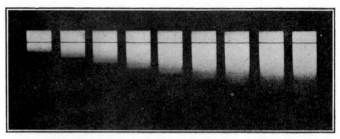

Figure 36. Sedimentation diagram of purified Eastern equine encephalomyelitis virus in the ultracentrifuge. The photographs were taken at 2.5-minute intervals during centrifugation at 15,000 g. Courtesy Dr. D. G. Sharp, Department of Surgery, Duke University, Durham, N. C.

the concentration of virus activity that remains in the capillary tube, the sedimentation velocity can be determined.

With the modern ultracentrifuges, measurements are made while the centrifuge is in motion by means of the so-called "analytical" heads, in which a beam of light is sent through centrifuge tubes (or cells) with transparent walls. The virus preparation must possess a high degree of purity and must be present in high enough concentration to give measurable absorption and scattering of the light. As the virus material sediments, the optical density increases toward the bottom of the centrifuge tube and decreases at the top. If all particles responsible for light absorption sediment at the same speed, there will be a sharp boundary migrating from the top down. The presence of such a boundary can be determined in two ways: either by photographic absorption measurements through the column of liquid (figure 36), or by locating the boundary as a region at which the refractive index of the liquid column shows an abrupt change (the *Schlieren* technique). Besides giving information on the sedimentation properties of a pure virus material, the method can also be used to obtain information on its degree of purity and homogeneity. A suspension of identical particles should give a single boundary, whose sharpness is only limited by diffusion.

With viruses ultraviolet light is often employed in the measurement of optical density. The high nucleic acid content of most viruses makes their absorption of ultraviolet light strong enough to allow analysis of relatively dilute solutions (0.01 mg per ml).

Diffusion measurements are made with a variety of apparatus, all of which involve careful layering of a virus suspension against the medium alone, after which the changes in concentration at various distances from the boundary formed at the layering point are measured. Optical methods similar to those employed in the ultracentrifuge can be used. It appears from the literature that diffusion measurements require even greater skill and are more liable to error than sedimentation measurements.

It may be pointed out that the use of physical methods to determine changes in virus concentration requires careful and painstaking work to justify the identification of the material with the virus. An example of the results obtained by these techniques may be instructive (405). The tomato bushy stunt virus studied in the dry state by electron microscopy and x-ray diffraction has been found to have spherical particles of 21.8 mμ diameter. This corresponds to a mass of 13 Mh (density 1.3). Diffusion and sedimentation measurements indicated a discrepancy between the diameters calculated from diffusion constant and from sedimentation constant, respectively. The discrepancy could be explained either by a fairly high degree of asymmetry—contradicted by the known spherical shape of the particles—or by an amount of hydration corresponding to 0.76 gram of water per gram of virus. The latter interpretation was confirmed by crystallographic measurements on crystals of virus in the wet state. The mass of the hydrated particle is 18 Mh units.[3]

Results of the same type were obtained with a number of spherical or nearly spherical particles associated with animal viruses. Sedimentation studies of sperm-shaped bacteriophages indicate the occurrence of a double boundary, probably due to the formation of aggregates of different shapes (592). Diffusion measurements on phage, when properly made, give results in agreement with those of centrifugation (318; 525; 539).

Electrophoresis and light scattering. There are additional methods that can provide information on the size, shape, and homogeneity of

[3] As a comparison, the reader may recall that the dry mass of a small bacterial cell is of the order of 10^5 Mh units.

virus particles. In *electrophoresis* we measure the speed of migration of particles in an electric field. The migration of particles depends on their overall electrical charge, which depends in turn on the electrolytic dissociation of the acidic and basic groups. This is controlled by the *p*H of the medium. The method is useful in purifying and identifying proteins and in checking their degree of purity, and has been applied to several viruses (*485; 539*).

Light-scattering measurements are based on the fact that a suspension of particles scatters light from an incident beam to an extent depending on the number of particles and on their volume (*189*). Measurement of the amount of light scattered at different angles may also be used to calculate the degree of asymmetry of elongated particles.

SUMMARY ON THE SIZE AND SHAPE OF VIRUS PARTICLES

The illustrations in figures 15–26 and the data in table 6 give a representative picture of the types of elements that are the carriers of

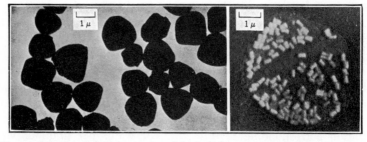

Figures 37–40. Polyhedra and polyhedral disease viruses from Lepidoptera. *Figure 37* (left). Polyhedral bodies from *Choristoneura fumiferana*. From: Bergold, *Can. J. Zool.* **29**:17, 1951. Courtesy Dr. G. H. Bergold, Laboratory of Insect Pathology, Sault Sainte Marie, Ontario. *Figure 38* (right). A polyhedron from *Prodenia praefica* partly dissolved in alkali, showing the polyhedral envelope and the virus bundles. From: Hughes, *J. Bact.*, **39**:189, 1950. Courtesy Dr. K. M. Hughes, University of California, Berkeley.

virus activity in the extracellular state. These elements are generally called "virus particles," a term that does not commit us to any interpretation as to their nature. The particles are the objects capable of initiating production of more virus upon introduction into new susceptible hosts.

The information on virus particle size and shape does not reveal any basic trend or similarity among viruses as a group. The shapes vary

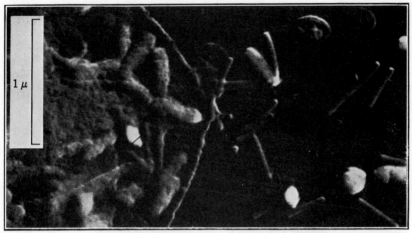

Figure 39. A polyhedron from *Porthetria dispar* in dissolution. Rod-shaped virus particles are seen singly and in bundles. Some are within "developmental" membranes, which are also seen empty and collapsed. From: Bergold, in: *The Nature of Virus Multiplication,* Cambridge University Press. Courtesy Dr. G. H. Bergold, Laboratory of Insect Pathology, Sault Sainte Marie, Ontario.

Figure 40. Particles from polyhedra of *Bombyx mori* (silkworm) in various stages of disintegration, showing empty "intimate membranes." From: Bergold, in: *The Nature of Virus Multiplication,* Cambridge University Press. Courtesy Dr. G. H. Bergold, Laboratory of Insect Pathology, Sault Sainte Marie, Ontario.

from spheres to greatly elongated rods. Internal structures are often evident, possibly due to local accumulations of nucleic acid. The possibility of artifacts in electron microscopy should not be overlooked, however. Complex shapes such as tadpole-like particles, sometimes with double tails, have been observed mainly in phages. Similar forms for the Newcastle disease agent and other viruses may be arti-

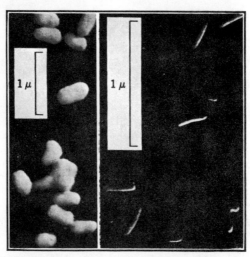

Figures 41–43. Capsules and virus particles from granuloses of Lepidoptera. Courtesy Dr. G. H. Bergold, Laboratory of Insect Pathology, Saulte Sainte Marie, Ontario. Figure 41 (left). Capsules from *Choristoneura fumiferana*. From: Bergold, in: *The Nature of Virus Multiplication*, Cambridge University Press. *Figure 42* (right). Virus particles from capsules of *Choristoneura fumiferana*.

facts (37; 591). On the other hand, the filaments observed regularly in recently isolated strains of influenza (131; 494) seem to be images of forms really produced by infected host cells. These filaments have the same transverse diameter as the spherical particles of these viruses and give similar reactions with red blood cells. . They appear to split into spherical particles (figure 19). Filaments described as the normal form of poliomyelitis virus (248) may, instead, have been artifacts.

Among the rod-shaped particles of several plant viruses, there are differences in thickness, length, and flexibility. The particles of tobacco mosaic virus are rods 15 mμ thick and about 300 mμ long. Their tendency to lengthwise and sidewise aggregation has rendered their study by hydrodynamic methods a most perplexing problem for the physicochemist (405).

A most interesting group of rod-shaped particles comprises the agents of the capsular and polyhedral diseases of insects (*66; 67; 68a; 627*). The virus particles are contained in characteristic intracellular inclusions (figures 37–43). In capsular diseases (*granuloses*) the capsules or granules are mainly intracytoplasmic. In polyhedral diseases, the polyhedra are intranuclear. The virus particles are rigid rods, mostly around 40×300 mμ, somewhat larger for some of the viruses (*627*). The rods are present singly in each capsule. In the

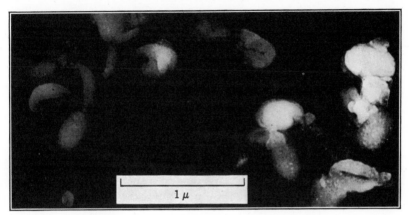

Figure 43.   Empty capsules from *Cacoecia murinana.*

polyhedra they are in bundles (figures 37–40). Each polyhedron contains several hundred virus particles, contained in a protein matrix with a distinct membrane.

Other particles of varying morphology are also found in the polyhedra, and have been used in reconstructing a developmental cycle of the rods from small spherical elements (*68; 68a;* figures 39, 40).

The individual insect virus particles possess an *intimate membrane* and seem to be formed in bundles within a common *developmental membrane*. These details are best observed in polyhedra that have been partially disintegrated with alkali. In some diseases the polyhedra contain mostly spherical particles, only exceptionally rod particles (*611*).

There are obvious limitations to the usefulness of information on the morphology of extracellular forms in the study of intracellular parasites. Increasing evidence is accumulating to show that viruses during their reproduction in the intracellular state differ in morphology and organization from the free virus particles, which may be thought of as resting stages of microorganisms that go through complex life cycles (*41; 439*). Even in the present rather primitive state of our knowledge on the organization of virus particles, several facts suggest that many of them differ from the reproductive form of the virus by possessing some kind of protecting covering or membrane. This is clearly so with some bacteriophages. Upon infection of a bacterium, the protein envelope of the phage is left on the surface of the host cell (*313*), and new protein envelopes are formed late in the process of maturation of the new particles (*175;* see chapter 8).

Among other viruses, vaccinia particles seem to have a membrane. The capsules of some insect viruses may have a protective function (see *355a*). Any such coverings would have to function also as a device for bringing or releasing the reproductive element of the virus into its new host cell. Further discussion of these ideas will be found in chapters 8–13.

Purification and Chemical Composition of Virus Material

THE MEANING OF PURITY

The material that carries virus activity in crude preparations is mixed with large amounts of foreign matter. Before any study on its chemical composition can be made, the specific virus material must be separated from the extraneous materials. We can define the goal of purification as the preparation of material carrying virus activity in a form as free as possible from noninfectious matter. Immediately we meet with theoretical difficulties, many of which have been pointed out by Pirie (520). Any method of purification will depend upon what we consider as pure. Criteria of purity are by no means definite. They vary with the interest of the investigator. An analytical chemist would aim at obtaining a virus preparation consisting of particles identical in size and chemical composition, each carrying equal and full activity and representing a "molecule" of virus, according to the usual definition of molecule as the minimum amount of matter endowed with all the chemical properties of a substance. A physicochemist, by the use of his techniques, would tend to consider as pure a population of particles of uniform size that also satisfy additional criteria, for example, the possession of uniform numbers of acid and of basic groups as measured by electrophoresis. A biologist would probably consider as ideal a purification method that could separate *all* particles with virus activity (ability to reproduce) from all inactive material.

None of these criteria is either clear-cut or operationally satisfactory. The uniformity of chemical composition may fail both as a theoretical criterion—since a variety of chemical forms and configurations may be compatible with a given virus activity—and as a practical criterion—since the gross chemical composition of most proteins is very similar and their finer organization is still beyond our means of study. For example, the chemical differences between active virus particles and particles inactivated by mild treatments are generally well beyond the analytical techniques of the most skillful chemist. The same can be said of the purely physicochemical criteria, which force upon virus material requirements for uniformity in size, shape, or electric charge, while neglecting more relevant information. For example, a mixture of active and radiation-inactivated tomato bushy stunt virus crystallizes in exactly the same way as a "pure" preparation of active virus. Is the mixture still "pure"?

The biological criterion of activity may also be deceiving, both practically, by requiring an often impossible separation of active from inactive particles, and theoretically, by postulating that association of activity with a given material identifies all this material with the virus and that all inactive material is nonvirus. We should remember that the definition itself of the minimum amount of material required to initiate virus production presents several ambiguities. On the one hand, the "true virus" might be adsorbed on inert carriers, still removable without impairing virus activity. On the other hand, the elimination of all material not essential for virus infectivity, as tested by reinoculation, may lead to the neglect of some important aspect of the virus. In fact, there is no reason to assume that only what is strictly necessary for infectivity is virus. By similar reasoning, we should say, on the basis of experiments on artificial insemination, that the only material that can be defined as a male animal is its sperm. In other words, the criterion of infectivity—ability to enter a sensitive host and to reproduce in it—may be too restrictive, since it may ignore specific portions of the virus which are connected with virus activity only when the virus is in its intracellular state (50; 522).

Some of these problems may appear to be peculiar to viruses, but we must remember that the question of purity, interpreted in chemical terms, is raised for viruses and not for full-fledged organisms, because the small size and presumably simple organization of virus particles suggest for them a simpler, more easily interpretable chemical structure.

If we decide that all criteria of purity must be operational, that is, defined in terms of meaningful, performable operations, we can state the problem of the physical and chemical structure of virus particles in the following form: Is a certain material, present in a virus suspension, specific? If so, what are its chemical and physical properties? Is its presence necessary for virus transmission and reproduction? Is this material related to specific, noninfectious materials present in the same suspension? Is the infectious material present in one form only (homogeneously dispersed, chemically uniform)? What components of the suspension are necessary or responsible for the various phases of the virus interaction with the host? Is there any detectable relationship between the specific material and some nonspecific component of the host?

In these general terms, the problems of virus purity cover practically the entire field of virology. This formulation, however, gives us some guidance in the more modest task of analyzing the properties of those particles with which it appears reasonable to identify, at least in first approximation, the specific virus material in infectious preparations. It has been pointed out that the very process of extraction can modify virus material. For example, viruses affecting strawberry plants can hardly be studied in vitro in strawberry extracts because of the presence in the plant sap of enough tannic acid to precipitate not only the virus but also most protein materials (47). Another case in point is that of pneumonia virus of mice, which, if extracted by grinding the infected lung tissue, becomes associated with a nonspecific host component (160).

When virus activity has been attributed on reasonable grounds to certain material particles, these can be separated and their chemical composition can be analyzed. The process of purification should be accompanied by an increase of virus activity per unit mass of the purified material. This is not always so, however, because of occasional losses of activity in the course of the purification process, either by inactivation, or by irreversible aggregation, or by loss of a portion of activity that was associated with other materials. These losses sometimes make it difficult to use the results of purification procedures as evidence for the identification of virus activity with one or another type of particles. Since all viruses have been found to consist in large part of protein material, a convenient way of following the decrease in foreign material in the course of purification is to measure at different stages of the process the number of infectious units per unit weight of protein nitrogen. An increase in virus titer per milligram of protein nitrogen indicates a removal of noninfectious proteins.

Activity measurements on purified virus preparations, although giving some indication as to the extent to which impurities have been eliminated, can seldom be considered as a test of purity, because of the low efficiency of most titration methods, as discussed in chapter 3. The best preparations of tobacco mosaic virus, for example, are infectious in concentrations of 10^{-13} to 10^{-14} gram of protein per ml. This still represents over 1000 particles 40 Mh in weight. Still, suspensions with such a low virus content do not give any of the usual tests for proteins, which at best are sensitive to concentrations of 10^{-5} gram per ml. This explains, without justifying them, early claims for "protein-free virus preparations."

Small amounts of impurities can be detected in purified preparations of plant viruses by the very sensitive serological tests. Chester (*130*) found that the uterine horn of a guinea pig sensitized with normal plant sap would respond with an anaphylactic contraction to the addition of purified tobacco mosaic virus preparations to the surrounding fluid (Shultz-Dale technique). In some cases, the impurities could be removed by treatment with proteolytic enzymes, which do not attack the virus. Bacterial impurities in purified phage preparations can be removed by precipitation with antibacterial serum (*146*).

METHODS OF PURIFICATION

The methods employed for the separation of viruses are borrowed from protein chemistry. We can employ chemical treatments such as "salting-out" procedures, which consist of the addition of high concentrations of very soluble salts, for example, ammonium sulfate (neutralized). Proteins are forced out of solution at salt concentrations that fairly well characterize different groups of them. For example, serum albumin is defined as a serum fraction that precipitates at 100% saturation with ammonium sulfate, whereas serum globulins precipitate at 50% saturation. It is also possible to precipitate viruses by adding alcohol or by adjusting the pH of the medium to the point of minimum solubility (isoelectric point). Both types of treatment can be used in the purification of tobacco mosaic virus, which precipitates at $\frac{1}{3}$ to $\frac{1}{2}$ saturation with ammonium sulfate and is stable at its isoelectric point (pH 3.4). Some viruses, for example, those of foot-and-mouth disease and of poliomyelitis, have been separated by first adsorbing them with colloidal precipitates of $Al(OH)_3$ or $CaSO_4$ and then eluting them. Large virus particles can be precipitated by treatment with protamine sulfate, which leaves in suspension particles 50 mμ or less in diameter (*664*).

Physical methods of virus separation are generally based on size differences between the virus particles and other materials in suspension. Centrifugation is used in a series of cycles alternating low-speed centrifugation, which removes tissue debris or bacterial contaminants, and high-speed centrifugation, which collects the virus in a pellet. Some virus particles, such as the elementary bodies of vaccinia, can be sedimented in fast centrifuges of the ordinary type; alternate cycles at

3000 rpm in a horizontal centrifuge and at 4500 rpm in an angle centrifuge yield fairly pure suspensions of elementary bodies (155). For smaller viruses, faster centrifuges can be used, equipped with so-called "quantity heads" that carry several large centrifuge tubes. The Sharples centrifuge, in which the material is sedimented from a thin layer of fluid covering the inner surface of a rotating hollow cylinder, is also suitable for virus purification. A procedure that promises to be very useful is "density gradient centrifugation" (100a). The virus particles are concentrated in specific layers, as they sediment in a medium with a density gradient from top to bottom.

All these methods allow only separation of viruses which differ in size from nonviral components of the crude suspensions. These methods may cause the loss of some virus, if the virus consists of a variety of particles of very different sizes. Control of the activity in each discarded fraction during a purification procedure should avoid the overlooking of any important active fraction, but may not reveal small amounts. A certain loss of activity always occurs, particularly in the centrifuge, because of incomplete sedimentation. For example, in vaccinia virus, centrifugation always leaves in the supernatant some activity, which has been shown to be accounted for by elementary bodies.

Some procedures employed in virus · purification are based on peculiarities of the individual viruses themselves. Treatment with proteolytic enzymes, as employed in purification of several viruses, is based on the fact that the virus itself is not attacked as long as it is active. Influenza virus particles can be purified by allowing them to become specifically adsorbed onto red blood cells at low temperature. The cells are collected, and upon incubation at 37° C there is elution of the virus, which can then be easily separated from the cells by centrifugation (233). Influenza viruses can also be purified by adsorption and elution on cation exchange resins (496a).

The purified material obtained by various procedures can be submitted to a number of tests to study its properties and its relation to virus activity. An important phase of this study is the comparison with materials obtained by similar procedures from uninfected hosts. A step forward in the identification is the proof that an identical material can be isolated from different hosts infected with the same virus, whereas no similar material can be obtained from uninfected hosts. At the same time, a comparison of the properties of the purified virus with those of normal host components may provide some lead to the mode of virus production.

PURIFIED VIRUS PREPARATIONS

Physicochemical analysis. Some plant viruses are particularly suitable for purification studies, because the specific materials can be obtained in large amounts from infected plants (up to 10% of the dry

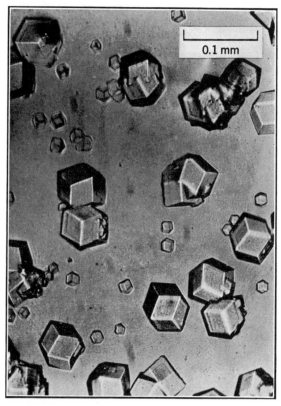

Figure 44. Dodecahedral crystals of purified tomato bushy stunt virus. From: Bawden and Pirie, *Br. J. Exp. Path.* **19**:251, 1938. Courtesy Dr. F. C. Bawden, Rothamsted Experimental Station, Harpenden, England.

weight of the plants for tobacco mosaic virus). These materials can often be purified without loss of activity, to yield protein preparations as homogeneous as those of the best-known proteins. A number of these "virus proteins" are obtained in beautiful crystalline forms. Tomato bushy stunt virus gives uniform rhombic dodecahedral crystals (figure 44); tobacco necrosis virus yields a variety of regular crystalline forms. Southern bean mosaic virus, turnip yellow mosaic virus (figure 45) and squash mosaic virus also give fairly perfect crystals. Some of these crystals have been shown (see 688) by electron-microscopic study of their surfaces to be made up of very orderly arrays of spherical or nearly spherical particles of great uniformity (figure

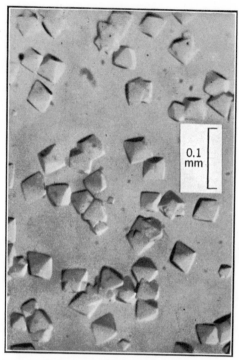

Figure 45. Crystals of turnip yellow mosaic virus. From: Markham and Smith (473). Courtesy Dr. K. M. Smith, Molteno Institute, University of Cambridge.

46). The size of the particles in the crystals can be estimated by crystallographic methods such as x-ray diffraction analysis, by which the distance between successive planes of symmetry within a crystal structure is calculated (475). A comparison of dry and wet crystals of tomato bushy stunt virus (70) has indicated that upon hydration the distance between the centers of individual particles increases by an amount corresponding to about 70% hydration by weight, in agreement with the conclusions derived from sedimentation and diffusion experiments.

The formation of regular crystals has been claimed as evidence for both the purity and the simplicity of constitution of these crystallizable virus proteins. As far as purity is concerned, crystal formation is a good but not an absolute criterion. The possibility exists that foreign materials may gain some degree of hospitality within a crystal. Inactive bushy stunt virus crystallizes just as well as active virus, although its chemical structure must be somewhat altered. Moreover,

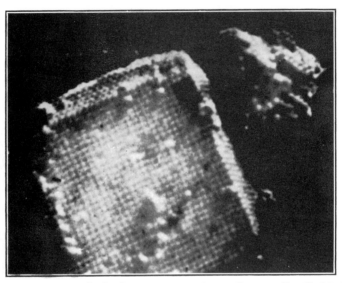

Figure 46. A crystal of tobacco necrosis virus. Courtesy Dr. K. M. Smith, Molteno Institute, University of Cambridge. Photographs from the same study were published by Markham et al. (*475*).

the bushy stunt virus in combination with substances such as clupein (a protamine) or heparin also crystallizes in regular forms.

A second group of plant viruses, including potato yellow dwarf and tomato spotted wilt, consists of particles about 100 mμ in diameter, whose electron-microscopic appearance is that of flattened spheres or ellipsoids (*100b*). These viruses have not been crystallized.

A third group of plant viruses yields purified preparations (*622*) consisting of very elongated particles. This group includes, among others, tobacco mosaic virus, some cucumber viruses, and potato viruses X and Y (see figures 20, 21). The particles of the potato viruses are apparently less rigid and more flexuous than the tobacco mosaic virus rods (*688*). The physical properties of purified preparations of these viruses reflect the asymmetry of the individual particles.

Tobacco mosaic virus is probably the virus whose purified preparations have been most thoroughly investigated and have raised not only complex physical problems but also heated polemics among virologists. Preparations from plants infected with tobacco mosaic virus were shown by Stanley in 1935 (622) to yield a highly infectious precipitate consisting of microscopic needles, which Stanley considered to be crystals of virus protein. All subsequent work has confirmed the identification of the needles with the specific virus nucleoprotein and has shown that the needles are highly organized bundles of the rod-shaped virus particles regularly arranged side by side (69).

Lauffer (403) lists the following evidence for the identification of the tobacco mosaic virus protein with the virus itself: constant association with virus activity; independence of the host on which the virus is grown; similarity among the proteins corresponding to related virus strains; similarity between the ultraviolet absorption spectrum of the virus and the action spectrum for virus inactivation; equal pH stability range for virus activity and protein homogeneity; similar sedimentation rates for the infectious material (measured in the separation cell of the ultracentrifuge) and the protein.

Electron micrographs of tobacco mosaic virus material always contain a variety of particles of very uniform thickness (about 15 mμ) but of somewhat variable length, from 40 to 500 mμ or more, with a mode around 290–300 mμ (688; figure 20). This observation has suggested that the protein may be present in the form of small units in different states of linear aggregation. This raised the question as to what the true "virus particle" and its real significance may be. Some workers (see 43) have pointed out that infected plants yield some virus protein in the form of less asymmetric elements than the long particles visible in electron micrographs. They suggested that the virus in the native state consists of elements shorter than 300 mμ, which aggregate linearly upon extraction. Stanley and several other workers, however, have shown that infectivity is never present in preparations which do not contain particles of approximately 280–300 mμ, and consider these elements as *the* infectious particles (507).

The best purified preparations sediment in the ultracentrifuge (in albumin solutions) with a sharp single boundary corresponding to a sedimentation constant of 230S$_0$, suggesting homogeneity of size and a particle size about 15 × 300 mμ (405). The presence of a variety of particle lengths in electron micrographs has been attributed to breakage or aggregation in the drying process. In spray-drop patterns, in which a fine mist of virus suspension is sprayed onto electron-microscope specimen holders and the patterns formed by individual droplets are photographed, practically all the virus fragments that differ from the typical 300-mμ unit in any given individual pattern add up to this basic unit length or to its small multiples. This suggests that they are produced within the droplets by breakage of units of the 300-mμ length or of dimers or trimers of them (678).

There is certainly no doubt that the virus protein is the virus material, in the sense that the virus activity is embodied in particles consisting of the protein. There is also little doubt of the constant association of virus activity with the "Stanley unit" (15 $\times$ 300 mμ particle). The objections raised to these conclusions have served, however, to focus attention on the fact that the virus protein and its component units may provide information not only on the nature of the infectious virus particles but also on the organization and production of virus inside the host cells.

Preparations of tobacco mosaic virus and other rod-shaped plant viruses exhibit a number of interesting properties, reflecting the tendency of the rod-shaped particles to orient themselves in parallel and to organize into bundles. *Flow birefringence* (641) results from the grating action exerted on polarized light by highly asymmetrical particles that become oriented in a moving column of fluid. Concentrated suspensions of virus protein tend to separate into two layers (*layering phenomenon;* 43), the bottom layer being a more concentrated and more rigidly oriented solution, representing what is called a *liquid crystal*. In the liquid phase, the rod-shaped particles orient themselves sidewise into "tactoids," which then settle into the liquid crystalline phase. Microscopic tactoids can actually be seen at the border between the two layers by examination in polarized light (figure 47). Bernal and Fankuchen (69) have shown by x-ray diffraction analysis that the crystalline needles obtained by precipitation are similar in organization to the tactoids of the liquid crystal phase. In the needles, which should more correctly be called "paracrystals," the individual rods are oriented sidewise with great regularity, but are not spaced regularly lengthwise. Indeed, the needles may not be produced as such by accumulation of particles, but may represent isolated portions of a more extensive gel of liquid crystalline properties.

The x-ray diffraction studies have provided further interesting information (69). In dry paracrystals, the centers of adjacent particles lie 15.2 mμ apart, a value close to the thickness of the virus particles as shown by electron microscopy. Upon wetting, the dry crystals take up water, and the sidewise spacings increase to as much as 23 mμ before the paracrystals show signs of disorientation. The persistence of the spatial relation between wet particles separated by several layers of water molecules has suggested that the particles are kept together by long-range forces. These need not be specific forces acting at a dis-

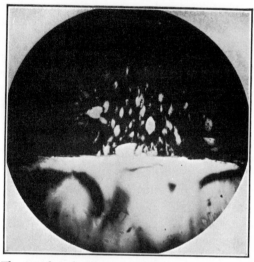

Figure 47. The interface between top and bottom layers of a concentrated solution of tobacco mosaic virus, photographed in polarized light. Birefringent, spindle-shaped droplets (tactoids) form in the upper layer and settle in the bottom layer. From: Bawden and Pirie, *Proc. Roy. Soc.* (London), *B*, **123**:274, 1937. Courtesy Dr. F. C. Bawden, Rothamsted Experimental Station, Harpenden, England.

tance (no such physical force having been proved to exist). Bundles of oriented particles of great length may manage to retain between one another more layers of oriented water molecules than ordinary proteins, so that the oriented water layers provide stabilizing forces for the bundles. It is also possible that a few points of contact among the long particles may be sufficient to preserve their orientation in the wet state.

Both x-ray diffraction studies (69) and high-resolution electron microscopy (676a) indicate that the individual virus rods have a hexagonal cross-section. Concerning the internal structure of the particles, x-ray diffraction analysis has suggested the occurrence of regular subunits. A particle would consist of a repeated series of subunits piled on top of one another like coins in a roll.

The particles of tobacco mosaic virus can be disintegrated in vitro by mild alkaline treatment into progressively smaller fragments; it has been claimed that each class of fragments possesses a high degree of homogeneity (587). The fragments have been supposed to originate by regular cleavage of successive subunits or groups of subunits from a native particle 15×300 mμ. All fragments seem to carry the full serological specificity of the virus, although some of the smallest ones lack the nucleic acid component. None of the fragments possesses infectivity. The chemical integrity of the fragments was supposedly confirmed by electrophoretic analyses, which indicated that the ratio of free acid to basic groups was the same in the fragments as in the large particles. The remarkable claim was made that upon mild acid treatment the fragments could come together again and reconstitute a particle with the physical properties of the original one, although inactive. This work requires confirmation.

The suggestion that a virus such as tobacco mosaic virus consists of repeated subunits implies that the specific element, which is replicated in the course of intracellular reproduction, is the individual subunit rather than the particle as a whole. Such a conclusion requires subsidiary hypotheses to explain why the infectivity, that is, the ability to initiate reproduction upon inoculation, is limited to the specific level of polymerization corresponding to the Stanley unit.

In virus-infected cells are found hexagonal crystals which have been thought to consist of protein elements smaller than the infectious virus particles. Recently, however, such crystals have been isolated by micromanipulation from frozen-dried cells and have been shown to contain almost exclusively the typical rod particles (625a; see frontispiece). These intracellular crystals may consist of layers composed of full-length virus particles standing side by side (676).

Chemical analysis. The chemical analysis of many purified viruses reveals differences among individual viruses and groups of viruses, differences which, although as yet insufficient to allow a chemical interpretation of virus specificity and reproduction, have helped placing the viruses in their proper company among biological objects. In all viruses, a high content of protein is found to be accompanied by the presence of nucleic acid. All viruses may be said to contain nucleoproteins. Purified plant viruses have been found to yield only protein, nucleic acid, and small amounts of ash, indicating a very simple composition. Moreover, the protein component for each plant virus appears chemically to be all of one type (405).

Nucleic acids (280) consist of combinations of nucleotides, each nucleotide containing a purine or pyrimidine base linked to a pentose molecule, which in turn is linked to phosphoric acid by its C atom in position 5. Successive nucleotides are held together by phospho-ester bonds between the phosphoric acid residue of one nucleotide and the pentose of the next one, at the carbon atom in position 3. The pentose is found to be ribose in the nucleotides of nucleic acid from yeast and desoxyribose in nucleic acid extracted from the thymus gland. Every nucleic acid fraction extracted from any one source has been found to contain either a pentose or a desoxypentose. The corresponding sugars are assumed to be ribose and desoxyribose, respectively ("ribonucleic acids" or RNA and "desoxyribonucleic acids" or DNA). Chemical and microchemical methods to distinguish between the two types of nucleic acid are available, based on the stronger aldehyde function of the desoxypentose than of the pentose. The Feulgen test for DNA, widely used in cytochemistry, is based on this difference. The purine and pyrimidine bases isolated from a given nucleic acid preparation consist generally of two purines and two pyrimidines, so that each nucleic acid contains four types of nucleotides. Some nucleic acid preparations contain five rather than four bases (471). The possibility for a variety of specific nucleic acid structures results from differences in the nature and seriation of the bases (128; 687a). The purines are adenine and guanine; the pyrimidines are cytosine and uracil in RNA, cytosine and thymine in DNA. Cytosine is sometimes accompanied and partly replaced by methyl-cytosine (although not in viruses); in one group of bacteriophages (see chapter 8) cytosine is replaced by hydroxymethyl-cytosine. The molar ratios (adenine: thymine) and (guanine:cytosine) are always close to unity in various DNA preparations; the ratio (adenine:guanine) varies rather widely in DNA from different sources.

The purine and pyrimidine rings of nucleic acids are responsible for the characteristic absorption spectrum of these compounds in the ultraviolet range, with a minimum at 2500 A, a maximum around 2600 A, and a rapidly decreasing absorption between 2600 and 3000 A (figure 48). The presence and intensity of the 2600-A maximum can be used for approximate quantitative determinations of nucleic acid. The high phosphorus content of nucleic acids (approximately 10%) accounts in part for the relative opacity of nucleoproteins in electron micrographs. An important reaction of nucleic acids is their depolymerization by specific enzymes or *nucleases*. Two such enzymes have been isolated from pancreas, a ribonuclease and a desoxyribonuclease. The fact that all known nucleic acids (after separation from the conjugated proteins) are split by either one or the other enzyme confirms the hypothesis that all nucleic acids belong to one of two groups, differentiated by the pentose they contain.

The protein components of the viruses appear to share the structure of proteins in general (294); they consist of amino acids joined into

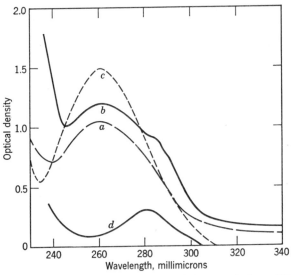

Figure 48. Ultraviolet absorption spectra. (a) Bacteriophage T2. (b) Tobacco mosaic virus. (c) Yeast nucleic acid. (d) Serum globulin. The optical density in the wavelength region beyond 320 mμ is due to light scattering. Note the resemblance between the spectrum of the nucleic acid and that of the phage, which contains about 40% nucleic acid. In the spectrum of tobacco mosaic virus, which contains 94% protein, the absorption due to proteins is more evident.

polypeptide chains by peptide bonds. From the peptide-chain skeleton depart side chains representing the individual amino acid residues, whose nature and proportions give a protein its specific composition. Proteolytic enzymes split proteins by hydrolysis of peptide bonds, the specific site of attack of an enzyme (for example, pepsin or trypsin) being regulated by the nature of the adjacent amino acid residues. The characteristics of the surface groups determine a number of the properties of a protein. Affinity for water is regulated by the amount of polar hydrophilic groups. The acidic or basic character of a protein depends on the ratio of acidic residues, such as those of the dicarboxylic amino acids, to the basic residues of arginine, histidine, and lysine. The aromatic amino acids (tryptophan, tyrosine, phenylalanine) give proteins a characteristic ultraviolet absorption with a maximum around 2800 A (figure 48). The organization of the peptide chain is well known only for certain fibrous proteins, along which the successive amino-acid residues have been found by x-ray analysis to be ranged at distances of 3.3 to 3.5 A. Most proteins, however, are in globular form, with the polypeptide chains folded in complex ways.

In summary, our knowledge of protein (and nucleic acid) structure is too inadequate to permit any attempt to interpret the biological activities of a protein or nucleoprotein in terms of chemical structure. The specificity of a protein depends at least as much on the fine details of the folding of its polypeptide chains and on the resulting peculiarities of its reactive surface as on its amino acid composition. The role of either level of structural organization in determining specific biological properties is practically unknown. Very slight changes in configuration of a folded peptide chain might be compatible with uniformity of physical and chemical characteristics but not with biological activity. Such slight differences in configuration may be involved, for example, in the transformation of certain inactive enzyme precursors into the corresponding active forms (499).

A number of proteins are associated with fairly simple nonprotein groups (prosthetic groups), which sometimes consist of metal ions and sometimes of organic compounds. In proteins with enzymatic activity, the prosthetic groups may be necessary for this activity. There is no evidence whether the relation of nucleic acids to proteins resembles that of prosthetic groups. The linkage of nucleic acid to protein is still a matter of controversy. Salt linkages between the acidic and basic groups of the nucleic acid and of the proteins, respectively, are probably involved. It is even doubtful that we are justified in speaking of "nucleoproteins" as chemical entities. The association of nucleic acids with proteins is a matter of joint extractability from natural sources.

In spite of our ignorance of the chemical function of nucleoproteins, some ideas on their possible biological role have been derived from a knowledge of their distribution and relative amounts in living matter (150). Thus, nucleoproteins are found wherever we have reason to suspect the presence of the determinants of specificity for newly formed biological material: in the cell nucleus, in the self-reproducing cytoplasmic units such as the chloroplasts of plant cells, and in the viruses. Moreover, nucleoproteins are probably involved in protein synthesis. They increase in amount in cells actively involved in synthetic processes. Desoxyribonucleic acid is generally found only in nuclei,

whereas ribonucleic acid is more common in the cytoplasmic constituents of most cells.   Speculations on the role of nucleic acids include the possibility that the orderly array of phosphate residues serves
to channel the energy required by synthetic processes in the geometrically organized fashion that may be required for synthesis of large
specific molecules.   This suggestion is based on analogy with the role
of various nucleotides as coenzymes in hydrogen transfer.   It has also
been suggested (293) that the nucleic acids may supply the rigid
framework required for the maintenance of the configuration of a
protein in the unfolded, two-dimensional state, in which a protein
molecule, acting as a model for production of similar molecules, might
have to arrange itself in order to make possible an identical, point-by-
point replication.   Finally, it seems likely that the nucleic acids may
themselves be, in part or exclusively, the carriers of specific biological
configurations (32).

Watson and Crick (666a) have proposed for DNA a structure consisting of two helical polynucleotide chains coiled around the same
axis and held together by bonds between the purine and pyrimidine
bases.   This structure accounts for the molar ratios of various bases
in DNA and suggests a mechanism by which specific sequences of
nucleotides can be duplicated exactly.   Thus, the proposed DNA
structure would make possible the reduplication of specific genetic
properties embodied in DNA organization.

PLANT VIRUSES

All the nucleic acids isolated from plant viruses resemble yeast
nucleic acid in containing only ribose.   Some differences exist between
the purines and pyrimidines of tobacco mosaic and of yeast nucleic
acids (472).   The amount of nucleic acid varies greatly among different
virus proteins, as shown in table 7.   The amounts of purines and
pyrimidines isolated from different plant viruses differ (table 8), the
more closely related viruses being more similar in composition (471).
It is likely that each virus will be found to contain a variety of nucleic
acid elements of different structure.

The size of the nucleic acid "molecules" isolated from plant viruses
depends on the mode of isolation.   Tobacco mosaic nucleic acid, if
extracted by alkali, is in the form of small units (about 11,000 mol.
wt.); if extracted by rapid heat treatment it is in the form of long
filaments (300,000 mol. wt.).   These have been supposed to represent
the native form of nucleic acid, possibly holding together small blocks

Table 7.   The nucleic acid content of plant virus proteins

From Markham (471)

Virus	Per Cent Ribonucleic Acid
Tobacco mosaic and strains	6
Tomato bushy stunt	16
Tobacco necrosis	17
Southern bean mosaic	21
Potato X	6
Turnip yellow mosaic	35

Table 8.   Purine and pyrimidine composition of the nucleic acids from plant viruses related to tobacco mosaic

From Markham and Smith (472)

(The molar proportions of the four bases (mean = 1) together with their standard errors are given. The figures in italics differ significantly from the corresponding values for tomato mosaic virus nucleic acid.)

Strain	Adenine	Guanine	Cytosine	Uracil	Number of Determinations
Aucuba mosaic	1.20	0.95	0.78	1.05	5
Type tobacco mosaic	1.24 ± 0.026	*1.17* ± 0.023	*0.62* ± 0.021	0.96 ± 0.019	4
Ribgrass	1.17	1.08	0.69	1.05	6
Cucumber 4	*1.04* ± 0.009	1.03 ± 0.009	0.74 ± 0.006	*1.19* ± 0.012	4
Tomato mosaic	1.18 ± 0.007	1.04 ± 0.014	0.73 ± 0.004	1.05 ± 0.037	4
Mean of all strains	1.17	1.05	0.71	1.06	23
Yeast nucleic acid	1.03	1.25	0.80	0.93	11

of protein in the elongated particles (148).   In view of the ready tendency of nucleic acids to aggregate in vitro into long fibers, the heat-extracted filaments might be artifacts.   Treatment of tobacco mosaic with alkali has suggested that the nucleic acid may belong in the smallest fragments derived from the surfaces of the particles (587). For turnip yellow mosaic virus, it has been suggested (473) that the nucleic acid is contained inside a shell of protein.

The purine and pyrimidine components and the amino acid composition have been studied for several plant viruses (table 9).   Inter-

Table 9.   Amino acid content of highly purified preparations of some strains of tobacco mosaic virus *

From Knight (380)

TMV = tobacco mosaic virus. M = Holmes' masked strain. J14D1 = a variant of TMV. GA = green aucuba mosaic virus. YA = yellow aucuba. HR = Holmes' ribgrass strain. CV3 and CV4 = cucumber mosaic viruses 3 and 4.

Amino Acid	Strain								M.D.†
	TMV	M	J14D1	GA	YA	HR	CV3	CV4	
Alanine	5.1	5.2	4.8	5.1	5.1	*6.4*		*6.1*	0.2
Arginine	9.8	9.9	10.0	*11.1*	*11.2*	9.9	*9.3*	*9.3*	0.2
Aspartic acid	13.5	13.5	13.4	13.7	13.8	*12.6*		13.1	0.2
Cysteine	0.69	0.67	0.64	0.60	0.60	0.70	*0*	*0*	
Cystine	0		0		0	0		0	
Glutamic acid	11.3	11.5	*10.4*	11.5	11.3	*15.5*	*6.4*	*6.5*	0.2
Glycine	1.9	1.7	1.9	1.9	1.8	*1.3*	*1.2*	*1.5*	0.1
Histidine	0	0	0	0	0	*0.72*	0	0	0.01
Isoleucine	6.6	6.7	6.6	*5.7*	*5.7*	*5.9*	*5.4*	*4.6*	0.2
Leucine	9.3	9.3	9.4	9.2	9.4	9.0	9.3	9.4	0.2
Lysine	1.47	1.49	*1.95*	1.45	1.47	1.51	*2.55*	*2.43*	0.04
Methionine	0	0	0	0	0	*2.2*	0	0	0.1
Phenylalanine	8.4	8.4	8.4	8.3	8.4	*5.4*	*9.9*	*9.8*	0.2
Proline	5.8	5.9	5.5	5.8	5.7	5.5		5.7	0.2
Serine	7.2	7.0	6.8	7.0	7.1	*5.7*	*9.3*	*9.4*	0.3
Threonine	9.9	10.1	10.0	10.4	10.1	*8.2*	*6.9*	*7.0*	0.1
Tryptophan	2.1	2.2	2.2	2.1	2.1	*1.4*	*0.5*	*0.5*	0.1
Tyrosine	3.8	3.8	3.9	3.7	3.7	*6.8*	3.8	3.7	0.1
Valine	9.2	9.0	8.9	8.8	9.1	*6.2*	8.8	8.9	0.2

* The values given in the table represent percentages of the indicated amino acids. In order to facilitate comparison, the values which are considered to differ significantly from those of TMV are in italics.

† Mean deviation of the values of single determinations from the averages given.

esting differences are correlated with the presumed degree of genetic relationship (380). Distant relatives, such as tobacco mosaic and Holmes' ribgrass virus, differ in a number of respects, whereas more closely related viruses differ in their content of only one or two amino acids or in the proportions of some aromatic bases. The differences represent changes of several hundred or thousand residues per virus particle. This again suggests a repeat structure for these viruses. Differences in amino acid composition are also reflected in differences in electrophoretic behavior among members of the tobacco mosaic group (243). Interestingly enough, the proteins extracted from many viruses are acidic, not basic like those found associated with nucleic acids in nucleoproteins extracted from most cells (protamines and histones). Protein and nucleic acid also appear to be more firmly bound in viruses than in cellular nucleoproteins (see 381). Cucumber mosaic viruses 3 and 4 seem to contain no sulfur amino acids; absence of sulfur is clearly not adequate evidence for absence of protein.

A number of workers have produced artificial chemical modifications in tobacco mosaic (624). Rather extensive chemical changes can be made without impairing virus activity. For example, 70% of the free amino groups can be blocked with acetyl radicals without loss of activity, and all —SH groups can be covered with iodine. Further iodine treatment, causing the transformation of tyrosine residues into diiodotyrosine, produces inactivation. In all cases, new virus produced by inoculation of the modified but active forms into plants is of the normal type. In view of the improbability that the host plants may possess enzymes that remove the covering groups prior to reproduction, Stanley suggested that only certain parts of the structural configuration of the virus particle are necessary to initiate the reproductive process. It is possible that only the viral nucleic acid is involved in the reproductive function. Some of the chemically modified viruses have different residual activities in various host plants. This may be due to differences in opportunity for penetration or in requirements for reproduction.

BACTERIOPHAGES

Several strains of bacteriophage have been highly purified. The purification process is relatively easy, since bacterial lysates contain no other elements of size comparable to the characteristic phage particles. Differential centrifugation has been mainly employed; precipitation methods have also been successful (499; 661). Except for one unsubstantiated claim for phosphorus-lacking phage (364), several coliphages and one staphylococcus phage have proved to contain protein and DNA, the DNA in amounts as high as 40% or more of the dry weight. Amino acid analyses show small differences among related strains (table 10). The presence of lipids and RNA in some preparations was originally reported (645), but careful work, including removal of traces of bacterial debris by serological precipitation (146), makes it likely that lipids and RNA are not essential constituents of virus particles.

The structure and genetic complexity of bacteriophages indicate the great degree of differentiation that phage nucleoprotein must exhibit within each particle. Recent work has indicated that a large fraction, and possibly the totality of the protein of some large phages, forms an

Table 10. Amino acid analyses of bacteriophages

Analyses on preparations of bacteriophage purified by differential centrifugation. The degree of purity of all preparations is questionable. Note the relatively good agreement for preparations of a given phage analyzed by the same method.

Preparations 1–5 analyzed by microbiological assay; Henderson, Sheek, and Luria (unpublished). Preparation P. and W. analyzed by paper chromatography; Polson and Wyckoff (*526*). All figures represent content of a given amino acid in the virus protein.

Amino Acid	Phage T2			Phage T4		
	Prep. 1	Prep. 2	Prep. 3	Prep. 4	Prep. 5	P. and W.
Aspartic acid	—	10.3	10.7	—	—	11.97
Glutamic acid	—	—	—	—	—	11.97
Alanine	—	—	—	—	—	9.40
Glycine	—	—	17.2	13.6	10.2	7.34
Serine	—	5.6	5.8	2.3	—	4.77
Threonine	6.1	5.7	5.4	5.9	6.2	7.0
Methionine	3.2	2.9	2.9	2.7	2.35	< 1.3
Cystine	—	0.19	0.24	—	—	—
Leucine	5.9	5.7	5.5	5.5	5.7	6.51
Isoleucine	7.1	7.4	7.5	6.0	5.05	3.90
Valine	—	6.3	6.7	6.2	6.1	6.51
Phenylalanine	4.8	5.1	5.0	5.3	5.3	4.16
Tyrosine	4.3	4.3	4.7	5.5	4.6	3.74
Tryptophan	—	0.91	0.88	—	—	—
Proline	3.0	3.7	3.7	—	—	5.00
Arginine	5.9	5.6	5.6	3.5	4.5	6.51
Lysine	7.6	6.9	7.4	4.0	4.3	8.46
Histidine	1.1	0.97	0.95	0.60	0.68	<2.6

outer coating that does not participate in phage reproduction (*313;* see chapter 8). If the nucleic acid should prove to be the true reproductive material of these phages, we would have to visualize it as differentiated and organized in the complex way necessary to account for the genetic properties of the phages (see chapter 9).

The dry weight of 1 infectious unit of a purified preparation of a large coli-phage is of the order of 10^{-15} gram, in good agreement with the weight calculated for the particles from their size. This, of course, reflects the high efficiency of the titration method (between 1 and

2.5 particles per infectious unit in good preparations; see page 52). The phosphorus content of a coli-phage such as T2 is approximately 5×10^5 atoms per infectious unit, corresponding to 2×10^5 to 5×10^5 nucleotides per particle (*319*). The DNA of phages T2, T4, and T6 of *E. coli* contain an unusual pyrimidine, hydroxymethyl-cytosine, instead of cytosine (*687b*). The new pyrimidine has not been isolated from any other source and may represent a unique constituent of these phages. Phage T2 contains 32.0 moles of adenine, 33.2 of thymine, 17.9 of guanine, and 17.0 of the new pyrimidine per 100 moles of nucleotides.

The discovery of hydroxymethyl-cytosine represents a remarkable advance not only in our knowledge of nucleic acids but also in our realization of the degree of specificity of the chemical processes that must be involved in virus synthesis and of the level at which an infecting virus must act upon the synthetic machinery of the host cell (see chapter 8).

ANIMAL VIRUSES

The purity of even the best preparations of animal viruses is open to question, because of the intrinsic difficulties involved in effective purification and in the estimation of purity itself. On the one hand, the viruses must be extracted from tissues, in which they represent a small minority component. Normal components, in the form of particles of size similar to that of viruses (microsomes), are also present and often contain nucleoproteins. The titration methods are seldom sensitive enough to permit any close correlation of one infective unit with an amount of virus of the order of one virus particle. Yet, analyses of several viruses carried out in different laboratories with different techniques have given reasonably consistent results, so that some generalizations are possible. Most of the chemical information available concerns the largest viruses, purifiable either by centrifugation or by precipitation (*56*). The smallest viruses can now be somewhat purified by removal of the larger impurities by protamine sulfate precipitation combined with trypsin treatment (*664*).

No animal virus has yet been obtained in crystalline form, although viruslike particles extracted from certain forms of human warts show crystallike formations in electron micrographs (*633*).

The chemical composition of some of the best preparations of several viruses is given in table 11. Opinions as to the validity of these analyses vary rather widely. It seems safe to assume that in the case of large, easily purifiable viruses such as vaccinia the chemical analysis

Table 11. Chemical analysis of purified preparations of animal viruses

Modified from Beard (56).   All values are per cent dry weight.

| | Whole Complex | | | | Lipid | | | | Nonlipid | | | Nucleic Acid | |
	Carbon	Nitro-gen	Phos-phorus	Carbo-hydrate	Total	Phos-pho-lipid	Choles-terol	Neutral Fat	Total	Protein	Carbo-hydrate	DNA	RNA
Vaccinia	33.7	15.3	0.57	2.8	5.7	2.2	1.4	2.2	94.0	89.0	2.8	5.6	
Papilloma	49.6	15.0	0.94	6.5	1.5				98.5	90.0		8.7	
Equine encephalo-myelitis (Eastern strain)	62.2	7.7	2.2	4.0	54.1	35.0	13.8	9.6	53.0	49.1	7.2		4.4
Influenza A (PR8 strain)	53.2	10.0	0.97	12.5	23.4	11.3	7.0	5.1	77.5	65.0	7.3	1.5	?
Influenza B (Lee strain)	52.7	9.7	0.94	13.1	22.4	11.2	3.7	7.2	76.4	63.6	9.4	1.2	?
Swine influenza	51.4	9.0	0.87	10.0	24.0	10.7	5.7	7.7	77.6	67.6	10.0	+	?

is fairly descriptive of the virus. DNA is probably the only constitutive nucleic acid in vaccinia virus. The evidence that some animal viruses, including those of the equine encephalomyelitis group, contain only RNA and no DNA is not fully convincing; nor is the evidence for the high lipid content of these viruses. Rous sarcoma virus appears to contain RNA (*137*).

Little use can be made of the results of chemical fractionation into major components (proteins, nucleic acid, lipids, carbohydrates) for an understanding of virus properties. It seems possible that the infectious particles of most viruses will be found to contain only one type of nucleic acid (either DNA or RNA), although excellent preparations of viruses of the influenza group yield both types (*378*). These highly purified preparations of influenza virus also contain some host-specific antigens, which might represent impurities, but which might also be incorporated into the particles as a necessary consequence of their mode of reproduction in the host cells (*142; 377*).

The presence of DNA or RNA in the particles of a virus may suggest its possible natural relationship with nuclear or cytoplasmic nucleo-protein granules. The implications of this line of thought will be developed more fully in chapter 18.

Amino acid analyses of repeatedly purified influenza virus preparations (*379;* table 12) have revealed significant quantitative differences between virus types. These differences are more marked than those observed among different strains of tobacco mosaic virus.

Even the purest preparations of some of the largest animal viruses show a complex composition resembling that of bacterial cells. Elementary bodies of vaccinia virus, obtainable in amounts of 2 mg per rabbit, contain several protein fractions that can be separated and shown to be different by chemical and serological tests (*606*). The difficulty in deciding what really belongs to the virus is well illustrated by the presence, in purified vaccinia virus, of cholesterol in definite and constant amounts, which, however, can be removed by proper solvents without loss of activity. Should the cholesterol be considered an impurity? Or is its presence an indication of a role it plays in virus production? These questions will become more meaningful when biochemical studies of virus growth are more advanced.

Other interesting questions are raised by the presence in purified vaccinia virus preparations of certain enzymes or coenzymes. Phosphatase, catalase, and lipase activity are present in most virus preparations. They may be due to enzymes accidentally adsorbed onto the virus particles during purification, since purified particles adsorb such

Table 12. Amino acid content of highly purified PR8 and Lee influenza virus particles and of the sedimentable particles of normal allantoic fluid

From Knight (*379*)

Amino Acid	PR8 Influenza Virus (per cent)	Lee Influenza Virus (per cent)	Normal Allantoic Particles (per cent)	M.D.* (per cent)
Alanine	2.5	2.6	—	0.1
Arginine	5.0	4.0	3.9	0.2
Aspartic acid	7.4	7.3	6.2	0.1
Glutamic acid	7.7	6.2	6.1	0.2
Glycine	2.5	2.9	1.8	0.1
Histidine	1.4	1.5	0.8	0.03
Isoleucine	4.1	4.2	3.2	0.1
Leucine	5.3	5.5	4.3	0.1
Lysine	3.6	4.7	2.5	0.1
Methionine	2.3	2.1	1.1	0.1
Phenylalanine	3.7	3.4	3.6	0.2
Proline	2.6	2.7	2.8	0.2
Serine	2.2	2.2	2.1	0.1
Threonine	3.7	4.0	3.8	0.1
Tryptophan	1.1	0.7	0.7	0.02
Tyrosine	3.1	2.1	2.2	0.05
Valine	3.4	3.2	3.2	0.1

* Mean deviation of the values of single determinations from the averages given in the table.

enzymes from solutions. Most careful tests for enzymatic activities of pure virus particles on simple substrates have been negative (*41;* table 13). Adenosine triphosphatase has been reported in a fowl leucosis virus (*486a*).

Biotin and riboflavine are present in constant and definite proportions in vaccinia virus and are apparently essential components of the virus particles (which also contain small but appreciable amounts of copper: 0.05%). The role of these substances as coenzymes in some of the energy-yielding systems of many cells is well known. Their presence in virus particles has been interpreted in the light of the theory that viruses may have originated from free-living forms. Supposedly, the viruses became obligate parasites through loss of certain

Table 13.   The occurrence of enzymes and other metabolic factors in the elementary bodies of viruses

Modified from Bauer (41)

Virus	Absent	Present	Comments
Vaccinia	Zymohexase Enolase Phosphoglucomutase Adenosine nucleosidase Peptidase Triosephosphate dehy- drogenase		
		Phosphomonesterase Phosphodiesterase Ribonuclease Deoxyribonuclease	Probably absorbed onto virus from tissue of origin
	Cytochrome oxidase Cytochrome C		
		Riboflavine Copper Biotin	Probably an integral part of the virus body
Influenza		Mucinase	Action on cell receptors
	Deoxyribonuclease Phosphatase Xanthine oxidase Adenosine triphosphatase Succinic dehydrogenase		

essential functions, for which they became dependent on the host. Thus, they may still occasionally possess some of the constituents of enzyme systems functional in their ancestors. Of course, the substances in question might instead represent components of host-cell systems that are operative in virus synthesis, and that become incorporated into the virus because of the peculiarities of its (unknown) mode of multiplication.

As a whole, the absence of enzymatic activity on substrates of metabolic significance is in line with the view that viruses utilize, for their growth and reproduction, the energy-yielding machinery and the building-block-synthesizing systems of their host cells. Enzymatic activities to be expected in virus particles, if any, are more likely to be exerted on substrates that may be encountered by the virus in penetrating or coming out of the host cell. In fact, the only well-established enzymatic activity of virus particles is the *receptor-destroying activity* of the viruses of the influenza group and of other hemagglutinating viruses, which can destroy the surface receptors of red blood cells and other related substrates (*330*). The details of this enzymatic reaction and its possible role in virus-host cell relation will be discussed in chapter 13.

A chemically well-investigated group of animal viruses is that of the insect viruses, which can be obtained in large amounts and consist of characteristic, easily purifiable rod-shaped particles (*66*). They contain DNA, protein, and little if anything else. In the specific inclusions, polyhedra, or capsules, the virus particles are associated with large amounts of a specific, noninfectious protein. This polyhedral protein consists of elements much smaller than virus particles, with a molecular weight of 200,000–400,000 (*68a*). The polyhedra, which are surrounded by a membrane, may be formed by precipitation of the specific protein, which is quite insoluble at its isoelectric point.

Some types of polyhedra liberate no rod-shaped virus particles, give a pitted appearance after treatment with sodium carbonate, and appear to have no membrane surrounding them (*611*).

These findings emphasize the importance of investigating not only the infectious virus particles but also other "specific" substances found in virus-infected hosts in order to gain an understanding of the various phases of virus production and function.

SPECIFIC, NONINFECTIOUS SUBSTANCES IN VIRUS INFECTION

The evidence for such substances is rapidly increasing. For *plant viruses*, we have, for example, the noninfectious crystallizable protein found in plants infected with the Rothamstead strain of tobacco necrosis virus. This specific protein consists of homogeneous particles about one-half the diameter of the infectious spherical particles (*49*). Turnip yellow mosaic virus preparations (*471; 473*) can be separated into two fractions, both consisting of spherical particles of equal size, some (about 60%) infectious and containing RNA, the others (about 40%) without it. There are reasons to believe that the RNA-less particles are not artifacts, but are actually present in the sap. They are antigenically similar to the virus, though less active.

Similarly, *bacteriophages* and *animal viruses* are often accompanied by specific protein materials, which are often smaller than the viruses. Besides the polyhedral protein, we may list the soluble antigen of vaccinia virus (*606*), the complement-fixing soluble antigens of influenza and of several other viruses (383), and the "ultrafiltrate factor" in phage lysates that blocks phage-neutralizing antibodies (111). In the few cases in which chemical analysis has been possible, these substances have proved to be proteins related to some of the proteins of the virus. Evidence is growing that at least some of these proteins represent intermediate products of virus synthesis; some may represent "mistakes" in virus production or breakdown products. Some such incomplete particles are sometimes produced instead of complete virus under the influence of chemical inhibitors. For example, bacteria infected with certain phages in the presence of the acridine dye proflavine liberate incomplete, nucleic acid-free particles (175).

There may be a whole range of cases intermediate between the production, along with the virus, of an excess of small building blocks and the production of a mixture of active and inactive virus particles. It is also possible that some of the specific, noninfectious virus products derive from the breakdown of virus particles. The amounts of these products vary greatly. For bacteriophages, the "ultrafiltrate factor" represents a small fraction of the total virus material produced; the virus appears to waste little in byproducts. In the polyhedroses of insects, on the other hand, the virus is a small fraction of the specific material of the polyhedra, the noninfectious bulk of which may fulfill some protective function for the virus inside the cell.

These examples emphasize the importance of not limiting our attention to the infectious particles themselves. Even the fact that virus particles may be inactive, when extracted from their host cells, because they are combined with inhibitors of cellular origin, may suggest a possible role of these inhibitors in virus production.

The fact that at least some of the "specific soluble substances" of viruses are proteins without nucleic acid and can be demonstrated separately from the virus particles raises a point of some interest. Are the same proteins, when in the virus particles, bound to nucleic acid or not? The ease of extraction of soluble antigen from vaccinia virus, as compared with the difficulty of removing any nucleic acid, seems to answer in the negative. Thus, the proteins of a virus particle may consist partly of nucleoproteins and partly of other proteins without nucleic acid ties.

As a whole, chemical investigations on purified viruses have as yet shed little light on the basic problems of virology. The fault rests neither with the chemists who have worked on these problems nor with any peculiarities of viruses, but with the disparity between the questions asked and the techniques available. The goal is to interpret biological functions, such as reproduction, host-range specificity, and tissue specificity, in terms of chemical structure. Present-day chemistry, however, lacks the proper tools to supply the answer. Protein and nucleic acid structure is understood only in some of its grossest phases, and nothing is known of the chemical basis of those specific properties of a protein that are of biological importance, such as antigenicity, species specificity, and enzyme function. The present gap in our chemical knowledge will be filled only by the development of a new biochemistry, covering the area of specific differentiations of large organic molecules of biological importance.

VIRUS COMPOSITION AND THE PROBLEM OF THE LIVING NATURE OF VIRUSES

The crystallization of plant virus proteins started widespread speculations and controversies as to the nature of viruses, some workers considering them "molecules," and therefore "nonliving," and others considering them "living organisms." The emotional root of the controversy lies in the reluctance of the chemist to call living something simple enough to crystallize in a test tube, and on the hesitance of the biologist to admit the existence of molecules capable of reproduction. The semantic aspect of the controversy, however, is more important, since it illustrates the fact that both the terms "molecule" and "living" must be redefined before we can utilize them as categories in which entities such as viruses can be classified unequivocally.

On the one hand, no definitions of the word molecule, as given by the chemist, can be applied without ambiguity to particles of biological material. Actually, no protein has ever been synthesized, the details of protein structure are obscure, and the structural homogeneity of even the most purified protein is questionable. Like viruses and visible cell components, proteins are synthesized only inside living cells. The term "molecule" is inadequate as a pigeonholing device in classifying such objects.

On the other hand, the confusion that would arise if all proteins were classified as "living" in view of their cellular origin is illustrated by a simple example: could we consider a preparation of egg albumin as "living"? This suggests that the limits of applicability of the term "living" in its everyday, common-sense meaning become hazy as we reach the domain of protein chemistry.

We should, then, investigate the possibility of redefining the word "living" in a way that may be meaningful and useful in this borderline field. The redefinition must aim at selecting criteria for the classification of objects in such a way that fewer and less important ambiguities will arise. As an analogy, the reader may consider the problem of adopting criteria that make the distinction between "table" and "chair" as useful as possible even in the borderline field of flat-top stools.

A point of departure may be the consideration that all properties of biological systems reflect their material structure and are not manifestations of metaphysical "life forces." Life, however defined, will be a manifestation of certain organized material objects that we call "living organisms."

Throughout the physical world, we observe that certain new properties arise as a result of organized agglomerations of parts, or, as is usually said, at certain levels of integration, not because the new properties are metaphysically superimposed over and beyond the properties of the component parts, but because the observations by which they can be defined can be made only on the whole and not on the isolated parts. For example, the social behavior of an individual cannot be defined in terms of the individual taken in isolation, outside of any social situation. The requirement for operational definitions, that is, for criteria based on feasible observations, can also be illustrated with the well-known example of the clock. All mechanical properties of a clock reflect the mechanical properties of its component parts, but the meaning and the very existence of the clock as a time-measuring device only arise upon its being assembled and observed by a time-minded agency.

Having decided that life must represent a manifestation of certain organized portions of matter (organisms), we realize, however, that each individual property of organisms, as listed in textbooks of biology, becomes somewhat ambiguous at the borderline between simple organisms and large units or molecules of organic matter. Some writers have, therefore, despaired of the feasibility of defining life. Rejecting such pessimism, we may consider that a property of all "unambiguous organisms" is their ability to reproduce, that is, to introduce a structural and functionally specific organization similar to their own into other material of simpler chemical organization.

The property of reproduction, however, if used as the sole criterion for defining life, would face two objections. First, crystal growth sometimes results in the formation of chemical complexes that do not exist as such in the mother solution, and, therefore, in an increased degree of specific chemical organization. Second, the nature of the synthetic mechanisms underlying biological reproduction is unknown, and it may be suggested, for example, that some or all proteins, in their native intracellular state, take part in reproduction. The simple criterion of reproduction is, therefore, of little value in formalizing the differences between groups of objects in the field under discussion; it fails because it is not strictly definable in terms of observable events and performable operations.

A further approach can be made, however, by taking into consideration the historical aspect of biological phenomena. There exists in the material substrate of the biological world a unity derived from its common origin and continuity. This unity is embodied in the two fundamental tenets of biology: the rejection of spontaneous generation and the theory of evolution. Unity and continuity reflect the presence of certain specific materials, which regulate the assimilation of outside matter and its transformation into more of the specific components. These specific materials, capable of change and evolution, represent the elements of continuity in the cycle of organic matter, by which simpler, nonspecific building blocks are organized into more protoplasm. A satisfactory operational definition of a living substance or organism might, therefore, be the following: "A material is living if, after isolation, it retains a specific configuration that can be reintegrated into the cycle of organic matter."

This definition, by making life identical with the possession of an *independent, specific, self-replicating pattern of organization,* gives a tangible criterion of classification. It differentiates, for example, between most cell proteins, which once isolated are unable to reenter the cycle of organic matter without being broken down below the level of biological specificity, and the viruses, which can reintroduce their own pattern into the network of biological syntheses. It also excludes, deliberately, the individual cells of multicellular organisms unless they are capable of reproducing more cells, for example, in tissue cultures.

Our definition does not involve any assumption as to the mechanism by which the pattern of specificity is preserved and reproduced or as to the influences that may alter it. It requires only that any change or mutation that maintains the living character must give rise to a new self-replicating pattern. The operational character of the definition is illustrated by the fact that a virus, for example, can only be considered as "more living" than any other cell constituent extracted along with it by performing the proper test of reintroduction into a suitable environment.

It will be realized that our definition classifies as living such entities as the "transforming principles" responsible for induced specific bacterial changes (*210*), but excludes, among other things, individual genes that cannot (yet?) be isolated and reintegrated into cells (see, however, page 351; *32; 695*).

It should be pointed out that some of the areas left ambiguous by our definition involve such biological enigmas as those plant diseases supposedly caused by viruses but transmissible only by grafting. The only reason to suspect the presence of a virus is the repetition of an abnormal symptomatology. Whether such hypothetical "viruses" that cannot be isolated are to be called living is anybody's choice.

6

Serological Properties of Viruses

Virus particles contain large amounts of protein. Since most proteins are good antigens, it is to be expected that viruses will have antigenic properties. An *antigen* is defined as a substance that, introduced parenterally (not by mouth) into an animal organism, stimulates the production of *antibodies,* that is, of modified serum globulins which circulate in the blood serum and can react specifically with the antigen. An antigen-antibody reaction involves combination between the two, in the case of viruses as well as of other antigens. Serological reactions are specific. Their specificity, determined by the chemical nature of the antigen, is of very high grade, since it distinguishes among proteins whose chemical differences are well beyond the analytical methods of present-day chemistry. Serological reactions, therefore, can be considered as a refined tool for the structural analysis of proteins and other antigens and of particles containing such antigens.

Reactions between an antigen and an antiserum prepared against another antigen (*heterologous* as opposed to *homologous* reactions) indicate the possession by the two antigens of common or very similar chemical configurations. Incomplete antigens or *haptens* are substances that, although incapable of stimulating antibody formation, react with antibodies against antigens with which they share certain chemical configurations.

Since all the specific properties of a virus, whether in the extracellular or in the intracellular state, ultimately depend on the chemical structure and organization of the virus material, serological methods are a precious tool for the study of viruses. We have already mentioned that the present methodology of protein chemistry and physicochemistry—including elementary and amino acid analysis, sedimentation, diffusion, light-absorption measurements, and electrophoresis—tells us very little about the structural basis of the biological specificity of proteins. This specificity must depend on details of organization and folding of polypeptide chains, details which disappear in the course of chemical analysis and which are not revealed by physico-chemical methods. Serological analysis, however, represents a finer chemical tool. An antibody is a chemical reagent capable of distinguishing those details of organization on which functional specificity may depend. Indeed, antibodies may distinguish between proteins prepared in identical ways from the same tissue of different related species or even of different individuals of the same species (397).

Each virus contains specific antigens, distinct from those of the host in which it grows and from those of other viruses. Antiviral antibodies permit not only the recognition and identification of individual viruses but also the recognition and measurement of virus material inside the host, even when this material is not extractable in an infectious state. Serological methods allow us to recognize similarities and differences among virus strains. They provide us with useful criteria for virus classification and with valuable epidemiological information. Serological reactions are the basis for most of the diagnostic procedures in virus diseases of man and animals. The animals used for laboratory production of antiviral antisera are generally rabbits, although guinea pigs, chickens, ferrets, and horses are sometimes used for special purposes.

ANTIGEN-ANTIBODY REACTIONS WITH VIRUSES

When an antigen is mixed with homologous antiserum, the reactions observed depend on the physical properties of the antigen and on the multiplicity of distinct antigenic functions it possesses. The types of reactions by which antigen-antibody combinations are manifested may be divided into three groups. First, there are reactions in which we observe changes in the state of dispersion of the antigen, such as precipitation or agglutination. In the precipitate, individual molecules or particles of the antigen are held together by antibody molecules in a framework or "lattice." According to widely accepted immunochemical theories, both antigen and antibody must be multivalent or at least bivalent to allow formation of such a lattice, since each antigen particle must combine with at least two molecules of antibody, and vice versa, to bring about formation of an extensive framework. The extent of lattice formation depends on the relative concentrations of the reagents. There will be an optimum ratio for lattice formation (equivalence point), and a lattice may fail to be formed if either reagent is in large excess. The term *precipitation* is used for antigens such as protein molecules; *agglutination* refers to larger particles such

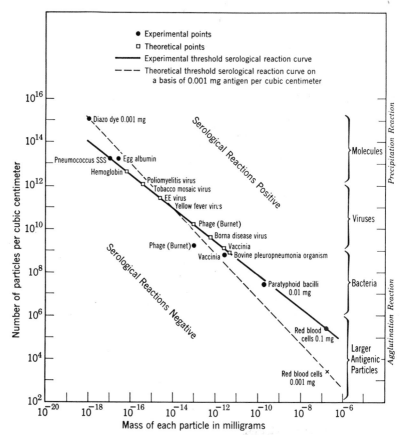

Figure 49. The relation between the mass of a particle and the number of particles needed for visible precipitation or agglutination by specific antiserum. From: Merrill (*480*). The mass values for several viruses should be somewhat modified in the light of present-day information.

as bacteria. The distinction is rather immaterial in the case of antigens such as virus particles. Large amounts of antigen are needed for the production of visible reactions; with viruses, the minimum amount required is of the order of 0.1 to 1 μg of virus material (*480*). Assuming the need for a constant minimum mass of antigen, a relation can be derived between the size of virus particles and the number of particles required for visible precipitation, as shown in figure 49.

Agglutination of virus particles may be visualized microscopically or ultramicroscopically, for example, in the electron microscope. A modified test is the agglutination by antiviral serum of relatively large particles, such as collodion granules or bacterial cells, which have been artificially coated with virus. The coating may be aspecific, as for vaccinia virus on collodion particles (258), or specific, as for bacteriophage on heat-killed bacteria (121).

The second type of reaction is one in which, after mixing antigen and antiserum, we test for a modification of some properties of the serum due to combination of the antibody with the antigen. Typical of this is the complement-fixation reaction, based on the fact that, in combining together, antigen and antibody often bind a normal constituent of blood serum, called *complement*. A complement-fixation test is made by adding to the mixture of antigen and antibody a known amount of complement, that is, of normal guinea pig serum. The disappearance or fixation of complement is then tested by means of an "indicator system," which consists of sheep red blood cells treated with antisheep cell serum. If complement is present, hemolysis of the cells occurs; absence or reduction of lysis shows that complement has been removed. The complement-fixation test is of great diagnostic value in animal virus diseases, in testing sera of suspected patients for the presence of virus antibodies. The virus preparations used as antigens in the complement-fixation test need not be as pure and concentrated as for agglutination or precipitation tests. Complement fixation, however, does not occur in all antigen-antibody reactions.

The third type of reaction involves changes in the infectivity of the virus as a result of combination with antibody. This is the so-called *neutralization reaction,* in which we observe a reduction in the infectious titer of virus. Loss of virus activity as a result of combination with antibody suggests that some essential portion of the virus particle is prevented from functioning by combination with antibody. This indicates the possibility of identifying specialized structures in the virus with certain antigens. As already mentioned, an antigenic function depends on the presence in the antigen of certain specific chemical groups or configurations, the "antigenic determinants," which induce the formation of antibody molecules capable of specific combination with these determinants. These may vary in complexity from rather simple functions, such as aromatic groups, to large portions of a protein molecule. Complex entities such as virus particles may carry several distinct antigenic determinants. An antiserum prepared against a virus may then contain a variety of specific antibodies.[1]

The multiplicity of viral antigens can be illustrated for vaccinia virus (606). On the one hand, injection of intact virus particles gives antisera that neutralize and agglutinate virus particles. On the other hand, antigenic fractions can be obtained which give rise to antibodies that agglutinate but do not neutralize the virus particles. It is clear, then, that this virus contains at least two types of antigens. The tests for multiple antigens are often delicate. For example, precipitation of a specific antiserum with particles of papilloma virus removes all antibody activity from the serum (105). The same is true for bacteriophage particles and antiphage serum. Yet, we can obtain phage antigen, in the form of immature particles, that react with antiphage antiserum but do not combine with phage-neutralizing antibody (175).

The most probable interpretation of virus neutralization is that combination of a virus particle with antibody blocks certain surface groups that are required to initiate infection. Combination with antibody apparently does not destroy the virus. It is often possible to recover active virus upon removal of antibody by a variety of treatments.

Several treatments suppress infectivity without altering the antigenicity of viruses. This indicates either that the changes involved in inactivation by these treatments are of a finer chemical nature than can be detected by tests of serological specificity, or that the groups affected in the inactivation process are not directly involved in the determination of antigenic specificity, that is, are not part of antigenic determinants. This is understandable, since inactivation may result from slight changes in one localized point of a virus particle. Usually the treatments that leave the virus antigenic but not infectious (for example, formalin or radiations) are those that inactivate the virus without extensive protein denaturation.

The problem of the possession of multiple and different antigenic determinants by certain viruses is connected with the problem of cross-reactions. It is generally found that a serum reacts more strongly or at higher dilution with its homologous antigen than with heterologous

[1] This fact is not necessarily reflected in the differences of the reactions observed, since the reactions depend entirely on our methodology. For example, there is no a priori reason to consider the agglutinating and the neutralizing antibodies as different antibodies, since agglutination and neutralization of virus particles may both be due to combination of the same antigenic determinant with the same antibody, the combination being tested in different ways.

antigens. If any cross-reaction occurs at all, the difference between homologous and heterologous antigens is clearly proved by absorption tests. Absorption with the homologous antigen generally removes from a serum all antibodies, while absorption with a heterologous antigen may only remove part of the antibodies, leaving a certain amount of reactivity with other antigens. The situation is illustrated for a group of related plant viruses in table 14. A virus could, thus,

Table 14. **Cross-precipitation experiments with plant viruses and cross-absorbed antisera**

From Bawden (*43*).   +, ++, +++, ++++: degree of precipitation at optimum antigen-antiserum ratio.

Antiserum	Antigen Used for Absorption	Precipitation Tests — Antigen				
		Tobacco Mosaic Virus	Aucuba Mosaic Virus	Enation Mosaic Virus	Cucumber Mosaic Virus 3	Cucumber Mosaic Virus 4
Tobacco mosaic virus	TMV	−	−	−	−	−
	AMV	−	−	−	−	−
	EMV	++	++	−	−	−
	CV3	++++	++++	++++	−	−
	CV4	++++	++++	++++	−	−
Aucuba mosaic virus	TMV	−	++	++	−	−
	AMV	−	−	−	−	−
	EMV	++	++	−	−	−
	CV3	++++	++++	++++	−	−
	CV4	++++	++++	++++	−	−
Enation mosaic virus	TMV	−	+	++	−	−
	AMV	−	−	+	−	−
	EMV	−	−	−	−	−
	CV3	++++	++++	++++	−	−
	CV4	++++	++++	++++	−	−
Cucumber mosaic virus 3	TMV	−	−	−	++++	++++
	AMV	−	−	−	++++	++++
	EMV	−	−	−	++++	++++
	CV3	−	−	−	−	−

be considered a mosaic of several discrete antigens, some shared and some unshared by related strains.

This formal interpretation, however, may be misleading. Cross-reactions of this type are not always the expression of a mosaic of discrete antigens, but may represent the fact that the virus strains possess antigens similar but not identical to each other. The antibodies produced as a response to a given antigen may consist of a variety of antibody molecules with varying affinity for the common antigen. Heterologous antigens remove only those antibody molecules that have a stronger, less discriminating affinity, leaving the weaker, more specific ones behind. Cross-reactions may then be considered as an indication of chemical similarity and relation, but not necessarily as proof of the possession of a number of identical antigenic groups in common.

SEROLOGY OF BACTERIOPHAGES

Bacteriophages illustrate well the serological specificity of viruses, since practically every strain of bacteriophage isolated in nature is found to be an antigenically distinct entity. Some bacteriophages are better antigens than others, as measured by the potency of the antisera that can be obtained against them. Two bacteriophages active on the same bacterium are often completely distinct serologically. Cross-reactions generally occur only among bacteriophages that are similar in other properties, for example, in morphology, and the strength of the cross-reactions may be taken as an indication of the degree of relatedness. As a consequence, serological properties provide a convenient basis for phage classification. For example, a large number of coli-dysentery phages fall into eleven major serological groups that do not cross-react (110). No serological relation exists between phage and host; antibody against the host gives no evidence of combination with the phage, and vice versa. A typical group of related phages includes the T-even (T2, T4, T6) series of coli-phages (169). Results of cross-neutralization experiments are given in table 15.

Agglutination reactions can be observed with highly concentrated phage suspensions, particularly if the phage is a "large-particle" one, or with phage-coated bacteria (121). The *neutralization reaction* is, however, far more important, particularly because the titration methods for phage allow precise quantitative studies of the neutralization process.

The basic finding is expressed by the so-called "percentage law," which states that a given concentration of antiserum in a given time will inactivate a given proportion of the phage present, independent of the total amount of phage (29). This law holds true as long as the amount of phage present is small as compared with the amount of antibody, so that the antibody available to each particle is not influenced by the number of particles present.

The second rule is that phage inactivation is a practically irreversible reaction. Serum-inactivated phage is not reactivated by dilution. Some phages, however, can be reactivated by sonic vibration (21) or by treatment with papain, which digests the antibody (366).

The third rule is that the logarithm of the fraction of phage that remains active after a certain time in a mixture with antibody is proportional to the time of contact and to the concentration of antibody. This is expressed in the following equations:

$$\frac{P}{P_0} = e^{-ktC} \qquad \log_e \frac{P_0}{P} = ktC \qquad \log_{10} \frac{P_0}{P} = 0.43ktC \qquad [9]$$

where P_0 is the initial phage activity; P is the residual active phage after t minutes of contact with a concentration C of antiserum; k is a constant ("fractional rate of inactivation"), which, within the limits of validity of equations 9, characterizes the rate of inactivation of a given phage by a given serum. Experimental data illustrating this relation are given in figure 50.

The interpretation of the relation is not completely clear. The equation is that of a first-order reaction or of a bimolecular reaction with one reagent in large excess. It suggests that one antibody molecule can bring about inactivation of a virus particle. If several molecules were needed, there would be an initial lag in the rate of phage inactivation, when few or none of the particles have as yet combined with the minimal numbers of antibody molecules necessary for inactivation. Not every molecule of antibody that combines with phage inactivates it, however. The phage particles that survive antibody treatment are already modified by combination with antibody. They are adsorbed less rapidly by sensitive bacteria and sometimes are not adsorbed at all by some of their host bacterial strains (365). Upon ultrafiltration, they show an increased size. Probably, antibody molecules can combine with different sites of the phage surface, but only the molecule that happens to block a certain spot suppresses the activity. This spot may be unique on the phage particle, or it may become singled out a posteriori, in the sense that, if a phage utilizes for attachment to a bacterium a serum-inactivated spot, the result may be a failure to grow. Indeed, it is known that some serum-inactivated phages retain at least part of their ability to be adsorbed by bacteria.

Equation 9 is not always strictly followed. An initial lag in inactivation is often present for low serum concentrations. Another frequent deviation is the occurrence of a more resistant fraction of phage, which, however, is not genetically resistant, since it does not give rise to a

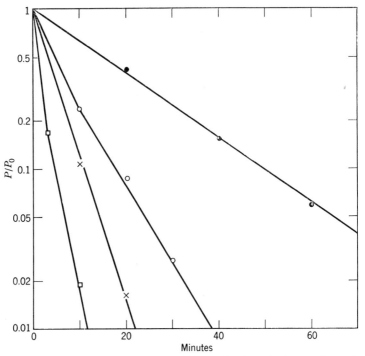

Figure 50. Neutralization of bacteriophages by homologous or heterologous antiserum. The fraction P/P_0 of residual infectious phage as a function of time of exposure to antiserum at 37° C. •: Phage T2 + anti-T2 serum diluted 1:64,000. o: Same, diluted 1:16,000. □: Same, diluted 1:4000. x: Phage T4 + anti-T2 serum diluted 1:4000.

resistant progeny. The resistant fraction may represent physiologically different phage particles. It might possibly consist of particles that have combined with antibody molecules without being inactivated and in such a way that some necessary portion of their surface, although still unblocked, has become protected from further antibody molecules by steric hindrance on the part of the antibody already adsorbed.

Analysis of precipitates formed by phage and antibody shows that some of the large bacteriophages, for example, coli-phage T2, can take up as many as 90 antibody molecules before losing activity. Up to

5000 antibody molecules of rabbit antiserum may be adsorbed by 1 phage particle (*317*). Absorption of a serum with a sufficient amount of phage, active or inactivated by formalin, can remove all the neutralizing antibody of the serum.

Equation 9 is of practical importance in phage research. Once the value of k, the fractional rate of inactivation, is known for a given serum-phage combination, we can calculate the serum concentration that will give any desired amount of survival in the desired interval of time. The values of k for a given antiserum and different phages indicate the degree of serological relationship among the phages. An unrelated phage will give a k value of 0; a weakly cross-reacting phage will have a k value much lower than that of the homologous phage (table 15).

Table 15. Cross-neutralization by representative antisera against bacteriophages T1–T7

Serum	k = fractional rate of inactivation, equation 9 (min^{-1})						
	T1	T2	T3	T4	T5	T6	T7
Anti-T1	80	0	0	0	0	0	0
Anti-T2	0	400	0	150	0	80	0
Anti-T3	0	0	120	0	0	0	30
Anti-T4	0	75	0	250	0	20	0
Anti-T5	0	0	0	0	80	0	0
Anti-T6	0	200	0	40	0	500	0
Anti-T7	0	0	75	0	0	0	120

Although serum-inactivated phage cannot be reactivated by dilution, it has been rendered active again by digesting away the antibody with the proteolytic enzyme papain (*366*). This indicates that the virus particle was coated by antibody but not destroyed.

An important observation (which appears to be valid for all viruses) is that phage-neutralizing antibody cannot prevent the multiplication of phage that has already been taken up by sensitive cells (*167*). This fact will be discussed again in chapter 8. In line with this observation, it is impossible to eliminate with antiserum the phage carried inside lysogenic bacteria, which continue therefore to carry latent phage after having grown in antiphage serum.

Complement fixation by phage-antiphage serum combinations occurs. Its specificity, as measured by the extent of cross-reactions, is similar to that of neutralization reactions with the same serum (*399a*). The role of complement in the neutralization reaction itself is obscure. Addition of complement reduces the serum-neutralization rate for phage T1, for example, but increases the rate for phage T2 (*311*).

Phage particles are not the only phage-specific antigen. Lysates of several phages contain a smaller, ultrafiltrable component, which combines specifically with antiphage serum even when the antiphage serum has been produced by injection of purified phage. These phage-specific soluble substances or *ultrafiltrable factors* are detected by their serum-blocking power, that is, by their ability to reduce the phage-neutralizing activity of a serum (see table 16). They have the

Table 16. The serum-blocking power of phage and of ultrafiltrate of phage lysate

From DeMars et al. (*175*)

Preincubation of antiphage serum with ultraviolet-inactivated homologous phage or with the phage-free ultrafiltrate of a lysate of the homologous phage reduces the phage-neutralizing ability of the serum.

Tube Number	Contents				Assay of Test Phage	Per Cent Survival of Test Phage
1	Broth	4 hr at 48° C	Add test phage T2r	4 hr at 48° C	7.7×10^5	100
2	Serum *				2.2×10^4	3
3	Serum + 7.0×10^9 T2 (UV inactivated)				7.7×10^5	100
4	Serum + 2.3×10^9 T2 (UV inactivated)				4.8×10^5	62
5	Serum + 7.7×10^8 T2 (UV inactivated)				1.8×10^5	23
6	Serum + 2.6×10^8 T2 (UV inactivated)				4.3×10^4	6
7	Serum + 8.7×10^7 T2 (UV inactivated)				1.6×10^4	2
8	Serum + ultrafiltrate diluted 1 : 3				1.7×10^5	22
9	Serum + ultrafiltrate diluted 1 : 9				5.3×10^4	7
10	Serum + ultrafiltrate diluted 1 : 27				2.5×10^4	3

* Serum anti-T2 1 : 40,000.

same serological cross-reactivity as the corresponding phages. They are of interest because they may represent specific phage building blocks and may throw some light on the process of phage synthesis.

Immature phage particles produced by infected bacteria in the presence of the dye proflavine and resembling empty phage heads (see page 71 and figure 28), fix complement with antiphage serum but do not combine with neutralizing antibodies (175). Thus, there is more than one type of antigen in some phages. The antigen that gives rise to neutralizing antibodies is apparently localized in the phage tail, whereas another antigen, recognizable by complement-fixation tests, is located in the phage head (399a). Antibody against the head antigen does not neutralize the phage. These observations are in line with the conclusion (see chapter 8) that the phage tail represents the organ of attachment of phage to the host cell.

SEROLOGY OF PLANT VIRUSES

The antigenic properties of plant viruses were discovered relatively recently (536). The serological methodology is influenced by the fact that relatively large amounts of virus material are often available, for example, for tobacco mosaic virus. It is feasible, therefore, to run *precipitation* tests. These can actually be used to measure the amount of virus material in a preparation (see 43). Two methods are employed: In the optimum precipitation method, a constant amount of virus suspension is mixed with various concentrations of antibody, and the mixture in which precipitation first appears is considered as the optimum for the reaction. In the end-point method, one determines the smallest amount of antigen that reacts with a constant amount of antibody. In these tests, as in all precipitation reactions with plant viruses, it is important to distinguish between specific and aspecific precipitation, since the viruses tend to be precipitated out of solution by a number of foreign materials, particularly proteins.

Antisera have been obtained against several plant viruses. Those viruses against which no antibodies have been found may simply have been present in amounts too small to give visible precipitation. Complement fixation, which has been successfully applied to plant virus work (641a), may be useful in detecting smaller amounts of virus.

Neutralization of plant viruses by antibody must be distinguished from the aspecific neutralization which occurs with normal sera. It is generally recognized that specific neutralization occurs, but that the combination of virus with neutralizing antibody is somewhat reversible upon dilution of the mixture. Tobacco mosaic virus can be recovered in active form from a mixture with antibody by digesting the antibody with enzymes. Quantitative studies on the rate of neutralization have been few and relatively inconclusive. They are complicated not only by the aspecific neutralization by normal serum, but also by the fact that, due to the low efficiency of the methods for testing infectivity, large amounts of virus must be used, so that the concentrations of antigen and antibody are of the same order. Therefore, the results are very sensitive to small variations in the concentration of either reagent.

Since viruses like tobacco mosaic virus are available in large amounts we can easily perform absorption tests, in which the antibodies that react with a virus are removed by prolonged treatment with an excess of that virus, and then the reaction of the antiserum with a different virus is tested. By this method, the serological cross-reactions among plant viruses have been studied in some detail. The patterns of relationship obtained in this way are in agreement with those derived from other methods, especially cross-protection tests. The results of a typical cross-precipitation test with absorbed antisera are shown in table 14.

Crude preparations of plant viruses, like those of bacteriophages and of animal viruses, often contain materials that share the serological specificity of the virus particles but not their infectivity (49; 473). These materials may even be antigenically more powerful than the virus itself. Their exact relation to the virus particles, as precursors, breakdown products, or abnormal forms, is currently a matter for speculation.

SEROLOGY OF ANIMAL VIRUSES

The serological reactions of animal viruses, discovered very early after the recognition of virus diseases, comprise a major portion of medical virology. Antibodies play an important role in the course of animal virus diseases and in a variety of important procedures in the prophylaxis, diagnosis, and therapy of these diseases. Serological reactions have been studied both in animals that can support virus growth and in animals that cannot. In those that can, the role of antibodies in immunity phenomena has been thoroughly investigated.

In vivo tests of the infectivity of mixtures of a virus with the homologous antiserum show a reduction of activity, commonly interpreted as due to a combination of the virus with neutralizing antibodies. This interpretation had been challenged because the combination is difficult to demonstrate. Indeed, virus activity can often be recovered from neutralized mixtures with antibody either by dilution or by centrifugation. It was, therefore, suggested that antiserum acts by stimulating the resistance of the host tissues (570). Good evidence has been obtained, however, for actual combination of the virus with neutralizing antibodies (see *121*). In the first place, the recovery of activity from virus-antiserum mixtures becomes progressively less complete the longer the mixtures are allowed to stand. Second, actual absorption of the neutralizing power of a serum by washed virus particles has been demonstrated. Burnet and his collaborators, using for virus titration the accurate method of pock counting on the chorioallantoic membrane of the chick embryo, showed that the neutralization of a variety of viruses by antiserum can best be interpreted in terms of a reversible combination between virus and antibody. The reversibility is more or less complete depending on the virus. With rabbit myxoma virus, for example, concentrated antisera give irreversible neutralization, whereas with louping ill virus the reaction seemed to be completely reversible. With influenza viruses, it can be shown by absorption tests that the neutralizing antibodies are at least in part the same as those that prevent red blood cell agglutination by the virus in vitro, under conditions where the antibody must certainly act on the virus itself.

It is now certain that the mechanism of action of virus-neutralizing antibodies is not fundamentally different from any other antigen-antibody reaction. The outcome of an inoculation with a virus-antiserum mixture depends upon the availability of the surface groups of the virus particle needed for infection at the time of the contact of the virus with a susceptible cell. This conclusion is supported by the finding that intradermal injection of antiserum against vaccinia protects a rabbit against dermal infection if given 24 hours previous to, or simultaneously with, the injection of virus, but not if given as little as 5 minutes after virus injection at the same site. This illustrates the inability of antibodies to affect virus that has already been taken up by the host cells. In general, the outcome of inoculations with mixtures of virus and antiserum will depend on the net balance of several processes: the reversibility of the virus-antibody combination, the rate of uptake of active virus by sensitive cells, and the rates of spread of the virus, the antibody, and the virus-antibody complexes through the tissues.

A possible biological significance of the reversibility of the combination of animal viruses with neutralizing antibodies has been suggested by Burnet (*121*). Reversibility favors the survival of the virus, both in its spreading within the host organism and in passing from host to host. The ability to combine reversibly with antibodies, being advantageous to animal viruses, would be favored by natural selection, whereas for bacteriophages irreversibility of the combination with antibody would not be a handicap for survival in nature, where phage does not generally meet antibody.

In vitro serological reactions of animal viruses, such as agglutination, precipitation, and complement fixation, reveal the antigenic complexity of most viruses. Crude virus preparations often contain, besides the virus particles, other virus-specific antigens. A good example of these noninfectious virus antigens, often called *specific soluble substances* (SSS), is the SSS of vaccinia virus (*606*). Centrifugation of a crude preparation of vaccinia from the rabbit's skin leaves a supernatant which, after being freed of residual elementary bodies, contains large amounts of a specific protein antigen, the so-called LS antigen. After purification, the LS fraction gives precipitation and complement-fixation reactions with antisera prepared either against the virus particles or against pure LS. The LS antigen has been found to consist of protein molecules, about 300,000 in molecular weight, carrying two distinct and separable antigenic functions L and S. The L function is suppressed by heating, the S function by treatment with chymotrypsin. The two antigenic functions are carried on the same molecule. This is shown by the fact that complete LS antigen is fully precipitated by antisera prepared against each of the partial antigens, L or S. Antibody against LS also agglutinates elementary bodies, indicating that some LS antigen is probably located on the surface of the virus particles, from which it can actually be extracted. The antibody against LS does not, however, neutralize the virus. The LS antigens of all viruses of the smallpox-vaccinia group appear to be identical, although the viruses differ in other antigens.

Extraction of vaccinia virus particles yields at least two other antigens, a nucleoprotein antigen removable by alkali and the so-called X-agglutinogen. Both antigens induce production of antibodies that agglutinate the virus particles but do not neutralize them. The antigens that give rise to neutralizing antibodies apparently cannot be extracted from the virus particles without being destroyed.

Many other viruses give rise to specific soluble substances comparable to the LS antigen of vaccinia in their relation to the viruses. For example, influenza viruses are accompanied by specific complement-fixing substances (*355*). These are virus specific, in the sense that the SSS of influenza virus A do not react with sera against the serologically unrelated influenza virus B. The influenza SSS are not strain specific, however; they are apparently identical in all strains of a given virus type (A or B). The virus particles themselves contain, besides complement-fixing antigens similar to their SSS, other complement-fixing antigens, which are often strain specific. Neither of these complement-fixing antigens is identical with the antigens that induce neutralizing antibodies.

The soluble antigens play an important role in diagnostic procedures. They are often readily obtainable in fairly large amounts, for example, from the dermal pulp of vaccinia-infected rabbit skin or from the spleen of animals with lymphocytic choriomeningitis. Complement-fixation tests may be used to reveal antibodies against soluble antigens or to detect the antigen itself in a patient's serum.

The soluble antigens are also of great theoretical interest. Indeed, they appear to represent portions of specific virus material produced in excess by the infected hosts. They may originate, either by excess formation of specific virus components or by breakdown of virus particles within the host. The first alternative seems to be supported by the appearance of complement-fixing SSS in eggs infected with influenza viruses several hours before any virus activity is recoverable (302; 353). This method for investigating virus synthesis by following serologically the formation of virus-specific materials will be discussed in chapter 13.

It has been suggested that the SSS may play a role in favoring the survival and spread of a virus within the host by acting as blocking agents for circulating antivirus antibodies (121). It must be mentioned, however, that a combination of SSS with neutralizing antibodies has not yet been demonstrated for animal viruses, but only for the "ultrafiltrable factors" that accompany certain phages.

The literature on serology of animal viruses gives the impression that their serological specificity is rather variable. Even in the same outbreak of a virus disease such as influenza several distinct antigenic types of virus may be isolated. This situation may be the result of natural selection. Indeed, a high rate of serological mutability would provide for a wider range of antibody resistance and would, therefore, be advantageous to the virus in its struggle for survival.

MEDICAL ASPECTS OF VIRUS SEROLOGY

The serological properties of animal viruses provide a basis for much of the diagnostic and prophylactic procedures of medical virology.

Antibodies are produced in an infected organism either in special tissues or possibly also in the very tissue in which the virus grows (581). The antibodies can prevent the spread of virus from cell to cell, but are probably inactive against intracellular virus. Circulating antibodies are also ineffectual against the spread of viruses that are transported along nerve fibers. By the time the symptoms of a virus disease manifest themselves, most of the cells that are going to be infected already contain the virus and protect it from circulating antibody. This seems especially to be so with neurotropic viruses.

Because of this, *passive immunization,* consisting of the injection of preformed antibodies, has mainly prophylactic applications, for example, during epidemics of measles. With diseases such as measles (and probably also poliomyelitis), the blood serum of a large number of human adults contains antiviral antibodies. It is therefore practical to use for passive immunization the gamma-globulin fraction extracted from large pools of human plasma.

The solid natural immunity that follows recovery from most virus diseases is partly due to the persistence of circulating antibodies, which may be found 20 years or longer after recovery, for example, in yellow fever. There is often a lack of correlation, however, between the degree of immunity on the one hand, and the presence and amount of neutralizing antibodies in the blood on the other hand (554). Tests for local antibody may be of greater significance since the degree of immunity is closely correlated with antibody present at the site of possible infection, as in bronchial washings in influenza (212).

The mechanism of the long persistence of antibodies against some viruses is obscure. Some authors incline to the belief that some virus or virus fragment remains permanently in the organism and stimulates antibody production (556). Other authors favor the idea that an antigen induces a modified pattern of globulin synthesis, which is then retained after the antigen has disappeared (112). Some nonviral and certainly non-self-reproducing antigens, such as bacterial polysaccharides, cause prolonged antibody formation, but the serological response is never as persistent as that which follows recovery from virus diseases.

Vaccination against virus diseases is of great prophylactic value. Its success—well illustrated by the case of Jennerian vaccination against smallpox by means of vaccinia virus, or by that of vaccination against yellow fever with an egg-passage variant—represents one of the major conquests of medical science. It was thought at first that the only vaccines that gave a satisfactory immunity were those containing active virus. This was probably due to the fact that the amount of antigen present in inactive virus preparations was usually insufficient to stimulate the production of an adequate antibody level. The purification of several viruses in large amounts has permitted the preparation, for example, with influenza, of powerful vaccines consisting of virus inactivated by treatments, such as formolization or ultraviolet irradiation, which preserve the antigenic power.

In vaccination by means of active virus, a low antigen content in the inoculum may be compensated by the production of more virus antigen in the vaccinated organism. Various methods are used in different cases. Partially inactivated virus vaccines have been employed. They may owe their effectiveness to the fact that they contain active and inactive virus in proper proportions, so that the level of antibody production under the stimulus of the inactive virus is, presumably, sufficient to keep the reproduction of the active virus at the nonpathogenic level. Vaccines consisting of a mixture of virus and antibody probably act through a mechanism of the same type. Their value will depend on the relative chances for migration and diffusion of the virus and the antibody from the site of inoculation and on the reversibility of the antigen-antibody combination. Some vaccinations may be made by inoculating infectious virus by an abnormal route, which prevents severe infection but not immunization. In all cases, the choice of an adequate vaccine is based on purely empirical criteria of effectiveness.

The most effective vaccines to date have been those consisting of mutant forms of viruses that possess the ability to multiply and cause antibody production in a host, for which they are either mildly pathogenic or not pathogenic at all. The best examples are immunization against smallpox with vaccinia or cowpox virus (from *vacca* = cow; hence the words vaccine and vaccination) and vaccination against yellow fever with a virus variant 17D that was isolated after repeated passages in tissue cultures and in chick embryos.

Vaccination is often complicated by the fact that what is considered as one virus may occur in a variety of serologically different, often unrelated strains. For example, three major serological types of poliomyelitis virus have been described. The recognition of such serological differences is of paramount importance for any effective serological treatment and diagnosis. An effective prophylaxis requires vaccines containing at least the most frequent serological types (*493*).

Serological procedures provide the most important and often the only reliable diagnostic tests for virus diseases, since the actual isolation of virus from patients is difficult and even in specialized laboratories succeeds only in a fraction of cases. The choice of serological method varies from virus to virus (*13; 345;* see *605* for an extensive tabulation).

The virus-neutralization test, in which we determine the reduction in infectious titer of a virus preparation after mixing it with the patient's serum, is laborious and not too satisfactory, but has till recently been the only available test with some viruses such as poliomyelitis (542), although complement fixation has been reported (125). For viruses that agglutinate red blood cells (see chapter 13) the serum to be tested may be examined for its power to inhibit hemagglutination. Flocculation tests (agglutination or precipitation) generally require too much virus antigen to be of practical use, but might be improved by using as antigens virus-coated bacteria or collodion particles. Complement-fixation reactions on the patient's serum are often the method of choice, using as antigen either the virus itself or its soluble antigens. The antigens need not be purified, but anticomplementary substances, particularly lipids, must generally be removed either by extraction or by other methods.

Skin tests have been devised for a few virus diseases. The Frei test for lymphogranuloma consists of intradermal injection of inactivated virus material. A positive reaction—a large papule at the site of inoculation—is generally present both in infected and in recovered, immune individuals. A similar skin test for mumps has been described (208).

Most diagnostic tests become positive late in the disease or even only during convalescence, a fact that reduces their value. Some reactions appear earlier than others, however; for example, complement fixation with soluble mumps antigen can often be detected in the first day of disease. Usually at least two samples of serum are tested, one taken very early during disease, the other during convalescence. Presence of antibodies against a virus in the first sample may indicate a previous history of virus infection and generally speaks against a role of that virus in the etiology of the current disease. Appearance of antibodies in the convalescent sample is the significant finding, but, of course, is more valuable in diagnosis and epidemiological survey than from the viewpoint of therapy. When feasible, repeated tests in the course of the disease provide the most useful information.

Environmental Effects
on Virus Particles

In this chapter we shall discuss the effects of various environmental agencies on the properties of free viruses. The range of detectable effects is limited by the number of observable properties of a given virus. Some of these are physical properties of the virus particles themselves, others are phases of virus-host interaction. Thus, we may recognize specific chemical changes of a virus, such as can be produced by chemical treatment of tobacco mosaic virus, for example. Or, we can recognize a disintegration or an aggregation of virus particles by changes in their size and shape. We may observe changes in antigenic or in hemagglutinating activity. And finally, we may observe losses of infectivity.

Where the process of infection has been analyzed in terms of individual steps of host-virus interaction, as for some bacteriophages, it may be possible to recognize virus changes that suppress reproduction by blocking one or another of the steps. For example, a virus particle may be inactive because of inability either to attach itself to a sensitive cell, or to penetrate through its wall, or to perform some of the later roles required for production of new virus.

Different environmental agents may inactivate virus particles in a variety of ways, by suppressing one or more of their activities. Indeed, many of these virus activities have been recognized from the study of inactive particles. For example, we know that the attachment of a phage to a bacterium is not necessarily followed by invasion and killing of the bacterial cells, because we find that by exposure to x-rays a phage may be rendered incapable of killing the bacterium, although it is still adsorbed by it (665). As a whole, the ability of various agents to cause a *separation of virus properties* is an invaluable tool in virus research. One important application of this separation is in the preparation of noninfectious virus vaccines.

135

Inactivation and disintegration studies on virus suspensions may provide some information concerning the structure and composition of the viruses. We must admit, however, that the information that has been gained from straight inactivation studies, including detailed analyses of the kinetics of inactivation, has been altogether disappointing. This is only an expression of our ignorance of the relation between structure and function in the chemistry of complex biological molecules.

The information available on the effect of chemical and physical agents on virus particles is different from that available, for example, for bacteria, partly because it has been gathered by investigators guided by different practical purposes. Problems of spoilage are hardly involved in work with viruses. The practical goals of inactivation studies on viruses are the preservation of virus activity in the laboratory, the separation of infectivity from serological activity for the production of vaccines, and the choice of suitable manipulations in the handling of viruses for purification and concentration. A more distant goal is the possible application of inactivating agents to the suppression of virus infectivity inside the host and to the chemotherapy of virus diseases.

We must be aware of the fact that the stability of virus particles exposed to various environments is a "chemical stability," that is, a static kind of stability. To alter a virus particle we must change its structure. The situation is somewhat different from the one encountered, for example, in the study of the stability of bacteria. Here we are dealing with an "organismic stability," that is, with a dynamic system in a state of continuous flux, into which and from which component elements are continuously incorporated, assimilated, eliminated, and broken down. In such a system, irreversible inactivation may occur following rather mild environmental changes, since any disturbance of the dynamic situation may lead to lack of protection against new situations produced by the organism's own activities. For example, a virus and a bacterium may be equally sensitive to a lowering of the pH. To inactivate the virus with acid, we must add acid. The bacterium, however, may be killed by a change in buffer concentration which allows it to accumulate enough acid from its own metabolic activity to bring the pH down to the toxic level. Studies on the stability of metabolizing bacteria are more properly to be considered as analogous to studies on the stability of viruses inside the host cells, a field that as yet has barely been developed.

Very few virus changes have been described that are not accompanied by loss of virus activity. To such nonlethal changes belong some changes by chemical treatment of tobacco mosaic virus (624), and the reproductive delays produced in bacteriophage by small doses of radiation (433).

Changes in the infectivity of virus particles brought about by external treatments can be classified into three major categories: reversible inhibition, inactivation without loss of antigenicity, and disintegration. Reversible inhibition of bacteriophage infectivity by combination with bacterial debris has been observed. Inhibition of infectivity of many plant viruses by a variety of substances, including proteins, enzymes, and plant and insect extracts, has been described repeatedly. Some has been attributed to a reversible combination between virus and inhibitor (43). Usually, however, the inhibition of infection is better explained by an effect of the inhibitor on the host cells rather than on the virus (281a; 621a). A variety of plant extracts can affect plant virus reproduction, even when sprayed on infected leaves as late as 1 day after inoculation with the virus.

Inactivation without disintegration of the virus particle is generally effected by treatments that do not cause extensive protein denaturation. Radiation and mild treatments with chemicals such as formalin or hydrogen peroxide often produce this result. Protracted or intense treatments with an agent that at first only causes a loss of activity lead to extensive denaturation and disintegration, often accompanied by changes in shape and morphology of the virus particles and sometimes by their actual breakdown, as for tobacco mosaic virus or vaccinia virus treated with alkali. Occasionally several properties of a virus can be suppressed one after the other by progressive treatment with one single agent such as ultraviolet radiation (301). The properties that are destroyed first are probably those that require the greatest degree of structural integrity and are, therefore, suppressed even by a slight chemical alteration. The ability to reproduce is generally lost very soon, whereas antigenicity is very stable, apparently requiring for its suppression a far-reaching alteration of the virus proteins.

It is important to keep in mind that the effect of any treatment on viruses is influenced by such conditions as the composition of the medium and the temperature. Sometimes it is difficult to decide which agent is actually responsible for the observed virus change, since a number of unfavorable conditions all present together may cause more damage than would the sum of their individual effects.

PHYSICAL AGENTS (EXCEPT RADIATION)

Temperature effects. In crude preparations or in other media of complex organic composition, most viruses are quite stable at room temperature; inactivation often becomes measurable at temperatures around 50–60° C, the range where denaturation of many proteins proceeds at an appreciable rate. Important differences among viruses are present, however. Thus, some plant viruses, like tobacco mosaic, are

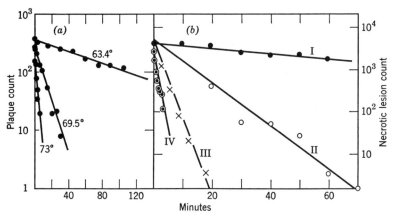

Figure 51. The inactivation of viruses by heat. (*a*) Phage T5 in broth at various temperatures. From: Adams (*6*). (*b*) Plant viruses in plant sap. I. Tobacco ringspot, 50° C. II. Tobacco mosaic, 90° C. III. Tobacco necrosis, 86° C. IV. Alfalfa mosaic, 62.5° C. From: Price, *Arch. ges. Virusforsch.* 1:373, 1940.

practically stable at 65° C and are only inactivated at an appreciable rate around 70° C. Aster yellows virus and certain other viruses are rapidly destroyed even at comparatively low temperatures. The aster yellows virus is inactivated in its insect vector at 32° C (*389*). Infected plants can be cured by immersion in warm water (*390*). The situation may be different, however, for such inactivation in the host. For example, a bacteriophage quite stable at 50° C is inactivated if phage-infected cells are kept at 43° C (*432*).

The kinetics of inactivation of viruses at different temperatures is exponential. The ratio of the virus activity V to the initial activity V_0 diminishes with increasing time t of exposure, according to the equation for a first-order reaction: $V/V_0 = e^{-kt}$. Deviations from this rule are generally due either to aggregation of virus particles or to heterogeneity of their heat sensitivity. The course of inactivation of several viruses at different temperatures is illustrated in figure 51.

Because of the exponential inactivation just described, we cannot speak rigorously of a "thermal inactivation point" for a virus, since survival always depends on the duration of exposure to heat and on the initial virus concentration. Many statements in the literature concerning thermal inactivation points of viruses reflect the occurrence of a narrow temperature range within which the inactivation rate passes from low to very high values; that is, virus inactivation generally has a high temperature coefficient. The range of thermal stability is that temperature range in which the inactivation rate is so low that no decrease in activity can be detected.

The exponential inactivation, expression of a first-order reaction, indicates that a constant fraction of the particles undergoes an inactivating chemical change in each unit of time and that one such change is sufficient to inactivate a particle. The temperature effects, according to chemical kinetic theory, reflect the fact that in a population of molecules there is a distribution of molecules with different energies. The only molecules that can undergo reaction (with a fixed probability) are those that possess at least a certain "energy of activation" characteristic for the reaction in question. The frequency of molecules whose energy equals or exceeds the activation energy increases with temperature. The rate constant k as a function of the absolute temperature T is given by the Arrhenius equation

$$k = Ae^{-E/RT} \tag{10}$$

where R is the gas constant (1.987 calories per mole per degree C); A and E are constants characteristic for a given reaction; and E is the energy of activation. A monomolecular reaction type results from the fact that the rate at which the activated molecules react is slow compared with the rate at which the equilibrium among molecules of different energies is established, so that at each time the fraction of molecules with energies greater than the activation energy is a constant fraction of the total number of molecules. Thus, the reaction rate measures the fraction of molecules whose energy equals or exceeds the activation energy necessary for the reaction.[1]

---

[1] The dependence of the reaction rate on the temperature is more fully expressed, according to the theory of absolute reaction rates (256a), by the equation

$$k = \frac{\kappa T}{h} e^{-\Delta F^{\ddagger}/RT} = \frac{\kappa T}{h} e^{-(\Delta H^{\ddagger} - T\Delta S^{\ddagger})/RT} = \frac{\kappa T}{h} e^{-(\Delta E^{\ddagger} + P\Delta V^{\ddagger} - T\Delta S^{\ddagger})/RT} \tag{10a}$$

This formulation expresses the kinetics of two reactions, a first reversible one, in which the original molecules become activated, and a second one in which the

The validity of equation 10 is tested by the so-called Arrhenius plot; log k should be a linear function of $1/T$. Such a plot for the denaturation of tobacco mosaic virus is shown in figure 52. The slope gives the value of E/R, from which we can calculate the value of E. Data

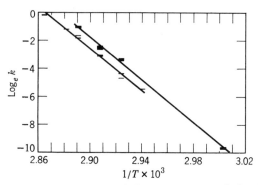

Figure 52. The natural logarithm of the rate constants k for denaturation of tobacco mosaic virus protein at various temperatures, as a function of the inverse of the absolute temperature T (Arrhenius plot). The straight lines indicate that the energy of activation is constant over the temperature range included. *Upper line:* 3 mg of virus per ml. *Lower line:* 6 mg of virus per ml. From: Lauffer, Price, and Petre (*405*).

for various viruses are given in table 17. The activation energy for thermal inactivation of most viruses is high, of the order of 30,000–150,000 calories per mole. Such high activation energies correspond to high Q_{10} values.[2] For example, an activation energy of 90,000 calories per mole corresponds to a Q_{10} of 50.

Activation energies of this order are unusual in ordinary chemical reactions but are observed for protein denaturation, a fact which sug-

activated molecules undergo the observed chemical change. In equation 10a, κ and h are the Boltzmann and Planck constants; $\Delta F^{\ddagger}$, $\Delta H^{\ddagger}$, and $\Delta S^{\ddagger}$ are the changes in free energy, in total energy, and in entropy in the activation reaction ($\Delta H^{\ddagger}$ corresponds to E in equation 10); $\Delta E^{\ddagger}$ is the change in energy at constant pressure; P is the pressure; and $\Delta V^{\ddagger}$ is the volume change in the activation reaction. Equation 10a explains why the reaction rate may be rapid even for reactions with high activation energy, if activation is accompanied by a large increase in entropy, so that the total change in free energy is small. Studies of reaction rates at various pressures can give information on the changes in molecular volume that take place in the transition to the activated state.

[2] The Q_{10} ($= k_{T+10}/k_T$) is the ratio between the reaction rates at two temperatures differing by 10° C.

Table 17.   Activation energy for the inactivation of several viruses
by heat

	E (calories per mole)	Source
Tobacco necrosis virus in plant sap	37,300	a
Alfalfa mosaic virus in plant sap	75,000	a
Tobacco ringspot virus (56.5–65° C) in plant sap	27,600	a
Tobacco ringspot virus (45–56.5° C) in plant sap	78,800	a
Tobacco mosaic virus (84–95° C) in plant sap	195,000	a
Tobacco mosaic virus (68–84° C) in plant sap	55,300	a
Tobacco mosaic virus (denaturation of virus protein)	153,000	b
Influenza virus A	34,000	b
Bacteriophage T1 in broth	106,000	c
Bacteriophage T4 in broth	131,000	c
Bacteriophage T5 in broth	86,000	c
Bacteriophage T7 in broth	77,000	c

Sources: a, Price, Arch. ges. Virusforsch. 1:373 (1940); b, Lauffer, Price, and Petre (405); c, Adams (6).

gests that thermal inactivation results from denaturation of virus proteins.   Indeed, the thermal inactivation of several viruses is closely paralleled by the loss of their serological specificity, which is dependent on the integrity of protein structure.   This is true, for example, for tobacco mosaic virus, latent potato mosaic virus, and several bacteriophages.   The role of nucleic acid changes in thermal inactivation is difficult to evaluate, since little is known about heat effects on nucleic acids.

Some plant viruses (tomato bushy stunt, tobacco necrosis) are rapidly inactivated by heat at temperatures lower than those which denature most proteins (see 43; 405).   The energy of activation for their loss of infectivity is rather low, and there is a wide range of temperatures at which these viruses are inactivated at measurable rates.   Thermal inactivation at the lower temperatures is not accompanied by loss of serological specificity.   One may suspect that in these cases thermal inactivation is due either to the destruction of some particularly heat-labile portion of the virus or to the thermal acceleration of virus inactivation by some other mechanism, possibly by combination with some medium component.

The observations reported above concern virus particles suspended in crude media or in relatively concentrated salt solutions. Viruses diluted in distilled water or saline solutions are often much less stable and become rapidly inactivated even at room temperature. Careful studies for various bacteriophages (6) have shown that the concentration of individual ions is the critical element. For example, coliphage T5 is as stable in presence of $10^{-2} M$ Mg^{++} or Ca^{++} as in nutrient broth, whereas in $10^{-1} M$ NaCl the rate of inactivation at the same temperature is over one million times faster. Higher concentrations of Na^{+} are protective. The energy of activation is not appreciably different in different solutions. Evidently the virus can combine with various cations to give reversible combinations, which are more stable than the virus particles in uncombined form. The inactivation rate observed at a certain ion concentration probably measures the fraction of virus present in uncombined form.

Heat treatment is not a choice method for effecting separation of various virus properties, since these properties are often lost at similar rates. An interesting exception is shown by the influenza viruses, which at 55° C lose their infectivity much faster than their hemagglutinating ability (327).

Effects of pH. The pH stability of different viruses is of interest mainly in connection with virus extraction and purification. At least for tobacco mosaic virus, the stability range of virus activity is nearly the same as the range of stability of the virus protein in respect to its physical characteristics. At pH above 8.5 the virus is broken into smaller units. It has been claimed that these can be rejoined together by lowering the pH, although without return of infectivity (587).

Most animal viruses have optimum stabilities around pH 7, with ranges varying widely around this point. Infectivity may be suppressed by acid or alkaline treatment without loss of antigenicity.

Drying and shaking. Most viruses withstand drying from the frozen state, a procedure commonly used for the preservation of virus specimens. Wide differences exist in the stability of different viruses in the dry state. Inactivation is probably brought about by oxidation in the course of the drying process. The presence of foreign proteins in the medium (as in blood serum, plant saps, and bacteriological media) exerts an appreciable amount of protection, probably due to a competition for oxidizing agents.

This is an instance of a very general situation, by which foreign proteins protect virus activity against inactivating agents by competition mechanisms, just as an excess of one protein protects another protein against denaturation. Similar protection by proteins is observed when a suspension of virus (phage) is shaken. Here the foreign protein prevents "surface denaturation" by competing for surface area (5). Addition of blood serum or beef extract is a common practice in virus preservation. For research purposes, salt-free purified gelatin is often used as a protective agent.

CHEMICAL AGENTS

In spite of many studies, it must be acknowledged that little fundamental information has yet come from the study of chemical treatments on viruses, mainly because of the difficulty of interpreting changes in virus properties in terms of chemical changes.

Enzymes. Enzyme studies are sometimes complicated by the occurrence of some reversible inhibition of virus activity by combination with enzymes just as with many other proteins. No meaningful pattern has emerged concerning the ability of one virus or another to withstand different enzymes. Moreover, viruses may be inactivated by nonenzymatic impurities in enzyme preparations. The resistance of tobacco mosaic virus and vaccinia to some proteolytic enzymes such as trypsin has been utilized in purification procedures to get rid of proteinaceous impurities.

In spite of their relatively large content of nucleic acid, virus particles are not inactivated by nucleic acid depolymerases from pancreas (ribonuclease and desoxyribonuclease). The nucleic acids and the proteins of viruses, however, after being extracted from the virus particles are rapidly attacked by nucleases and proteolytic enzymes, respectively. In their native form within the virus particles, they are evidently not accessible to enzyme attack, probably because of inaccessibility of the atomic groups upon which the enzymes can act. Thus, the organization of virus particles, like the organization of living cells but not necessarily by the same mechanism, protects the individual components against enzymatic breakdown. In some bacteriophages, protection against desoxyribonuclease is probably due to the protein membrane of the virus particles (308).

Other chemicals. Several chemicals, when used in the proper concentrations, produce inactivation of viruses without loss of serological specificity. Formalin and phenol have been employed successfully in the preparation of several noninfectious vaccines.

Different viruses are inactivated at different rates by the same chemical. The inactivation produced by chemical agents may sometimes be

reversed in vitro by suitable treatments. For example, formalin inactivation of tobacco mosaic virus may be partially reversed by dialysis
(561). Some bacteriophages, after inactivation by formalin, can be
partially reactivated by placing them in a medium with high protein
content (376). Mercuric chloride inactivation of several viruses has
been reversed by treatment with hydrogen sulfide. Apparently the
mercuric ion suppresses virus activity by combining with the sulfhydril groups of proteins, from which it can be displaced competi-
tively by other —SH compounds. Sulfhydril compounds can also
counteract the inactivating effect of several oxidizing agents, a fact
which identifies the —SH groups of the virus as the sites of the inactivating oxidation. In contrast with such reversible inactivation is
that produced by chemicals, such as urea, that cause extensive protein
denaturation. Virus particles inactivated by urea are often broken
down into fragments (405).

We already mentioned that certain chemical treatments can produce
chemical changes detectable by analysis of virus proteins without
suppressing the virus infectivity. Schramm and Müller (588) reported
that all the free amino groups of tobacco mosaic could be covered
without inactivation, but Stanley and his coworkers (see 624) concluded that only 70% of these groups (plus 20% of the phenol-plus-
indole groups) could be combined with acetyl or phenylureido groups
without loss of infectivity. The resulting virus was homogeneous in
size and differed electrophoretically from normal virus.

Iodine could block the sulfhydril groups of tobacco mosaic without inactivation, but iodine treatment prolonged enough to affect the
tyrosine groups was inactivating. The activity of the modified viruses,
although undiminished when tested in one host, was occasionally reduced in another host, a fact that indicates that virus growth in different host cells requires different levels of structural integrity.

From a practical point of view, the observation that most viruses will
remain active for several years in 50% glycerin, which kills most bacterial cells, has been utilized in preserving virus vaccines.

Virus inactivation and chemotherapy. Most of the agents that inactivate virus particles in vitro are not specific in their action on viruses,
but act because of their ability to alter proteins. The purpose of
chemotherapy being the suppression of a virus inside its host without
damage to the host, any chemotherapeutic agent must have a differential toxicity for host and parasite. Protein-denaturing treatments,
however, generally produce nonspecific protoplasmic destruction.
They will, therefore, be of little use in therapy. Exceptional cases

may occur. Inactivation of some plant virus diseases by heat treatment of infected plants is apparently due to the remarkable heat sensitivity of these viruses as contrasted with the host plants (390).

Antibacterial chemotherapy has been successful in the use of substances, such as antibiotics, chosen on empirical grounds and later proved to be inhibitory of enzymatic processes. Chemotherapeutic success depends on differential susceptibility of host and parasite, either because the host does not require the inhibited enzymes or because of different sensitivity or accessibility of host enzymes and bacterial enzymes. The classic example is that of the sulfonamides, which interfere with the utilization of paraaminobenzoic acid, the requirement for which is greater for many pathogenic bacteria than for animal organisms.

As we shall see in later chapters, viruses appear to use for their reproduction the enzymatic machinery of the host cells. It therefore seems likely, on the one hand, that the metabolic-inhibitor approach to antivirus chemotherapy will be less likely to succeed than in antibacterial chemotherapy. On the other hand, success might depend on the discovery of enzyme systems, either carried by the host cell or possibly by the virus itself, whose suppression would be tolerated by the host but not by the virus. Thus, the logical expectation is that a successful chemotherapy of virus diseases will be the outcome of a detailed analysis of the physiology and biochemistry of the virus-infected cell, which may reveal the vulnerable points of the enzymatic processes involved.

There are objections, however, to this reasoning. Our knowledge of the synthetic mechanism of cells is still very limited, and a clarification of virus-host metabolism may take decades. Indeed, an appreciable amount of information on cell metabolism has been obtained from a study of the mode of action of empirically chosen antibacterial chemotherapeutic agents, such as sulfonamides and various antibiotics. Clarification of virus-host metabolism may well follow rather than precede chemotherapy's successes. It is a fact that in bacterial diseases most of the enzyme inhibitors rationally discovered through metabolic studies have proved of no chemotherapeutic value.

The intensive search for chemotherapeutic agents against virus diseases has yielded some limited successes. Several infections produced by viruses of the psittacosis group in man (lymphogranuloma venereum, trachoma) respond to sulfonamide therapy, although psittacosis itself does not. Psittacosis, however, is successfully treated by penicillin, chloromycetin, and aureomycin. Aureomycin, terramycin, chloromycetin, and related antibiotics have been used widely in a variety of virus diseases, especially in the ill-defined group that goes under the name of "primary atypical pneumonia," but the therapeutic results are questionable (346). Aureomycin and terramycin have proved effective in checking certain virus diseases of mice (257).

Another possible line of approach to virus chemotherapy stems from the discovery of specific organic inhibitors of virus adsorption onto susceptible cells. Certain bacteriophages are not adsorbed by sensitive bacteria in the presence of indole (170). Influenza virus can be prevented from infecting sensitive cells by certain polysaccharides (346).

Formation of tobacco mosaic virus in isolated discs of tobacco leaf tissue can be inhibited by purine and pyrimidine analogues (151; 477). Amino acid analogues can prevent formation of influenza virus (2), but their potential therapeutic value is doubtful. Other approaches to virus chemotherapy include attempts to interfere selectively with the energy supply of virus-infected cells (199a).

RADIATION EFFECTS

Radiations occupy a special position among the environmental agents that can affect virus particles. They provide a powerful tool in virus research. To understand why, let us recall briefly some fundamentals of radiology.

Electromagnetic radiation includes infrared, visible, ultraviolet, roentgen, and gamma rays, each type of radiation being characterized by its wavelength. If a beam consists of a single wavelength it is called monochromatic. Radiation has a dual character, that of a wave phenomenon and that of a discontinuous sum of discrete packets of energy called *quanta*. The energy E of a quantum depends on the wavelength λ according to the relation $E = 12,400/\lambda$. If λ is given in angstrom units, E is obtained in *electron volts* (1 electron volt or ev is the energy of an electron accelerated by a potential difference of 1 volt). Yellow light of 5800 A consists of quanta with 2.14 ev; ultraviolet light of 2536 A, the major output of common germicidal lamps, has quanta of 4.9 ev; for x-rays of 0.1 A, the quantum energy is 124,000 ev.

All radiation effects are caused by the absorption of radiation energy in matter. They depend on the energy of the quanta and on the nature of the absorbing material. Irradiation, then, is a bombardment with a beam of quanta. Each electron belonging to an atom may "absorb" a quantum, and chemical change may ensue if enough energy is transferred to the electron. The energy required to pull an electron completely out of an atom or molecule (ionization energy) is of the order of 10 ev or more. A quantum of x-ray or gamma ray (ionizing radiations) can remove an electron from an atom, leaving a positive ion (*ionization*). The ejected electron generally possesses enough energy (fast electron) to act as a secondary bullet, ejecting electrons from other atoms or molecules until all its energy is spent. The ejected electrons will be captured by other atoms to form negative ions, so that for every electron that is ejected an ion pair is produced. A molecule from which an electron has been ejected has a high probability of undergoing chemical change in the course of the resulting electronic rearrangements.

Particulate radiations (beta rays or fast electrons, alpha rays, protons, deuterons) act like the fast electrons emitted under x-ray bombardment. The main differences consist of the more-or-less close packing of ionizations along the track of the particles through matter, which for heavier particles is practically an "ionization column."

Weaker quanta (visible and ultraviolet light) do not remove electrons, but can only produce *excitations,* that is, they can raise an electron to a state of higher energy (nonionizing radiations). The rearrangements that follow may lead to chemical change, but the probability of chemical change following excitation of complex organic molecules is generally much lower. Most excited atoms or molecules return to the original condition without chemical change, and the extra energy is dissipated into heat. Excitations are also produced by ionizing radiations. About one-half of the energy of x-rays is spent in producing such excitations.

There is a fundamental difference between ionizing and nonionizing radiations. Absorption of ionizing radiation is nonselective among the atoms and molecules exposed, and therefore the probability of ionization of an atom is unaffected by its chemical combination. Thus, the absorption ability of a substance depends only on its density and on the atomic number of the component atoms. Most biological materials differ little from one another (and from water) in average atomic composition.

Absorption of ultraviolet and visible light depends instead on chemical structure, since a quantum of a given energy will only be absorbed by electrons possessing the proper excitability, which is determined by intraatomic and interatomic forces. Thus, among substances of biological importance, nucleic acids strongly absorb ultraviolet by means of their purine and pyrimidine rings. The absorption coefficient (logarithm of the inverse of the fraction of energy absorbed by a 1-cm layer of a substance) for various wavelengths defines the absorption spectrum of a substance (see figure 48). Absorption spectra of purified virus suspensions are easily measured with a spectrophotometer.

Visible light is absorbed only by colored substances and is generally much less effective than ultraviolet in producing chemical change, the quantum energy (3 ev or less) being lower than the energy of most chemical bonds in organic materials.

We see then that the characteristic feature of the absorption of radiation is the production in the irradiated material of modified atoms and molecules distributed in a scattered way. The scattering will be geometrically more random in weaker radiations, where the full energy of one quantum is used in one single collision, than for ionizing radiations, where ejected electrons act as secondary bullets producing more or less concentrated clusters or columns of ionizations. Because of the discontinuous nature of the absorption processes, chemical change will be produced in discrete spots, as though the radiation energy brought each receiving molecule to a condition corresponding to a large rise in temperature.

The analysis of the frequency of a biological reaction (for example, the inactivation of a virus) as a function of the energy, the intensity, and the dose of radiation may provide information about the number of chemical alterations required, their location, and their nature. Moreover, the randomness of the bombardment often produces differential damage in different parts of a virus particle, resulting in dissociation of its various properties. Radiations actually represent a sort of microsurgical tool for the analysis of the dependence of various virus properties on the integrity of the virus structure.

We must distinguish between reactions produced directly, by primary absorption of radiation in biological material (*photochemical reactions*), from secondary reactions resulting from the chemical activity of substances produced by the primary reactions in the medium that surrounds the virus.

Ionizing radiation. A virus suspension, irradiated, for example, with x-rays, loses its reproductive activity at a rate that depends in part on the medium. With dilute or purified viruses in water or salt solutions, the inactivation is faster than in crude suspensions and is due mainly to toxic agents produced by radiation absorbed in the medium (*indirect effects*) (*239; 408; 444*). The toxic agents fall into two categories: unstable, short-lived agents, probably OH and H radicals, and more stable ones. These, which probably include peroxides, can be demonstrated by adding virus to a previously irradiated medium (*666*).

Most of the inactivation of viruses irradiated in salt solutions is due to the short-lived agents (see figure 53). The properties of particles inactivated in this way may differ from those treated with the long-

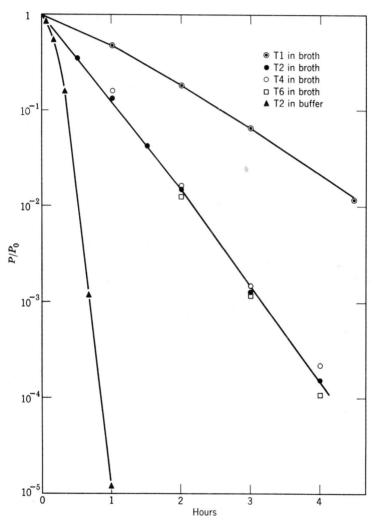

Figure 53. The inactivation of bacteriophages by x-rays, either in nutrient broth (direct effect) or in phosphate buffer (direct + indirect effects). Abscissa: duration of irradiation. Ordinate: proportion of residual infectious phage. X-ray intensity 80,000 roentgens per hour. Data from Watson (*665, 666*).

lived agents. For example, bacteriophage inactivated by immersion in irradiated buffer is still adsorbed by bacteria, whereas the same phage irradiated simultaneously with the buffer is quickly rendered unadsorbable.

These types of inactivation are not directly due to primary photochemical reactions, but are effects of chemical poisons produced by radiation in the medium. They share the properties (for example, the temperature dependence) of chemical reactions among solutes.

The indirect, secondary nature of this inactivation is shown by the fact that, if the virus is irradiated dry, or if an excess of some protective substance (gelatin, peptone, tryptophan, thiourea) is added to the medium, so that it may compete with the virus for the radiation-produced poisons, the rate of inactivation becomes much slower.

Yet, even in the presence of any amount of protective substance there remains a residual, unprotectable inactivation. This is presumably due to a *direct effect* of radiation absorbed within the virus itself (*444*). The rate of direct inactivation (see figure 53) generally follows the exponential law

$$V/V_0 = e^{-kD} \qquad [11]$$

where V_0 is the initial virus titer, V the residual one, and D the dose of radiation, usually measured in roentgen units.[3]

The rate of this direct inactivation is independent of the temperature and of the time over which the dose is spread. Thus, the process has the characteristics of a true photochemical reaction. Equation 11 is similar to the rate equation for monomolecular reactions. It indicates that each virus particle is inactivated by one independent event or "hit," corresponding to one primary act of absorption (generally one ionization). Considerations of this type are the basis of the so-called "hit theory" of radiation effects (see *407*).

One virus particle is inactivated by one radiation hit. Let us go a little further. If the dose D in equation 11 is measured in number of ionizations per unit volume, k becomes the volume ("action volume") within which one ionization occurs at the dose for which $V/V_0 = e^{-1}$ (since then $kD = 1$). This action volume can be measured experi-

---

[3] One roentgen or r is the dose of x-rays or gamma rays that liberates in 1 cm^3 of air an amount of ions carrying 1 electrostatic unit of electrical charges. This corresponds to about 1.8×10^{12} ion pairs (one negative and one positive) in 1 cm^3 of water or of material with the average composition and density of protoplasm. Doses of particulate radiations, like protons or alpha particles, are often given in "roentgens equivalent physical" or rep.

mentally and compared with the volume of the virus particles; several results of such comparisons are given in table 18. This analysis is less

Table 18. The inactivation of viruses by x-rays

Virus	Particle Size (millimicrons)	Dose that Gives $V/V_0 = e^{-1}$ (roentgen)	Diameter of Target, Calculated according to Lea (407) (millimicrons)
Phage S13	16–20?	9.9×10^5	15.9
Phage T1	50 (+ tail)	$9 \ \ \times 10^4$	30
Phage C16	65×95 (+ tail)	$4 \ \ \times 10^4$	42
Vaccinia	210×260	$1 \ \ \times 10^5$	70
Rabbit papilloma	66	4.4×10^4	40
Foot-and-mouth	15–30?	2.8×10^5	27
Tobacco necrosis	17	9.4×10^5	16
Tomato bushy stunt	31	6.2×10^5	19
Tobacco mosaic	15×300	4.3×10^5	22

complicated than it may appear. The situation may be compared to one in which a man fires many shots at random into a large target containing an invisible bull's eye, which when hit rings a bell. If he knows the area of the target, the number of shots he has fired at it, and the number of times the bell has rung, he can calculate the size of the bull's eye.

Suppose that the dose of radiation that reduces the activity of a virus suspension to the level $V/V_0 = e^{-1}$ (≈ 0.37) is 60,000 roentgens, a dose that produces 10^{17} ionizations per cm^3. With this dose one ionization will occur on the average in each volume 10^{-17} cm^3. This will be the action volume. Similar calculations have also been used to estimate the size of genes from the rate of induction of gene mutation by x-rays (407).

Table 18 shows that smaller viruses have generally smaller action volumes, that is, are more resistant to radiation. Most authors have gone farther and have assumed that the action volume or "target" is a real volume, which represents that portion of a virus particle within which *every* ionization is effective, while outside of it the virus is wholly unsusceptible. For comparison of the action volumes with the actual volume of the virus, several refinements are made (*407*), correcting for the waste of ionizations that occur in clusters or in tightly packed columns (since one particle can be inactivated only once, a cluster of ionizations in one target can only be as effective as one ionization). For small viruses, the calculations give target sizes not too different from the sizes of the virus particles (table 18), whereas for large viruses the targets are much smaller than the particles. According to the assumptions of the target theory, the large viruses consist of an essential genetic portion, the target, and of a portion where radiation damage does not suppress reproduction. For several viruses, the target has a volume similar to the volume of the viral nucleic acid (*210a*).

Variations of the calculated target size with different radiations have been interpreted as due to nonspherical shape of the targets, and have been used to estimate the number of elements (supposedly spherical and corresponding to genes) in which a target must be resolved to account for the discrepancy in effectiveness of different radiations. This type of analysis may go farther than is justifiable by our knowledge both of radiation and of viruses and may, therefore, be misleading. We know now that a virus particle may be inactive (unable to reproduce) because of any one of a number of reasons—inability to attach to a host cell, or to penetrate it, or to reproduce in it. Each of these losses of function probably represents a damage to a different structure, and the probability that an ionization produces an inactivating damage may be different from one region of a virus particle to another. The main conclusion that we can derive from the analysis of the direct effect of ionizing radiations on viruses is that small viruses are inactivated by almost every ionization within them, while larger virus particles with more complex organization may survive several ionizations. Inactivation in all cases results from one successful ionization, not from the summation of the effect of several, as proved by the rate of inactivation (equation 11). The parallelism between virus size and x-ray sensitivity may be useful in estimating the size of a virus by interpolation in cases where other methods are unavailable or inapplicable (*684*).

Ultraviolet light. The rate of inactivation of viruses by ultraviolet light has generally been reported as exponential, obeying equation 11; more refined study sometimes reveals deviations from the exponential rate (figure 54), deviations whose interpretation is uncertain. Neglecting such deviations, one might conclude that the absorption of one quantum is the hit that inactivates a virus. Not all quanta are effective, however; the quantum yield, that is, the ratio *effective quanta/absorbed quanta* is often of the order of 10^{-4} to 10^{-5}, indicating that most of

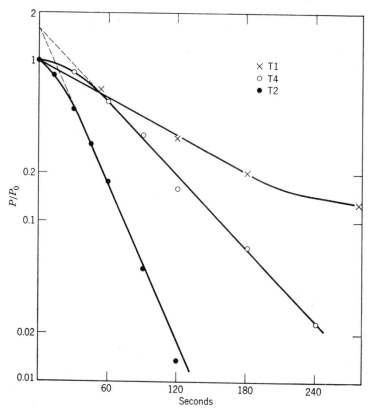

Figure 54. The inactivation of bacteriophages by ultraviolet light. Abscissa: seconds of exposure to ultraviolet light (2537 A; intensity 1 erg $\times$ sec^{-1} $\times$ mm^{-2}). Ordinate: proportion of residual infectious phage. The irradiation and assays were carried out under yellow, nonreactivating light. Note that the survival curves for the T-even phages are not exponential from the start, but extrapolate to an initial titer 1.6 times greater than the one experimentally measured.

the quanta absorbed by a virus particle either fail to produce permanent chemical change, or produce changes still compatible with infectivity (506). The surviving particles may show a delay in reproduction, however, as is found with bacteriophages (433). Indirect effects through the medium can generally be neglected for viruses irradiated with ultraviolet in water or salt solutions, which absorb very little of this radiation.

The action spectrum for inactivation, that is, the quantum yield for various wavelengths, has not been determined in detail for any virus, but from data on the relative effectiveness of various ultraviolet wavelengths it appears that for several viruses the relative effectiveness follows closely the absorption spectrum of nucleic acids. This indicates that most of the inactivating quanta are absorbed by these compounds.

Quantitative work on ultraviolet irradiation requires exposure of virus in nonabsorbent media (water, salt solutions) to prevent screening by ultraviolet-absorbing substances such as proteins and other organic compounds. Thin layers of opaque suspensions can be used; continuous flow techniques have been devised for use in ultraviolet irradiation for production of virus vaccines (416). Since glass and cellophane are opaque to ultraviolet, open or quartz-covered containers must be used.

Inactivation of some bacteriophages by visible light has been reported (402). It may be due to a photodynamic action of light through the agency of some component of the medium rather than to a direct photochemical reaction. Several viruses, indeed, have been shown to be inactivated by the photodynamic action of dyes in the presence of light (516).

Radioactive decay. An interesting experiment pertinent to radiation effects has been made (319) with bacteriophage grown in bacteria containing large amounts of radioactive phosphorus P^{32}. Phage particles containing many radioactive atoms are unstable and lose activity at an exponential rate, as the radioactive decay proceeds. On the average, a particle is inactivated by 1 out of 10 P^{32} disintegrations. All phage phosphorus is presumably in nucleotide form, 1 atom per nucleotide. Hence, the above observation suggests that there is 1 chance out of 10 that the alteration of a single nucleotide in the phage particle renders it inactive. Either some nucleic acid portions of the virus are intrinsically nonessential, or there is a limited chance for each of several alternate portions to be utilized in reproduction, so that the fraction of effective damages may correspond to the inverse number of such alternate portions.

Separation of virus properties by radiation. Probably every virus can be rendered uninfectious by radiation while retaining its antigenicity. Ultraviolet-inactivated virus vaccines have been perfected repeatedly for rabies, equine encephalomyelitis and other viruses. Moreover, radiation-treated virus may still react with its host cells even after losing its ability to reproduce. Such residual interaction has been studied especially with bacteriophages and influenza viruses.

Ultraviolet leaves to some phages the ability to be adsorbed by host bacteria and to kill them, although the phage has become unable to reproduce. The nonreproducing but killing phage disrupts the structure of the host cell, suppresses the synthesis of host enzymes, and interferes with the growth of other phages in the same cell, just like active phage. X-rays, acting directly on phage, can render it still

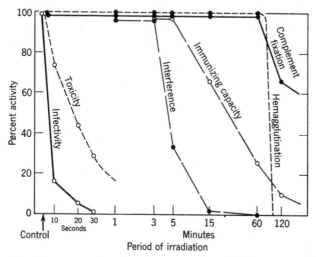

Figure 55. The suppression of various properties of influenza virus by ultraviolet light. From: Henle and Henle (*301*).

adsorbable but nonkilling and noninterfering, probably by suppressing its penetration into the cell.

For influenza viruses (figure 55) increasing doses of ultraviolet suppress, in the following order, infectivity, toxicity, ability to interfere with other strains, immunizing ability, and hemagglutination capacity (*301*). Similar observations have been made with other viruses.

Reactivation phenomena with irradiated viruses. Radiation-inactivated phage particles have been reactivated in two ways. First, ultraviolet-inactivated particles can be reactivated by causing them to be adsorbed to bacteria and then exposing these bacteria to visible light (*193*). This *photoreactivation* is an example of a general phenomenon occurring with ultraviolet irradiated organisms. It occurs to a very slight extent with x-ray-inactivated phage.

The second type of reactivation is observed when some phages inactivated by ultraviolet are mixed with host bacteria in such a way that each bacterium adsorbs several inactive phage particles. Some of the bacteria liberate active phage. The phage has been reactivated by interaction among inactive particles within the host cell (*multiplicity reactivation; 436*).

Both photoreactivation and multiplicity reactivation will be discussed in chapter 9. Similar reactivation phenomena have been described for influenza viruses (*303*). Their possible occurrence must be kept in mind, for example, in the use of radiation-inactivated vaccines.

Intracellular irradiation of viruses. Irradiation of virus-infected cells has been performed with a number of viruses. In some cases, as with papilloma virus of rabbits, the manifestations of disease can be suppressed by doses of radiation much smaller than those needed to inactivate free virus. The effect is probably due to a nonspecific action on the host cells (*240*).

With bacteriophages, no cure of the infected cells by radiation treatment has been observed, but the ability of the infected cells to liberate virus can be suppressed by radiation in a way that suggests a direct action on the intracellular virus. The changes of radiation sensitivity during the infection are indicative of the evolution of the virus inside the cell (*64;* see chapter 9). Radiations have also been found to induce mass lysis and liberation of phage from several strains of lysogenic bacteria (*454*).

Virus-Host Interaction
The Bacteriophage-Bacterium System

VIRUS-HOST INTERACTION

Up to this point we have discussed the properties of the material particles that represent the static, extracellular form of the viruses. In this form, viruses may be considered as in a resting state; no reproduction, no metabolism take place. We must now study how viruses perform, that is, how they interact with the hosts in which they reproduce. We do not know a priori to what extent the properties of intracellular virus resemble those of the extracellular virus particles. Inside the host cells, as we shall see, the virus behaves as a cell component, and little is known about the structure (and even less about the mode of performance) of any cell component as it exists in the cell in the native state. We know that the cell is not merely a bag containing a mixture of components, but an organized and integrated whole. Whatever the mechanisms of organization and integration, they may confer upon individual constituents properties that are lost or unobservable after extraction and isolation of each component. Actually, viruses provide very favorable material for the study of cellular integration itself.

The central problem in the study of the intracellular behavior of viruses is that of their reproductive mechanisms. On the one hand, clarification of these mechanisms would give us a better understanding of the nature of viruses and of their natural relationships, and, in the practical domain, would help us control their propagation. On the other hand, information on the mechanisms of viral reproduction may throw light on the central problem of biology, that of the reproduction of individual specific biological elements, such as genes. Reproduction of cells must be a consequence, a final result, of more elementary mechanisms, in which individual carriers of specificity, probably individual molecules, are replicated in identical form, except for mutations. Viruses carry specific genetic material. Since they can be studied in isolation and then transmitted to new host cells it may be possible to trace, qualitatively and quantitatively, the changes in the intracellular evolution of the specific viral material. Viruses may indeed be the material of choice for the investigation of biological reproduction.

In the interaction between a virus and its host, we distinguish a series of phases, including the entry of the virus into the host organism, its spread and localization, its reproduction inside susceptible cells, its liberation from these cells and secondary spreading to other parts of the host organism, and finally, its release from the host and transmission to new hosts. From the standpoint of virus biology, each of these phases raises problems related to specific virus properties. We wish to know how a virus particle acts on the surface of a sensitive cell; what part of the virus penetrates, and how; what effects it has on the properties of the cell; how the virus reproduces, and by what process it is released. Moreover, we ask what determines the ability of a virus to grow in one type of cell and not in another, that is, what properties make a given animal or plant, or a given tissue, capable of supporting reproduction of a given virus. Finally, we inquire as to the ecological relations between a virus and its hosts, which allow the continued propagation and survival of the virus in nature.

Virus-host interaction at the cellular level has been studied most thoroughly in bacterial viruses. These can be considered as simplified models because of the unicellular character of their hosts. We shall, therefore, start our discussion with an analysis of bacteriophage-bacterium relation. We must realize, however, that results valid for a group of viruses cannot a priori be assumed to be valid for other viruses. We already know that viruses are grouped together on methodological grounds rather than on grounds of natural relationship. Even among viruses active on the same host there are fundamental differences. It will be our task to describe what is known in well-studied cases and then, from the available material, to attempt whatever generalizations may be justified.

BACTERIOPHAGE-BACTERIUM INTERACTION

Even within the group of bacteriophages, it is impossible to generalize from one virus to another. We recognize, however, two major types of host-virus relationships, the *lysogenic* and the *lytic*. In the lysogenic relation, phage is carried by bacterial cells from generation to generation without conspicuous lysis and is occasionally liberated into the medium. We can recognize this phage if we have available another bacterial strain that reacts to it with visible lysis, so that plaques or clearing of cultures may be observed. The lytic condition is one in which the phage, after infecting a cell, causes it to lyse within a short time, generally before it divides again, with liberation of new phage.

Phage strains that can establish a lysogenic relation with bacteria are called *temperate phages*. Strains that do not establish lysogenicity, but regularly lyse the cells they infect, are called *virulent*.

The lysogenic condition is probably more important in perpetuating phages in nature and also in providing information as to the relation of phages to cell constituents and as to their origin. Yet, more is known today about the lytic condition, which is easier to analyze. Especially, a large amount of our information on virulent phages has been derived from the study of a few selected systems. One such system, illustrated in table 19, consists of 7 phages (T1, T2, T3, T4, T5, T6, T7), all active on a common host bacterium, *Escherichia coli*, strain B. In the past decade a large group of workers has deliberately concentrated on the study of these viruses in an effort to clarify the mechanisms of viral reproduction (*19; 169*).

THE LYTIC TYPE OF PHAGE-HOST INTERACTION

The broad features of the lytic condition can be visualized in the dark-field microscope or, better, in electron micrographs taken at intervals after mixing phage and bacteria (*448*). First, the phage particles stick to the bacterial surface. A period of intracellular events ensues, followed after a relatively short interval by a sudden lysis and liberation of large numbers of phage particles (see figures 29–31). All that is left of the cell structure is a lacerated cell wall, which later disintegrates.

The quantitative study of phage-bacterium interaction received its greatest impulse by the translation of this cycle of events into a quantitative procedure called the *one-step growth experiment* (*205*). Leaving the justification of each step for the following sections, we shall describe here the essential procedure (*174*).

Concentrated sensitive bacteria under standard cultural conditions are mixed with phage, and phage fixation (*adsorption*) is allowed to proceed for a brief period, shorter than the minimum interval between adsorption and lysis (the *latent period*). Then the mixture is diluted

Table 19. The T group of bacteriophages of *Escherichia coli*, strain B

Serological Group	{	{			{		{
Phage Type	T1	T2	T4	T6	T3	T7	T5
Morphology:: Head Tail	Prismatic, 50 mμ 150 × 10 mμ	Prismatic, 95 × 65 mμ 100 × 25 mμ			Prismatic, 45 mμ 15 × 10 mμ?		Prismatic, 65 mμ 150 × 10 mμ
Average plaque size	3 mm	1 mm	1.5 mm	1 mm	4 mm	4 mm	1.5 mm
Latent period at 37° C	13 min	21 min	24 min	26 min	13 min	13 min	40 min
Yield per cell, one-step growth experiment in nutrient broth	150	100	250	250	300	300	200
Mutant types	Host range; plaque type	Host range; plaque type	Plaque type; cofactor requirement	Plaque type	Host range	Host range	Heat resistance
Genetic recombination	Present	Present	Present	Present	Present	Present	Present (with other serologically related phages)

to such an extent that adsorption is practically stopped by the decreased frequency of phage-bacterium collisions. Platings are made at intervals for plaque counts, and results of the type shown in figure 56 are obtained. The low plateau represents the latent period; no lysis occurs and the count remains constant because each infected bacterium

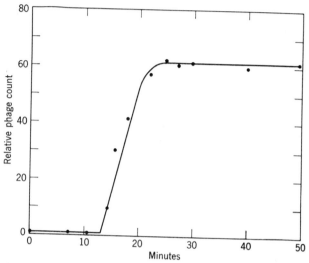

Figure 56. A one-step growth experiment with bacteriophage T1 on *Escherichia coli*, strain B, in nutrient broth at 37° C. Phage and bacteria, at a ratio 1:10, were mixed at time 0. The mixture was diluted after 4 minutes, when 45% of the phage had been adsorbed. Assays were made at intervals after dilution. Average phage yield per infected cell = 62 × 100/45 = 138.

that is plated produces only one plaque on the solid medium whatever its intracellular phage content at the moment of plating. The rise in plaque count corresponds to lysis (this can be checked by microscopic observations), and the final plateau is due to the fact that the newly liberated phages fail to meet any bacterium in the diluted mixture and, therefore, remain free and do not reproduce any further. This procedure thus isolates one step or cycle of growth; if dilutions were not made, there would be a series of steps blurring into one another, due to repeated, nonsynchronized cycles of adsorption and liberation, until lysis is completed or until bacterial growth stops, and with it phage reproduction. In a mass lysate of this kind, the titer often reaches 10^{11} infectious units per ml, or more.

The one-step growth experiment provides information on the duration of the intracellular phage development and on the amount of phage produced. Innumerable modifications can be devised in order to study many variables (single, multiple, mixed infection; temperature effects; medium composition). Several of them will be discussed in the following sections.

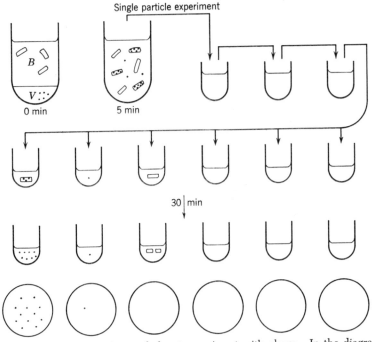

Figure 57. Diagram of a single-burst experiment with phage. In the diagram, one out of six tubes (second row) contains an infected bacterium, one tube contains an unadsorbed phage, and one tube contains an uninfected bacterium. After 30 minutes the infected bacteria have lysed. The contents of each tube are plated on individual plates for phage count. The first plate (left, bottom row) shows the yield of phage from the infected bacterium. From: Delbrück, *Harvey Lecture Series* 41:161, 1945–1946.

One important modification of the one-step growth experiment is the *single-burst experiment* (108; 205; figure 57). Here, after phage is adsorbed by the bacteria, the mixture is diluted until its content of infected bacteria is very low, say, 2 per ml; and many small aliquots, for example, 0.2 ml each, are distributed into a series of tubes before lysis begins. Most tubes will receive no infected bacterium (in the above example, a fraction $e^{-0.4} = 0.67$), some will contain one (a fraction $0.4e^{-0.4} = 0.268$), and very few will contain more than one (a fraction $1 - (1 + 0.4)e^{-0.4} = 0.062$). These frequencies are calculated from equation 1 (see page 49), assuming a random, independent distribution of infected bacteria in the various samples. The tubes are then incubated, and after lysis is completed the entire content of each tube is plated on one plate for plaque count. Most of the plates will have either no plaque or possibly 1 plaque or 2, representing residual nonadsorbed phage, which, of course, fails to reproduce. The other plates will have relatively large amounts of plaques, and most of them contain the yield ("burst") from a single bacterium. The burst size distribution is generally wide, showing great disparities in the amount of phage produced in individual bacteria (table 20).

Table 20. The distribution of yields from individual *Escherichia coli* bacteria infected with phage T2 (single-burst distribution)

(a) Average number of infected bacteria per plate, calculated from phage input   0.73

(b) Total number of plates   96

(c) Expected number of plates without bursts $96 \times e^{-0.73} = 46$

(d) Number of plates found without bursts   39

(e) Average number of infected bacteria per plate, calculated from (d) $\ln (39/96) = 0.9$

(f) Calculated number of plates with 1 burst $96 \times 0.9 \times e^{-0.9} = 35$

(g) Calculated number of plates with 2 bursts $96(0.9^2/2)e^{-0.9} = 16$

(h) Calculated number of plates with 3 or more bursts $96[1 - (1 + 0.9 + 0.9^2/2)]e^{-0.9} = 6$

Plate count distribution

9	67	92	114	161	260
31	67	92	117	163	278
41	70	99	118	165	291
45	75	101	124	192	298
48	76	102	130	201	407
49	81	103	130	206	413
55	86	105	132	209	477
56	89	106	135	215	
58	90	110	136	216	
65	91	110	151	230	

Total count   7938

Average yield, calculated from (e) $7938/(96 \times 0.9) = 92$

In experiments of the one-step or single-burst type, the unadsorbed phage can be eliminated before lysis begins, either by washing the bacteria free of supernatant fluid or, more conveniently, by adding to the mixture some antiphage serum, which inactivates the free phage without affecting the adsorbed phage (167). Serum action must be stopped by further dilution before lysis begins, to avoid inactivation of the newly liberated phage.

ADSORPTION OF BACTERIOPHAGE BY BACTERIA

Kinetics of phage adsorption. The fixation of bacteriophage particles on susceptible bacteria is easily demonstrated by electron microscopy. Quantitatively, it is studied by following the disappearance of free bacteriophage from a mixture with bacteria; the bacterial cells are separated from the free phage by centrifugation, and the free phage is titrated. To avoid liberation of new phage, all measurements must be made in the latent period before lysis, which can be prolonged by lowering the temperature. Sometimes we can use heat-killed bacteria, which retain the ability to adsorb certain phages (578); then the free phage can be measured without centrifugation, since phage adsorbed irreversibly on heat-killed bacteria is lost and forms no plaque.

Phage adsorption follows a first-order reaction in relation to the concentrations of both bacteria and phage:

$$dP_f/dt = -KP_fB \qquad P_f/P_0 = e^{-KBt} \qquad [12]$$

where P_f is the concentration of free phage, P_0 is the initial phage concentration, and B is the bacterial concentration. K (cm^3 min^{-1}) is the adsorption rate constant. This relation justifies the practice of interrupting adsorption by dilution, which decreases the bacterial concentration. From a knowledge of K, we can predict by means of equation 12 the amount of phage that will be adsorbed by a given number of bacteria in a given time. Equation 12 is valid for mixtures with either bacteria or phage in excess, up to ratios "phage"/"bacteria" of the order of 200 for large-particle phages. Thus, several phage particles can be adsorbed by each bacterium, until complete coating is reached.

The ratio P_{ads}/B (the average number of phage particles adsorbed per bacterium) is generally called the *multiplicity of infection*.[1] Since

---

[1] The term *multiplicity of infection* is something of a misnomer, since the ratio P_{ads}/B may be lower than 1. Indeed, expressions such as "multiplicity of infection 0.05" are commonly employed.

the adsorption ability of individual bacterial cells is approximately uniform, the fraction B_n/B of bacteria that adsorb n particles will follow a Poisson distribution:

$$B_n/B = \frac{(P_{ads}/B)^n}{n!} e^{-(P_{ads}/B)}$$

The number B_0 of bacteria without phage will be:

$$B_0 = Be^{-(P_{ads}/B)}$$

In typical cases, adsorption of one or more phage particles by a sensitive cell results in the death of a bacterium; a colony count of the surviving bacteria ($= B_0$) will, therefore, permit an estimate of P_{ads}/B. This method of measuring the adsorbed phage is particularly useful in the study of phage particles which have become unable to reproduce but which can still be adsorbed by bacteria and kill them.   Phage inactivated by ultraviolet light often behaves in this way (441).

Equation 12 is often followed only for the first 90–95% of reduction in free phage.   A less adsorbable phage fraction remains, which, however, after reproducing gives rise to a progeny of normal adsorbability. Combination of some phage with inhibitors may be the factor responsible for the less adsorbable fraction.

Chemical requirements for adsorption.   The adsorption of phage by sensitive bacteria is influenced by the physiological conditions of the bacteria (mainly through the smaller size of older cells, and possibly through the production of slime or capsules) and, even more markedly, by the composition of the medium.   In pure distilled water or in a concentration 10^{-4} M of monovalent ions (Na^+ or K^+), adsorption of phages of the T group fails to occur.   Increasing cation concentrations render adsorption possible; the optimum concentrations, that is, those permitting maximum adsorption rates, are characteristic for each phage and each ion.   Concentrations above optimum often reduce the adsorption rate of phage.   This is probably due to a combination between the ions and the bacterial surface receptors.   Some data are given in table 21.

Adsorption in salt solutions with low concentrations of cations is reversible, either by dilution or by transfer to distilled water.   At higher ionic concentrations reversible adsorption is promptly followed by a fast irreversible reaction.   The reversible adsorption does not lead to any detectable changes in the host cell ($250; 535$).

In complex salt-containing media or in buffers with optimum ion concentration, the adsorption rate constant K approaches values of 4

Table 21. Optimum salt concentrations for irreversible adsorption of the T phages onto *Escherichia coli*, strain B

The concentrations given below allow phage adsorption at the maximum rate. Data supplied by Dr. T. T. Puck.

T1	$10^{-3}\ M$ Mg^{++} or Ca^{++}; or $10^{-2}\ M$ Na^+ or K^+ or NH_4^+
T2, T4, T6	$10^{-1}\ M$ Na^+ or K^+ or NH_4^+
T3	$10^{-3}\ M$ Na^+ or K^+ or NH_4^+
T7	$10^{-2}\ M$ Na^+ or K^+ or NH_4^+; or $10^{-3}\ M$ Mg^{++}

to 5×10^{-9} cm³ min⁻¹. This is approximately the value that can be calculated for the rate constant, on the assumption that almost every collision between phage and bacterium results in adsorption, from the known values of the radius r of the bacteria and of the diffusion constant D of the phage ($K = 4\pi rD$; see 165).

This result, showing the enormous efficiency of the adsorption reaction, suggests that phage adsorption can occur following contact of the phage with any portion of the bacterial surface. Indeed, the maximum absorption capacity of 300 particles of a phage about 100 mμ in diameter corresponds to the coating of about one-third of a bacterial cell $3 \times 1\ \mu$.

The remarkable fact is that, although specific for each phage, the ion requirements for reversible adsorption are not specific for phage-bacterium combination. They are identical to the requirements for adsorption of phage particles to cation exchange resins or to glass (for example, to sintered glass filters), an adsorption which, biologically speaking, is clearly nonspecific (535).

A similar situation holds for another category of requirements for phage adsorption, namely *activation* by cofactors (see 17). Phages T4 and T6, among the strains of the T group, are only adsorbed by bacteria (or by glass filters) if there are present in the medium certain *cofactors*. L-tryptophan is the most effective cofactor of adsorption, other amino acids are much less effective. Substitutions in the aromatic ring of tryptophan (for example, in 5-methyltryptophan) may preserve cofactor activity; substitutions in the aliphatic chain abolish it. Indole, a tryptophan analogue, is a competitive inhibitor of tryptophan action (170).

The kinetics of tryptophan action is complex. The amino acid combines reversibly with phage, the reaction being rapid in both directions. The influence of concentration on activation and deactivation is best interpreted by assuming that each tryptophan molecule is adsorbed independently onto the phage particle, and that activation results from the formation on the phage surface of self-stabilizing complexes, each complex consisting of 5 molecules of the amino acid (628).

Together with the results on the influence of ions, the cofactor phenomena can be interpreted by assuming that the phage's surface—modified by the cofactor molecules, when these are needed—provides a base on which ions become attached to give the proper electric charges, which must be present to permit contact between the phage and the specific bacterial receptors. Irreversible adsorption or *fixation* will then occur by other more specific, possibly enzymatic binding mechanisms (250).

The activity of indole as a tryptophan inhibitor is remarkable, in that it provides an example of a potential specific defense mechanism against viruses (170). Indole is a product of the metabolism of tryptophan by *Escherichia coli*, the host bacterium for the tryptophan-requiring phages T4 and T6. If tryptophan is present in excess in the medium indole is produced and can act to prevent adsorption of these phages.

The nature of the bacterial receptors. As a rule, only bacteria that can grow a phage will adsorb it. Some cases are known in which the phage can be adsorbed by bacteria unable to support its growth and to be lysed; serological cross-reactions have been found between the normal host for a phage and the nonhost bacteria that adsorb that phage (545). This suggests a role of the antigenic constitution of the bacterial surface in phage adsorption. A fairly good correlation exists between the possession of certain antigens and the sensitivity to different bacteriophages (see 101). For example, the phages active on bacteria of the genus *Salmonella* can be divided into several groups, some active on rough strains only, some on smooth ones; smoothness and roughness of bacteria depend on the possession of certain antigens. Some phages against typhoid bacilli are specific for strains carrying the so-called V*i* antigen, which is present in virulent strains. These phages and their substrains (see page 206) are used in the *phage-typing method* for the identification of individual V*i*-strains of *Salmonella typhosa* (157; 157a). Phage typing is used with a variety of other organisms (156).

It seems plausible that the surface antigens of the bacteria are actually involved in the adsorption of phage. Sensitive bacteria yield fractions that inactivate homologous phage specifically, and these phage-inactivating agents, once purified, are similar to known bacterial antigens (*206; 263; 415*). The situation is by no means simple, however. Some workers report specific phage-inactivating power in polysaccharide fractions (*206*), others only in carbohydrate-lipoid-protein complexes in native form (*484*) or in their lipocarbohydrate portion (*257a*). Also, phage combines specifically with carbohydrate-free cell walls obtained by extracting the cells in a series of successive treatments (*668*). These residual cell walls are slowly destroyed upon incubation with phage, but the mechanism of this process is as yet unknown.

These facts and the numerous exceptions to the rule of similarity between antigenic properties and susceptibility to phages may be accounted for by the suggestion (*109*) that phage receptors and antibody receptors are not necessarily identical, but may represent variously overlapping portions of certain reactive patches of the bacterial surface.

THE LATENT PERIOD OF INTRACELLULAR DEVELOPMENT

Problems of phage reproduction. Following phage adsorption there is an interval before lysis during which, normally, more phage is produced. The average yield of phage per bacterium or *burst size*, as determined by one-step growth experiments, is the ratio

$$\frac{\text{(Final titer)} - \text{(Unadsorbed phage)}}{\text{(Initial titer)} - \text{(Unadsorbed phage)}}$$

The average yields for the T phages on young growing bacteria are shown in table 19; yields from old bacteria are lower.

The series of events between phage adsorption and lysis has to be reconstructed from more or less indirect evidence obtained by a variety of methods. The evolution of the virus-infected bacterium in the latent period is complex. Some stages can be recognized from the existence of abnormal situations in which the evolution of the system stops early. Thus, phage adsorption may not be followed by any other noticeable changes in the bacterium, which goes on dividing; this occurs, for example, with x-ray-inactivated phage (*665*). Or the bacterium may be killed but may fail to produce any active phage and to undergo lysis, as with ultraviolet-inactivated phage (*441*), or, for phages like T5 and others, in the absence of Ca^{++} (*7*).

A phenomenon, which contributes only indirectly to the understanding of the normal phage-bacterium evolution, is *lysis from without* (*166*); this is produced by rapid adsorption of a very large number of phage particles, active or inactive. This lysis apparently results from massive damage to the bacterial surface; no active phage is released, not even the original ones, and the cell does not undergo the specific cytochemical changes which, as we shall see, are often associated with phage-cell integration (445).

Phage reproduction, when present, takes place inside the bacterium. The new phage is not visible by electron microscopy on the bacterial surface, nor is it accessible to antiphage serum action. The phage-reproducing mechanism becomes refractory to antiphage serum action within seconds after phage adsorption. Direct observation of the phage inside the bacterium, either by dark-field microscopy or by electron microscopy, yields results difficult to interpret and of little value; indirect methods must be employed. Before describing and evaluating such methods and their results, let us consider briefly what we are looking for and what we may expect to find.

A virus particle infects a cell, and several minutes later several hundred particles emerge. What is the relation of the initial particle to the final ones? Does the initial particle penetrate the bacterium as a whole or in part? Does it appear as such among the progeny particles? Or does it contribute material to the composition of one or more of them? If so, are these materials specific?

How does the initial particle preside over the formation and specificity of the new ones? Does it cause a transformation into virus of a ready-made precursor, or a synthesis of virus from nonspecific building blocks? Are these supplied by the bacterial cell, by the external medium, or by both? Are they synthesized and put together by mechanisms provided by the bacterium, by the virus, or by both? What types of mechanisms are operative: enzymatic, autocatalytic, "patternlike," or others? And where does the necessary energy come from?

Does a virus particle "grow," that is, produce more viral material within its own borders, then split into two or more particles? Or is the new virus put together from scratch and all at once, by copying a preexistent virus that provides a model for assembly of nonspecific blocks? Or else are there intermediate levels of organization in which the building blocks, still free in the cell, become more and more virus-like through a series of stages of increased structural complexity and specificity?

It is clear that these problems deal with the functional organization of the virus-infected cell, and that little can be learned about them by analogy with other situations, since the functional organization of the cell, particularly at the level at which specific syntheses occur, remains as yet a field where even speculation has hardly dared venture. Virology may ultimately prove the field of choice for its clarification.

The sections that follow provide evidence of various types on intracellular phage development. They suggest a complex and by no means final picture, in which the phage particle introduces a specific portion of itself into the host cell, modifies the pattern of specific syntheses in the host, and utilizes, at least in part, the enzymatic machinery of the host to obtain building blocks, on which it impresses its own viral specificity. Most of this development takes place in stages. Mature, infectious phage particles are formed only as an end product of the process as a whole.

Premature lysis. Artificial breakage of phage-infected bacteria long failed to yield any active phage. Success was finally obtained by the use of a variety of methods: sonic vibration (for phages such as T3, that can stand this treatment) or "lysis from without" of the cells by an excess of a different phage (*182*); mechanical disruption of cells by decompression (*234*). Cyanide or some other metabolic inhibitor is generally added in order to stop the progress of phage development at a precise moment.

These methods reveal that increasing amounts of active phage are obtained from infected bacteria in the second half of the latent period (figure 58); in the first half, however, no active phage is recovered. Thus there is an *eclipse* of the infecting phage, a phenomenon that probably occurs for all virus infections, as shown by the nonrecoverability of most viruses immediately after infection. The eclipse is certainly real, and, as we shall see, the first virus particles that appear after the eclipse are not the infecting particles; they are already part of the final crop of new virus.

The rate of appearance of infectious, intracellular virus is nearly linear. An apparent increase in rate at the beginning is caused by an inhomogeneity in the time of appearance of the first active phage particle in individual bacteria. The rate of appearance of the new virus, however, does not represent the actual rate of phage synthesis, but only the rate at which individual phage particles "mature," that is, graduate to the infectious stage.

This is shown, for example, by the effect of addition of the dye proflavine (diamino acridinium sulfate) to bacteria infected with phage T2 (*227*). The dye allows lysis to occur normally, but only as many mature, active phage particles are liberated as were already present when the dye was added; none appears if the dye was added before the middle of the latent period. If one examines the materials liberated by these bacteria, one finds by electron microscopy that they contain many inactive, tailless, incomplete phage particles or "doughnuts" (figure 28, page 68), in numbers approximately similar to those of

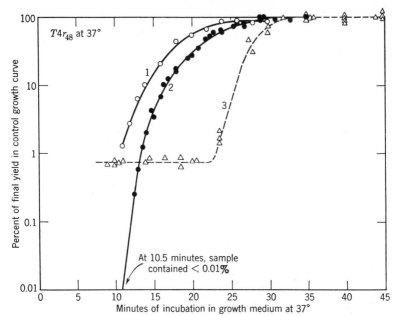

Figure 58. Premature lysis of *Escherichia coli* cells infected with phage T4r. Premature lysis was produced at intervals by diluting in a mixture of 10^{-3} M cyanide (to stop further phage production) and of phage T6 in excess (to induce lysis). Abscissa: time interval between infection and dilution in cyanide. Ordinate: amount of phage present in per cent of the phage yield that would be obtained by natural lysis. Curve 1: data from a single experiment, with 7 T4r particles adsorbed per cell. Curve 2: combined data from four experiments with single infection. Curve 3: control one-step growth curve; single infection. Note that the samples taken before 13 minutes contained less infectious phage than the original inoculum. From: Doermann (*182*).

active phage particles that would have been produced in the absence of the dye (*175*). These "doughnuts" are not adsorbed by bacteria. They contain little or no nucleic acid; they contain an appreciable amount of sulfur, presumably in protein. They fix complement with antiphage antiserum but do not combine with phage-neutralizing antibody.

The doughnuts produced in proflavine are similar in morphology to immature phage forms that can be seen in mechanically disrupted

bacteria before the mature phage particles appear (*417*). Counts of
the doughnuts and of tailed particles from bacteria disrupted at various
times reveal an increase in doughnuts, followed by an increase in tailed
forms. This suggests a transformation of the doughnuts into tailed
particles. In the presence of proflavine this transformation fails to take

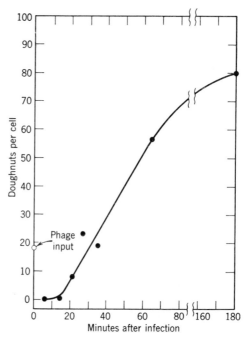

Figure 59. Increase in the number of immature phage particles ("doughnuts")
inside bacteria of *E. coli* B infected with phage T2 in presence of 4 μg of proflavine per ml. Electron microscope counts on extracts of prematurely lysed
bacteria. From: DeMars et al. (*175*).

place (figure 59). Thus the doughnuts appear to be organized precursor elements of the phage particles. At a later stage of evolution
one detects nucleic acid-free particles, which are still noninfectious but
are adsorbed by bacteria (*464*).

It is clear that phage synthesis goes through stages, the active phage
particle being a sort of final, mature form. Once in this form, as we
shall see later, a phage particle no longer multiplies in the bacterium
in which it has been produced. Ability to infect a new bacterium is
apparently acquired by a transformation of the particle, which stops its
reproduction within the cell of its origin. The rate of appearance of

active phage, as obtained from premature lysis experiments, probably represents the rate at which the final maturation reaction takes place, and may differ from the rate at which the production of individual phage replicas takes place.

The incomplete, tailless particles are not the only phage-specific material obtainable, besides active phage, inside infected bacteria. A serologically specific ultrafiltrable factor, which combines with phage-neutralizing antibody (see page 126), can be obtained by disruption of infected bacteria throughout the eclipse period (175). This factor increases in amount prior to and in parallel with the increase of active phage. Some of it is liberated, along with mature phage, upon normal lysis. The ultrafiltrable factor probably represents material on its way to becoming phage and containing the antigen responsible for neutralizing antibody.

Thus premature lysis experiments tell us that, following infection, the infecting particle is so altered as to be noninfectious. After an eclipse period lasting almost half the latent period, new phage-specific elements of various complexity can be detected in increasing number, until the mature particles are finally formed.

Transformation of the infecting phage following adsorption. For phage T2 infecting *E. coli* B, the disappearance of the infecting phages as infectious units and the meaning of the eclipse period have been explained by the brilliant work of Hershey and Chase (313), using isotopic tracers. Phage labeled with P^{32} in its nucleic acid (or with S^{35} in its sulfur-amino acids) can be obtained by growing it in labeled media and purifying it from the lysates. This phage can then be used to infect unlabeled bacteria, and the fate of the P or S of the infecting phage can be traced by measuring the radioactivity of various fractions (whole bacteria, extracts, medium, etc.).

Using labeled phage T2, Hershey and Chase found that the phosphorus of the infecting phage, that is, its nucleic acid, separates from the sulfur. The phosphorus apparently penetrates the bacterial cell and acquires some of the properties of the bacterial nucleic acid; for example, it becomes accessible to desoxyribonuclease action in bacteria heated at 80° C. Surprisingly enough, the sulfur appears instead to remain at the surface of the bacteria. It can be removed from the bacteria by violent shaking of infected bacteria in a rotary mixer (Waring Blendor) *without preventing the growth of phage in these bacteria and its normal liberation.*

This remarkable result can be visualized in the light of the known organization of the particle of this phage, which, upon osmotic shock (transfer from 5 N to 1 N NaCl), separates into a S-rich, P-free "ghost" or "skin" (see figure 28, page 68) carrying the main antigens of the phage, and a fraction of highly polymerized nucleic acid (308). Apparently, upon infection, the phage skin remains on the bacterial surface, whereas the nucleic acid, possibly accompanied by some S-free protein, penetrates and initiates the production of the new phage (figure 60). These observations on phage T2 have been confirmed for several other coli-phages of the T1–T7 system (see, for example, 401).

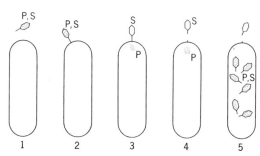

Figure 60. Diagram of the transformation of the infecting phage particles according to data by Hershey and Chase (313). 1. Phage and bacterium. 2. Adsorption. 3. Separation of the phosphorus-containing core (P, stippled) from the sulfur-containing skin (S). 4. Removal of skin by stirring in a Waring Blendor. 5. Production of new phage, containing phosphorus and sulfur without participation of the skin of the infecting phage.

These observations explain at once the eclipse of recoverable infective particles following infection and the inability of antiphage serum to stop phage reproduction. Complete phage particles cease to exist as organized units, and the phage skins, carrying most and possibly all the phage antigens, remain on the outside and take no part in the reproductive process.

The eclipse is thereby explained. The problem of phage production becomes that of the mechanism whereby the sulfur-free phage primordium or "nucleus" that penetrates the cell gives rise to the full, mature virus particles in the yield.

The discovery of hydroxymethyl-cytosine in phages of the T2 group (687b) has made it possible to follow the synthesis of phage DNA in infected bacteria (315a). When the phage-specific DNA and host-specific DNA are measured at intervals in infected cultures, the phage DNA begins to increase soon after infection, while the bacterial DNA decreases. After the appearance of mature phage the phage DNA continues to increase and is always in excess over the amount accounted for by the infectious particles. The excess phage DNA corresponds to the amount needed to supply 40–80 phage particles. If this phage DNA is in the form of immature phage "nuclei," we may conclude that during growth of phage T2 in a bacterium there is a population consisting of up to 40–80 immature particles. This population is presumably repleted by multiplication and depleted by maturation, and its size remains more or less constant. The multiplying noninfectious form of phage has been called the *vegetative* phage.

Thus, the phage DNA penetrates the bacterial host, while little or no phage protein does. Phage DNA increases very early after infection, while phage-specific protein is not observed, even by sensitive serological tests, until a few minutes before mature phage appears. It is therefore puzzling that the very first morphologically recognizable new phage elements that can be isolated from prematurely disrupted bacteria are DNA-free, antigenically specific particles—the doughnuts (417) or their tailed successors (464). It is possible that the phage proteins are produced around the phage DNA, but that they remain separable from it until a late reaction occurs, which binds them into stable form and puts the last touch upon the mature particle.

Origin of phage constituents in infected bacteria. The amount of new phage produced in a bacterium sometimes corresponds to as much as one-tenth or more of the mass of the bacterium. What is the origin of the materials that go to form the new phage? How are they synthesized? And where does the energy for their synthesis come from? Phages seem to contain only proteins and DNA. These substances could either derive from constituents of the bacterial protoplasm already present in the cell at the time of infection, or they could be assimilated from the medium after infection. Experiments with isotope tracers show that both sources contribute materials for phage synthesis. These experiments are carried out as follows (143):

Suppose we grow bacteria in a medium containing phosphorus compounds "labeled" by a certain content of the radioactive isotope P^{32} (one-half of whose atoms disintegrate in every 14.3-day interval, giving rise to S^{32} atoms). All the phosphorylated components of the bacteria will contain some phosphorus recognizable by its radioactive emission of beta rays. These bacteria are washed, resuspended in nonradioactive medium, infected with phage, and allowed to lyse. The new phage is purified, and the radioactivity, that is, the proportion of P^{32} in its phosphorus, is measured. If 25% of the phage phosphorus is derived from material present in the bacteria at the time of infection (*bacterial contribution*) and 75% comes from phosphorus taken in from the medium after infection (*medium contribution*), the ratio (P^{32}/P total) in the new phage will be one-fourth the ratio in the labeled medium in which the bacteria had been grown. Thus the P^{32} content of the new phage will be a measure of the amount of phosphorus that has been transferred from bacterial cell to phage. Of course, the "medium contribution" need not represent material that goes directly into phage. It is simply the material that has been taken up by the cell after infection.

Alternatively, unlabeled bacteria may be placed in labeled medium at any desired interval of time before or after infection, and the transfer of P^{32} from medium to phage may be measured. Or else, labeled phage, prepared by growth in labeled bacteria in labeled medium, may be used to infect unlabeled bacteria in unlabeled medium, to study the fate of the phosphorus of the infecting phage, as already discussed in the preceding section. Similar experiments can be done by labeling sulfur, carbon, or nitrogen with isotopes, either radioactive or stable; the stable isotopes are measured with the mass spectrograph. Since carbon and nitrogen are present in both nucleic acid and protein, they can be used to label either moiety, whereas phosphorus provides information only about the origin of nucleic acid, and sulfur only about that of sulfur-containing protein. We can also incorporate into bacteria certain preformed, labeled building blocks (purines, pyrimidines, amino acids), whose transfer from host to virus we can then follow.

The main results obtained from this type of study on phages of the T1–T7 group can be summarized as follows (*144; 237; 313; 384; 392; 463; 465; 627a; 667a*):

1. Of the phosphorus of the infecting phage, about 30–50% appears in the new phage; whether within one of them or distributed among many we do not know. The new phage in turn transfers the same proportion of its phosphorus to a following phage generation. With a yield of 100 particles per bacterium, the contribution of one infecting phage particle is not more than $\frac{1}{200}$ of the DNA of the new phage. Most of the parental phosphorus is found in the progeny produced in the first half of the latent period.

2. No sulfur is transferred from parent phage to progeny phage, as expected from the fact that the phage skin, containing all the phage sulfur, takes no part in reproduction. Likewise, no significant amount of amino acids is apparently transferred from parent phage to progeny phage.

3. About 20–35% of the nitrogen and of the phosphorus in the DNA of the new phage in T2, T4, T5, and T6 comes from the bacterial contributions; the rest (65–80%) comes from the medium. For T3 or T7, about 75% of the phosphorus comes from the host, and for T1 about 55%.

4. Purines and pyrimidines present in host DNA contribute 15% or more of the corresponding compounds in the new phage.

5. About 80–90% of the nitrogen of the phage protein is contributed from the medium, 10–20% from the host.

6. The phage protein nitrogen is derived from substrates in relatively rapid equilibrium with the medium, whereas the nitrogen and phosphorus in phage DNA are derived from a fairly long-lived pool of compounds (purine or pyrimidine bases, nucleotides, polynucleotides). This pool is fed partly by preexistent bacterial protoplasm, partly by new syntheses from the medium. The contribution of the infecting phage to the phosphorus of the new phage may either go into the pool or represent a transfer of intact chunks of phage DNA. Definite evidence on this point is still lacking. The bacterial contribution to the phosphorus pool derives predominantly from the bacterial DNA, but the ratios of various DNA constituents are not identical in bacterial and in viral DNA. This indicates that the bacterial DNA is not transferred in intact large chunks to the new phage.

7. By making labeled medium available at various times for 1-minute intervals only, preceding or following phage infection, and isolating the phage obtained after premature lysis at various times, it can be shown that each phage particle draws, from the available pool, materials that have entered the pool at any time during an interval of several minutes preceding its maturation. The average time between the uptake of a phosphorus atom from the medium and its appearance in mature phage is about 14 minutes; for sulfur atoms, about 7 minutes.

8. The phage particles that are produced last contain proportionally a higher medium contribution of phosphorus and pyrimidines than the particles formed first, as though the original bacterial contribution had become depleted.

These results should be viewed together with the following evidence obtained by chemical analysis of phage-infected bacteria (*144;* see figure 61). After infection with phage T2 the total DNA in the cells remains approximately constant, although phage DNA is already formed during this period (*315a*). Later, DNA increases at a rate about linear. The total RNA remains constant. The total protein increases linearly from the moment of infection (*144*).

The data as a whole fit the following picture of the synthesis of phages like T2 and its relatives. Phage infection stops the synthesis of bacterial RNA. It allows or stimulates a breakdown of bacterial DNA; it stimulates synthesis of new DNA and of new protein, both marked for use in phage synthesis. The phage protein derives mostly from the medium and from low-molecular-weight, acid-soluble nitrogenous fractions present in the cell at the moment of infection. The DNA derives

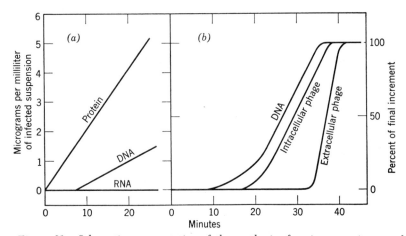

Figure 61. Schematic representation of the synthesis of various constituents of *Escherichia coli*, strain B infected with phage T4r. Infection takes place at time 0. *a*, The amounts of various chemical fractions; *b*, the relation of DNA synthesis to phage formation. Data from Cohen (*143, 144*).

from a pool fed by the medium and by breakdown of the bacterial DNA.[2]

Bacterial enzymes and the synthesis of phage constituents. We have seen that the phage-infected cell performs syntheses which lead to the formation of phage-specific materials. Several questions arise. Which portion of the new syntheses is carried out by bacterial machinery, and which by phage machinery? Is there synthesis of specific bacterial components or only of specific phage components? How are these syntheses directed?

Extensive evidence indicates that in bacteria infected with the T phages many bacterial enzymes that were present at the time of infection continue to work; they provide energy and synthesize nonspecific

[2] An older idea, according to which the phage simply catalyzed the conversion of ready-made precursor into active phage (*385*), is incompatible with the results of the tracer analysis.

building blocks, but these are used to build phage protoplasm rather than bacterial protoplasm. We use the word "protoplasm" as a convenient term to include all that is chemically and functionally specific in a given cell (enzymes, antigens, genetic substances), even though the chemical basis of the specificity still escapes us. We may list here some of the evidence for the above statement (see *144*):

1. After phage infection, bacterial respiration continues at the same rate as at the moment of infection. No rate increase occurs, even with bacteria that were actively increasing in size and in respiratory activity before infection.

2. Inhibitors that block the energy-yielding process of bacteria also prevent phage production. However, pretreatments that block cell division but allow bacterial metabolism to continue (penicillin, mustard gas, radiation) allow phage growth to take place (*18; 534*).

3. In bacteria that require for growth a supply of some essential building block—for example, an amino acid—phage synthesis requires the same supplement (*541*). It would be interesting to test whether this rule holds only for substances, such as amino acids, that actually appear in the phage protoplasm. Continued requirement for building blocks not present in phage particles would suggest that synthesis of some constituents of cell protoplasm takes place in phage-infected cells.

4. No enzymatic adaptation occurs after phage infection (*489*); even ultraviolet-irradiated phage, which is unable to reproduce but can still kill the bacteria, prevents enzymatic adaptation. It is well to remember that enzymatic adaptation requires actual synthesis of specific enzyme protein.

5. Only one enzyme activity is found to increase in *E. coli* B infected with phage T2. Desoxyribonuclease activity increases many times (*508a*). This may reflect an actual increase in amount of enzyme or only a decrease in a desoxyribonuclease inhibitor (*383a*). The desoxyribonuclease may play a role in the breakdown of host DNA and possibly in the synthesis of phage DNA.

The role of phage in the synthesis of new phage. The infecting phage appears to assume the direction of specific syntheses; it allows the bacterial machinery to produce the building blocks, but decides how these are to be put together. The mechanism by which the actual "patterning" of new protoplasm by the phage takes place remains unknown. It is on the same level as the mechanism of replication of any "self-reproducing" molecular structure in any cell.

The phage-infected bacterium, however, must synthesize certain substances that were not present in the uninfected cells. In fact, the

DNA of the T2, T4, T6 phages contains, instead of cytosine, the 5-hydroxymethyl-cytosine (687b). This compound, as far as we know, is not present either in the bacterial host or in any other biological material. The synthesis of phage DNA must entail a synthesis of this pyrimidine. Thus, the infecting phage does not simply redirect the assembly of building blocks produced by bacterial enzymes, but actually determines the synthesis of specific compounds. This determination might or might not require the intervention of enzymes contributed by the phage. It is possible, for example, that the presence in the cells of the vegetative phage primes or stabilizes the synthesis of the new compound by bacterial enzymes.

Phage infection and bacterial organization. A suggestion of the nature of the process by which the phage replaces the pattern of bacterial protoplasm with its own is provided by cytological observations (445; 498). One of the first changes noticeable in a bacterium after phage infection (within 2–3 minutes) is an alteration of the morphology of the bacterial nuclei, the DNA-containing bodies. In fixed and stained preparations of bacteria infected with phages like T2, the nuclei are seen to be broken into chromatic blocks, which move to the periphery of the cell. If the infecting phage is active, the nuclear disruption is followed several minutes later by appearance of new, granular chromatin, which is probably phage. Infection with inactive but killing phage (inactivated by ultraviolet) causes nuclear disruption and simply leaves the cells without organized DNA. With phage T5, where the latent period is longer, there is an interval of time between nuclear breakdown and appearance of new chromatin. During this interval no cell structure giving the cytochemical reactions of DNA is recognizable, although DNA is certainly present in the cells (figure 62).

The nuclear changes provide an explanation of the killing of bacteria by phage that cannot reproduce. They also suggest that the redirection of syntheses may be due to the elimination of the bacterial genes as determiners of protoplasmic specificity, with their replacement by phage genes in that role.

As for the synthesis of specific viral components, such as hydroxymethyl-cytosine, by phage-infected bacteria, the cytological picture suggests that the role of the phage may be to introduce specific genetic determinants for the production of the needed enzymes. Thus, the virus would indeed introduce new enzyme systems into the host cell, not, however, as preformed phage enzymes, but as genetic patterns for enzyme synthesis.

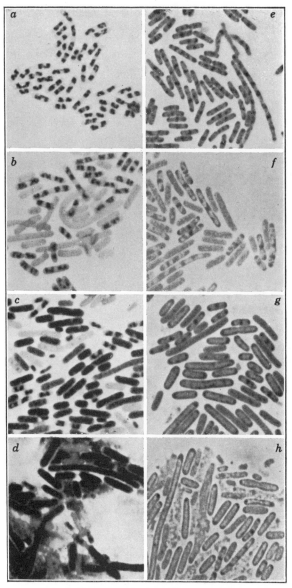

Figure 62. Cytological changes in *Escherichia coli*, strain B infected with phage T5. *a–d*, Chromatin stain (HCl-Giemsa). (*a*) Uninfected cells; (*b*) 15 minutes after infection; the infected cells show no organized chromatin; (*c*) 30 minutes after infection; the infected cells show variable amounts of granular chromatin; (*d*) 48 minutes after infection; the infected cells are filled with chromatin and undergo lysis. *e–h*, Cytoplasmic stain (thionine). The chromatin bodies remain unstained. (*e*) Uninfected; (*f*) 10 minutes; (*g*) 30 minutes; (*h*) 45 minutes. Note that this method gives the reverse appearance of the chromatin stain. (Courtesy Dr. R. G. E. Murray, University of Western Ontario, London, Ontario.

181

An interesting confirmation of this viewpoint is an observation on coli-cells sterilized by nitrogen mustard. These cells synthesize no DNA but accumulate RNA. Infection with phage T2 causes an immediate stoppage of RNA synthesis and a resumption of DNA synthesis, followed by lysis with phage liberation. Here the phage seems to have contributed the necessary DNA pattern for phage synthesis (307a).

The postulated substitution of phage genes for host genes as a result of infection has been described as "parasitism at the genetic level" (437). We shall see in chapter 9 that the situations observed with lysogenic bacteria fit, and in many ways enlarge, the concept of an intimate tie-up between the genetic apparatus of the host and that of the virus.

The cytochemical events observed with the T phages are not present in all phage-host systems, however. With many other systems, RNA and enzyme syntheses continue until lysis, and the only observable change in synthetic pattern is a delay of several minutes in DNA synthesis (603a). This is true of temperate phage, which can establish lysogeny, and also of their virulent mutants. This suggests that the shift in production from host DNA to phage DNA is the critical step, whereas the other changes in synthetic patterns may be restricted to special cases.

The Bacteriophage-Bacterium System (*Continued*)

GENETIC ANALYSIS OF PHAGE REPRODUCTION [1]

Examination of the phage produced by infected bacteria and of its relations to the infecting phage provides a great deal of information on phage development. The amount and composition of the new phage as a function of the amount and composition of the infecting phage permits us to analyze the genetic relations between the two. We shall discuss, first, the effects resulting from intracellular phage changes, and then the effects that follow modifications of the phage input.

Spontaneous phage mutations and the rate of phage reproduction. Bacteriophages as well as other viruses undergo spontaneous mutations (see chapter 15). Among the phage mutants, the most useful for genetic studies belong in two categories. The "host-range" mutants (*h*) are recognized by their ability to grow on bacterial strains resistant to the normal strain of phage (*434*). Thus phage T2*h* is active not only on *E. coli*, strain B, but also on strain B/2, which is a mutant of *E. coli* B resistant to T2. An *h* mutant attacks one or more strains of bacteria that are resistant to the parent phage. Sometimes the resistant bacteria have acquired their resistance by mutation from a sensitive bacterium; sometimes they are found to be resistant upon first isolation. The *h* mutants are easily recognized by plating with the resistant bacterium, on which they form plaques; the original, wild-type phage does not.

The plaque-type mutants of phages T2, T4, T6 belong to a series (see figure 63) characterized by plaques that are either smaller or sharper or larger or more completely lysed than those of the wild

---

[1] The student should be familiar with the basic facts of genetics to understand the material discussed in the following sections.

type (*309*). Most of these variations reflect quantitative changes in a property of these phages, the so-called "lysis inhibition": if a bacterium already infected is reinfected with phage before lysis occurs, it lyses late and produces a higher yield of phage (*181*). Mutations of the plaque-type series lead either to elimination of lysis inhibition (mutants *r* = rapid lysis) or to a reduced inhibition (mutants *w* = weakly inhibited). Exaggerated inhibition may be responsible for the *m* type

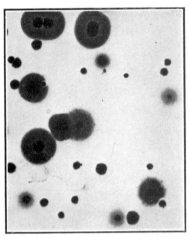 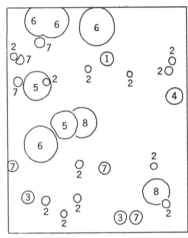

Figure 63. Plaques of phage T4 and of various plaque-type mutants. 1, wild type; 2, *m* (minute); 3, *tu* (turbid); 4, *tu tu* (double turbid mutant); 5, *r* (rapid lysis); 6, *r tu*; 7, *r m*; 8, *r tu tu*. Note the suppressive action of non-*r* plaques on the development of neighboring *r* plaques. Courtesy Dr. A. H. Doermann, Oak Ridge National Laboratory.

(minute plaque). The various mutant plaque types are easily recognized; they are frequently observed in platings of lysates of the T-even phages, the frequency of mutants being often between 0.01 and 1%.

The mutations that give rise to these phage mutants take place only during intracellular phage reproduction and are apparently spontaneous events, in the sense that the factors that control their occurrence are unknown. We only know that these factors act in a completely random fashion.

Let us now consider the mutation process more closely. When a mutation occurs in a bacterium, the phage yield contains both normal and mutant phage (*434*). The amount of the mutant phage present in the yield of the bacterium in which the mutation has occurred must depend on the mode of phage reproduction, or at least on the mode of reproduction of the portion of genetic material ("gene") responsible for the determination of the mutated character. New phage genes must arise by a replication of some sort from preexistent genes. If a mutation has a constant probability of occurring at each replication, the number of mutants to which a mutation gives rise in the bacterium depends on the sequence of replication. For example, if each phage replica is produced independently of the other replicas, mutated replicas will be distributed at random among the infected bacteria.

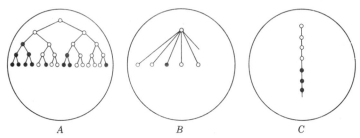

Figure 64. Diagrammatic representation of possible sequences of production of virus elements. A, Increase by repeated reduplications. B, Increase by successive replications of the initial element. C, Increase by replication of the last element produced. Solid dots indicate mutants. Mutants are produced in clones of identical sibs in case A, singly in case B, and in series in case C. Case A agrees with the experimental findings (Luria, *438*). From: Luria, *Ann. Missouri Botan. Garden* **32**:235, 1945.

If a phage replica, on the other hand, can in turn reproduce and give rise to further replicas, and so on, the mutated replicas will often be in groups or "clones" of mutated sibs.[2] These possibilities are illustrated in figure 64.

By counting all the mutant plaques T2*r* in the individual yields of several thousand bacteria infected with phage T2, it is possible to show that the mutants, when present in a bacterial yield, are grouped in clones of identical sibs (*438*). The distribution of clones of various sizes (1 mutant, 2 mutant, 3, 4, 5 · · · mutants per clone) is very close to a distribution that is calculated by assuming that the reproduction of phage genes is an exponential process, following the equation

$$N = 2^n \qquad [13]$$

where N is the final number of gene copies and n corresponds to the number of phage generations that have taken place.

[2] A "clone" is the group of all the individuals derived from one ancestor by vegetative reproduction.

This equation is formally analogous to the equation for clonal reproduction of bacteria, protozoa, or any other vegetative cell population. It tells us that the phage genes reproduce from 1 to 2 to 4 to 8, rather than by the successive production, 1 by 1, of single copies of the original gene brought into the bacterium by the infecting phage particle.

This result, we must remember, concerns individual phage properties; in itself it does not necessarily mean that all phage genes reproduce together as a single particle, giving rise to 2 particles, which then produce 4, and so on. All it means is that individual determinants of phage heredity reproduce exponentially by successive duplications. Whether or not they do so all together, assembled in a single element, has to be shown by other methods.

Multiple and mixed infection. When several phage particles attack the same bacterium, we speak of *multiple infection* if they are all alike, of *mixed infection* if they are of different types. The results are different and depend on the degree of similarity between the particles. Multiple infection gives results quite similar to single infection. The latent period, the phage yield, and the time of appearance of mature particles, as shown by premature lysis, are not significantly different. This similarity between single and multiple infection is not due to a limitation in the number of infecting particles that can penetrate the cell; rather, it indicates that the amount of phage produced in a bacterium is limited by some other mechanism.

When multiple infection consists of two infections with the same phage, separated by an interval of several minutes, the second phage contingent, after being adsorbed, is often actually destroyed, and part of its phosphorus is shed into the medium in soluble form (238). This may mean that the phage skin and nucleic acid separate, and that the nucleic acid is partly released outside. This second phage contingent does not participate in reproduction, nor does it contribute phosphorus to the phage progeny (237). It may, however, give sign of its presence, for example, by lysis inhibition.

Mixed infection with unrelated phages. Experiments on mixed infection are done using *indicator strains* of bacteria, which selectively reveal each phage in a mixture of phages. The usual indicator strains are bacterial mutants resistant to one or another of the phages. The spontaneous mutations of bacteria to phage resistance have proved very useful in the study of bacterial genetics (442). A mutation may produce resistance to one or more phages (see table 22). There is no obvious relation between the degree of relatedness of two phages and the cross-resistance pattern of various bacterial mutants to them (177).

Table 22. Bacteriophage resistant mutants of *E. coli*, strain B, with respect to bacteriophages T1–T7

Modified from Luria (*435*).
Each mutant is derived from wild type by a single mutational step.

	T1	T5	T2	T6	T4	T3	T7	Trypto-phan Require-ment
				*			*	
Wild type	S	S	S	S	S	S	S	—
Frequent mutants								
B/1	R	S	S	S	S	S	S	+
B/1, 5	R	R	S	S	S	S	S	—
B/6	S	S	S	R	S	S	S	—
B/3, 4	S	S	S	S	R	R	S	—
B/3, 4, 7	S	S	S	S	R	R	R	—
B/3, 4, 7	S	S	(S)	(S)	R	R	R	—
Complex mutants								
B/1, 3, 4, 7	R	S	(S)	(S)	R	R	R	+
B/1, 3, 4, 5, 7	R	R	(S)	(S)	R	R	R	—
B/2, 3, 4, 6, 7	S	S	R	R	R	R	R	—
B/1, 2, 3, 4, 6, 7	R	S	R	R	R	R	R	+

* The braces indicate serological relationship between phages.
( ) The parentheses indicate ability to produce phenotypically modified phage (see page 197).
S = sensitive; R = resistant.

Given a pair of phages, it is almost always possible to obtain a bacterial strain sensitive to one phage and resistant to the other. These resistant mutants are used as indicators to identify the phages in a mixture, in the following way (figure 65).

Suppose we plate a mixed suspension of phages T1 and T2 with bacteria of the mutant strain B/1, resistant to T1 and sensitive to T2; only phage T2 will produce plaques. If we use strain B/2 instead of B/1, only T1 will produce plaques. If we plate our phage suspension with mixed indicators, that is, with a mixture of bacteria B/2 and B/1, all plaques will be "turbid," since the plaques formed by each phage by lysis of the sensitive bacteria will be overgrown by the other bacterial type resistant to that phage (*168*). Clear areas will be observed where plaques of the two phages overlap.

This technique also makes it possible to test whether a bacterium sensitive to two phages, when infected by both of them, liberates both

types. The host bacteria are infected with the two phages, and a series
of samples are plated *before lysis*, with single and with mixed indicators. A bacterium that liberates only T2 gives a plaque on B/1, no
plaque on B/2, and a turbid plaque on the mixed indicators. A bacterium that liberates only T1 gives a plaque on B/2, none on B/1, and
a turbid plaque on mixed indicators. Only bacteria that liberate *both*
T1 and T2 give clear plaques on the mixed indicators.

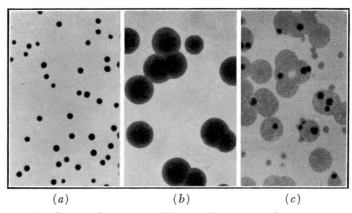

(a)   (b)   (c)

Figure 65. Platings of a mixture of bacteriophages T1 and T2 on various indicator bacteria. (*a*) Indicator B/1, sensitive to phage T2 only. (*b*) Indicator
B/2, sensitive to phage T1 only. (*c*) Mixed indicators B/1 and B/2; both phages
form turbid plaques, with clear areas of lysis where the plaques overlap. Enlarged about 2½×.

The results of mixed infection depend on the degree of relatedness
of the infecting phages. In the T series, if the phages are unrelated
by morphological and serological criteria, the resulting phenomena,
which have been grouped under the general term of *interference* (see
chapter 14), can be summarized as follows (*168*):

1. There is no interference in the adsorption process. Adsorption is
normal for both phage types, until extensive coating of the bacterial
surface becomes a limiting factor.

2. There is complete *mutual exclusion.* A given bacterium liberates
either one or the other of the unrelated phage types, never both.

3. There is a *depressor effect:* the excluded phage causes a reduction
in the yield of the successful one. This depressor effect can be counteracted, within several minutes after infection, by addition of antiserum
against the excluded phage. This suggests that the depressor effect is
exerted by some portions of the excluded phage that are located on

the bacterial surface and are still accessible to antiserum, possibly the skins of the excluded phage.

The mechanism of mutual exclusion is not yet clear. As we shall see later (page 202) a phage coming from outside may sometimes exclude maturation of a phage already present inside the bacterium, that is, of a lysogenically carried phage (669). In these and probably in all cases, mutual exclusion may involve a competition for some single piece of machinery needed for phage maturation. It is possible that the excluded phage multiplies in the mixed-infected bacteria and simply fails to mature.

Thus, mutual exclusion and depressor effect may result from different types of interactions in separate regions of the infected cell. The most remarkable feature of mutual exclusion between unrelated phages is its all-or-none character, no exception to which has been reported.

Mixed infection with related phages. When serologically related phages such as T2, T4, and T6 infect the same bacteria, mutual exclusion fails and most bacteria liberate particles of both types (173). If the phages are very similar, for example, if they are mutants of the same phage, every bacterium is a mixed yielder. In a mass lysate derived by mixed infection with a pair of mutants of the same phage, the ratio of particles resembling the two parent types is generally the same in the yield as in the infecting mixture. This indicates that little intracellular selection takes place for or against either phage type.

Participation of many infecting phage particles in reproduction is only possible, however, if infection is almost simultaneous. A few minutes of delay cause an exclusion between related phages (195). This exclusion is accompanied by destruction and partial release into the medium of the excluded particles (238).

Genetic recombination. When two related phages, differing from one another in at least two characters, infect the same bacteria, a new phenomenon is observed. This consists of the appearance of phage types that were not present in the input and that represent new combinations of the characters of the parents. Thus, infection with T4r and T2 gives rise to four types: T2, T2r, T4, T4r; infection with T2h and T2r gives T2h, T2r, T2hr, and T2 (173; 310).

The discovery of this "recombination" opened a new field in virus genetics. It soon became clear (314; 315) that each character that acted as a recombination unit represented one of two alternative forms of some discrete phage portion or gene, and that recombination was a reshuffling of these genes. Thus, we should write more correctly and in complete analogy with usual genetic terminology:

$$T2hr^+ \times T2h^+r \rightarrow T2hr^+, T2h^+r, T2hr, T2h^+r^+$$

The superscript $+$ indicates the normal (wild-type) form or *allele*. A single-step mixed-infection experiment of this kind is called a *cross*.

The important discovery was soon made (*314*) that independently isolated r mutants of the same phage are seldom, if ever, identical, and are actually not allelic, since upon mixed infection with two r mutants one obtains some r^+ recombinants:

$$T2r_1 \times T2r_2 \rightarrow T2r_1(r), T2r_2(r), T2r_1r_2(r), T2r_1{}^+r_2{}^+(r^+)$$

The letters in parentheses indicate the plaque character or phenotype of each phage. The scheme of figure 66 gives the genetic interpretation of these crosses.

It is clear that phenomena such as this may reveal essential features of the process of phage development; this process must be such as to allow for recombination of phage characters to take place. A quantitative analysis of genetic recombination may be as informative on phage development as the quantitative analysis of genetic data in higher organisms is in clarifying the nature and organization of the genetic material in their germ cells. A peculiarity of phage genetics is that quantitative data on recombination, that is, on the relative frequencies of various classes of progeny from a. cross, are obtained by examining the yield of many bacteria or, at best, the whole yield of individual bacteria. The exact number of phage particles of each parental type that infect individual bacteria is unknown; all we know is the average number of the infecting particles. Moreover, the process of recombination may occur many times within each bacterium. Thus, the final result we observe reflects an unknown number of crosses among an unknown number of parental particles and of their offspring. It has been pointed out that mixed infection of a single bacterium is equivalent to an experiment in population genetics rather than to a cross between two individuals.

The most salient features of the phenomenon of genetic recombination, as studied mainly with phages T2 and T4, may be listed as follows (*183; 184; 314; 315; 657*):

I. In *mass populations* derived in single-step experiments from bacteria mixed-infected with phage of two types:
   1. The yields of the two recombinant types are approximately equal and characteristic for each pair of character differences studied; for example, a cross T2h $\times$ T2r yields equal numbers of T2hr and T2h^+r^+.

2. Some characters are recombined independently (unlinked genes). In a mass lysate the frequency of each recombinant type in these cases is generally lower than 25% of the total, the proportion expected if there were random assortment of

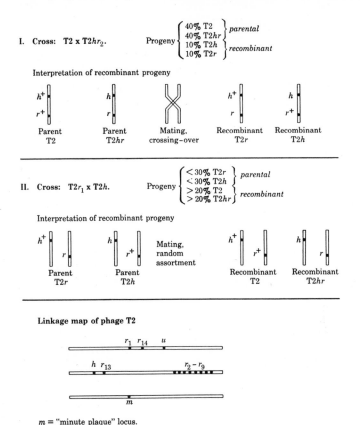

I. Cross: T2 x T2hr₂.   Progeny $\left\{\begin{array}{l} 40\% \text{ T2} \\ 40\% \text{ T2}hr \end{array}\right\}$ *parental* $\left.\begin{array}{l} 10\% \text{ T2}h \\ 10\% \text{ T2}r \end{array}\right\}$ *recombinant*

Interpretation of recombinant progeny

h^+ h h^+ h
r^+ r r r^+

Parent   Parent   Mating,   Recombinant   Recombinant
T2   T2hr   crossing–over   T2r   T2h

II. Cross: T2r₁ x T2h.   Progeny $\left\{\begin{array}{l} <30\% \text{ T2}r \\ <30\% \text{ T2}h \end{array}\right\}$ *parental* $\left.\begin{array}{l} >20\% \text{ T2} \\ >20\% \text{ T2}hr \end{array}\right\}$ *recombinant*

Interpretation of recombinant progeny

h^+ h Mating, h^+ h
   r r^+ random r^+ r
           assortment

Parent   Parent   Recombinant   Recombinant
T2r   T2h   T2   T2hr

Linkage map of phage T2

r_1 r_{14} u

h r_{13} $r_2 - r_9$

m

m = "minute plaque" locus.
u = "ultraviolet sensitivity level" locus.

Figure 66. The chromosomal interpretation of genetic recombination in bacteriophage.

two independent pairs of elements. The limitation is interpreted as due to the fact that not all the progeny particles have had an equal chance for biparental origin. The more phage is produced in a bacterium (for example, under conditions of lysis inhibition) the closer the recombinant frequencies become to the expected 25% value. In a cross between parents differing by 3 instead of 2 unlinked characters, the recombinants for a pair of characters are divided into two equal classes, each of which carries one of the two forms of the third character. For example, in a cross T2rhm × T2$r^+h^+m^+$ (r, h, m unlinked) one-half of the rh^+ (or of the r^+h) is m, the other half is m^+. Only three unlinked groups of characters have as yet been described in phage T2 (see figure 66).

3. Linked characters, which do not assort independently in a cross, have been found. They give frequencies of recombinants intermediate between the minimum observable (about 1%) and 25%. The results are compatible with the assumption that the corresponding genes lie arranged linearly on "chromosomes" and that the recombination frequencies reflect "crossover frequencies" or "distances" between genes on the same chromosome, that is, additive probabilities that groups of linearly arranged genes become separated by crossing over. Thus, a "3-point test" (using 3 linked characters a, b, c) tells whether a certain gene lies between two others or beyond one of them. If c is between a and b, the frequency of recombination for the pair a, b is approximately the sum of the frequencies of recombination for a, c and for b, c. The linkage map of figure 66 was constructed after experiments of this type. The validity of the linkage hypothesis is corroborated by "coupling and repulsion" experiments; if a cross ab × AB gives, say, 3% aB (and Ab), the cross aB × Ab gives 3% AB (and ab). For linked characters as well, the higher the phage yield, the higher the proportion of recombinants becomes.

4. A recombinant particle may exhibit characters derived from at least 3 parents. Thus, in a cross abC × aBc × Abc, some particles ABC are formed. These could not be formed by any type of exchange between two parental particles only. If, therefore, the elementary act of recombination is a mating of phage particles in pairs, followed by redistribution of genetic elements, there must then be several rounds of matings in each bacterium.

5. Recombinants are already present among the first mature phage particles that are obtained by premature lysis at the earliest time after infection; the frequency of recombinants in the premature yield is lower than in the final yield.

II. In *single-burst* experiments from mixed-infected bacteria:

6. The numbers of recombinants of opposite type produced in individual bacteria are neither identical, nor similar, nor even

significantly correlated. This holds both for final and for premature yield. If recombination is due to mating in pairs followed by reciprocal exchanges, the result of the individual pairings should be the production of equal numbers of the two recombinants. Possibly, some other event occurring later may distort the numbers of opposite new types that the mating produces. Unequal reproduction of recombinants after the exchanges could do so. Such unequal reproduction may reflect partly the nonsynchronization of phage multiplication, partly the removal of particles from the reproducing population by maturation.

As a whole, the recombination experiments reveal a tremendously complex genetic system in phage. Genetic recombination has been observed in all the coli-phages of the T systems in which it has been looked for (T1, T2, T3, T4, T5, T6). How it takes place we do not know with certainty. The most likely explanation seems to be a series of matings by random pairings, irrespective of genetic type, among haploid,[3] vegetative phage particles that have not yet become mature and infectious. Recombination in the paired phage would occur both by random segregation of chromosomes and by "crossing over," as in sexually reproducing higher organisms. Indeed, it is possible to predict the actual frequencies of recombinants in various crosses (for example, with parents in unequal numbers) and the lack of correlation between reciprocal recombinants on the basis of a model (657) consisting of repeated, completely random matings in a population of reproducing vegetative phages, with maturation (see page 170) removing individual phages at random from the sequence of reproduction and recombination. The remarkable feature is, of course, the tremendous frequency of repeated matings in the short period of a single intracellular cycle.

Heterozygotes. If matings among vegetative phages do occur, it would be desirable to demonstrate the existence of mating forms. Among the phage particles comprising the yield of any one cross, about 2% give progeny that contain particles of two types (312). For example, in the yield from a cross of T2r × T2r^+, about 2% of the new particles give progeny consisting of r and r^+ particles in equal amounts. These "segregating" particles produced in the cross are, then, *heterozygous* for the r locus. The heterozygotes, although they

---

[3] "Haploid" indicates a nucleus containing a single set of chromosomes; "diploid," a nucleus with two sets of homologous chromosomes.

fit the general picture of a mating mechanism, are difficult to explain in terms of the mating theory discussed above, especially because the heterozygous portions of their chromosomes appear always to be very small.

A study of linkage in heterozygotes of T2 (*416a*) has shown that the heterozygous regions of the chromosomes are those at which crossovers have occurred. The results suggest a special mode of phage reproduction, in which the chromosomes are replicated by a linear, zipper-like mechanism. Partial replicas, initiated at opposite ends of two homologous chromosomes, could join together and give rise to chromosomes with overlapping regions. If any allelic differences occur in the duplicated, overlapping regions the particles will be heterozygous for the corresponding genetic properties.

RADIATION ANALYSIS

Radiation treatments have been most valuable in attempts to clarify the intracellular phage development by modifying phage in such a way that its development stops at one stage or another. Thus we learn that phage adsorption is not necessarily followed by death of the bacteria, since x-ray-inactivated phage is adsorbed and disappears without stopping bacterial growth (*665*). Likewise, the following stage of invasion, characterized by bacterial death and nuclear disintegration, can be dissociated from production of new phage by ultraviolet treatment of the phage before adsorption (*441*). Moreover, new phenomena are observed in bacteria infected with irradiated phage, depending on the conditions prevailing upon infection.

Reactivation phenomena. An inactive phage particle is defined as one that fails to reproduce in the host bacterium. Upon adsorption of such an inactive particle (if adsorption can still occur) lysis fails to take place and even artificial disruption of the bacterium reveals no active phage. If bacteria infected with phage inactivated by ultraviolet light (UV) are exposed to visible light or near UV (3100–5000 A) a fraction of the bacteria produce active phage. This *photoreactivation* (*193*), an instance of a very general occurrence with cells modified by UV, is characteristic for each phage, is barely noticeable after x-ray inactivation, and has not been observed with phage inactivated by chemicals. No photoreactivation occurs if the irradiated phage is exposed to light in the free, unadsorbed state.

For phages like T3 or T7, the damage made by each UV quantum must be repaired by 1 light quantum, although some of the UV damage is irreparable. For phages like T2, the situation is more complicated, and the hypothesis of a 1:1 repair of individual damages requires some subsidiary assumptions (98a). The pigment responsible for the photochemical reaction may be a flavine. The dependence of photoreactivation on factors such as temperature probably reflects the effect of these factors on the production and utilization of the pigment.

Another type of reactivation is observed with several phages upon multiple infection with irradiated particles. Active phage is produced in many more bacteria than those which receive the few phage particles that register as active in single infection (443). This *multiplicity reactivation* indicates a cooperation among damaged phage particles in "pulling through" in the same bacterium. The particles must be either of the same type or of nonmutually exclusive types. It was thought at first that multiplicity reactivation was due to genetic recombination, with the formation of active particles by transfers of genetic material among genetically damaged particles. Further work showed however that the genetic recombination hypothesis was inadequate to fit all the aspects of the phenomenon (194). Multiplicity reactivation is probably due to a cooperation among damaged particles in performing some early step in the integration between phage and host cell. Reproduction can then occur if at least one of the particles is genetically undamaged. Such a genetically undamaged particle might arise by genetic recombination.

Intracellular irradiation. By exposing phage-infected bacteria to radiation, their ability to produce phage can be suppressed (447). In this case radiation acts on the virus itself rather than on the bacterial host. Actually, most phages can grow in bacteria that before infection had received doses of radiation much greater than those needed to suppress phage growth. This situation is not surprising, since we have already seen that the part of the bacterium used in phage synthesis is its enzymatic machinery (which is very resistant to radiation) rather than its more radiosensitive nuclear apparatus.

The analysis of intracellular suppression of phage as a function of radiation dose gives different results with different phages. With T7, a small and probably simple phage, the suppression curve in single-infected bacteria immediately after infection is identical with the inactivation curve of free phage. Then, after several minutes, it changes into a "multiple-hit" type of curve. The final slope, that is, the probability of an individual hit, remains approximately constant (64; figure 67). This indicates that suppression of the ability of an infected bacterium to liberate phage requires the inactivation of all the intracellular virus elements, and that the individual elements to be inactivated retain the same radiosensitivity as the free virus particles, while their number increases.

The situation with T2 is more complex (*64; 447*). The radiosensitivity of the infecting particle diminishes for several minutes, before

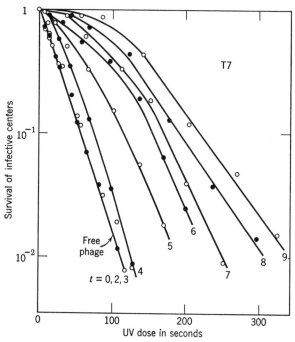

Figure 67. The intracellular inactivation of phage T7 by ultraviolet light. Abscissa: dose of UV light. Ordinate: the proportion of infected bacteria which retain the ability to liberate phage. Bacteria, infected at time 0, are chilled after various times of incubation, irradiated with UV, then plated for assay of plaque-forming ability. The number near each curve gives the time in minutes between infection and chilling. From: Benzer (*64*).

any increase in the number of radiosensitive units is seen. This behavior fits the idea that the phage has to perform an initial reaction, which requires the intervention of a specific radiosensitive portion. This portion may be needed only in the first few minutes, after which the phage reproduces in the form of less radiosensitive units. These, late in the latent period, give rise to mature particles.

SUMMARY ON THE DEVELOPMENT OF THE T PHAGES

From all lines of evidence, we can now construct a tentative picture of the events of phage development. This picture is, of course, provisional, and serves mainly a purpose of orientation.

With a phage like T2, irreversible adsorption is followed by a process of invasion. This depends on a penetration of the nucleic acid-containing phage portion into the bacterium. It is characterized, on the one hand, by a modification of the cell surface, in which a mechanism for the rejection of additional phage particles becomes established; on the other hand, by an incapacitation of the nuclear apparatus of the bacterium. In these stages, the phage is nonrecoverable in active form (*vegetative phage*). A radiosensitive phage portion becomes unnecessary and is possibly used up. Then, logarithmic reproduction of the genetic phage elements begins, accompanied by genetic recombination. The formation of infectious phage particles, which starts about the middle of the minimum latent period, is preceded by the appearance of immature elements related to various portions of the phage particles. The maturation probably consists of the acquisition of a "cytoplasm" as opposed to a "nucleoplasm" or genetic core of the phage. The cytoplasm includes the protein skin, the tail, and possibly other parts of the mature particle. Maturation renders a phage particle infectious for other bacterial cells and removes it from further participation in reproduction in the cell in which it was formed.

Other phages may be less differentiated into portions of different dispensability and of different function; they also differ in the extent to which they disrupt host functions and organization.

PHYSIOLOGICAL CHANGES INDUCED IN BACTERIOPHAGE BY THE HOST

The concept of a physiologically active, nongenetic portion of the phage, acquired late in phage development, is supported by the fact that growth in different hosts can induce transitory changes in phage particles (*76; 446*). An example of such phenomena, which are apparently fairly frequent and will be discussed in greater detail in chapter 15, is illustrated in figure 68. A phage, for example P2, when grown on a host strain Sh, is generally unable to attack another host B. A few particles attack B, however, and give rise to a new phage form (P2B) that can grow regularly on B. The change is not permanent, however, since a single cycle of growth of P2B on Sh returns it to the P2 form, which does not grow on B.

Changes of this type are strictly host controlled. They modify the ability of a virus to grow on a given host. In some cases, as in the

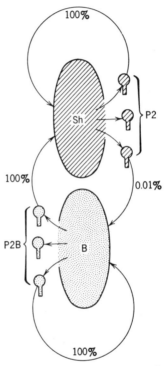

Figure 68. Scheme of host-induced modification. The percentage figures near the arrows correspond to the fraction of cells in which the phage can grow. Phage P2, after 1 cycle of growth in strain Sh, can only grow in 1 of 10⁴ cells of strain B. After 1 cycle of growth in strain B, P2 is in the P2B form, which can grow in every cell of either B or Sh. Modified from: Bertani and Weigle (76).

one mentioned above, they allow repeated growth on the new host. In other cases, instead, they may prevent continuous growth on it. The importance of such phenomena is that they represent the only known modifications of virus properties directly induced by the host. The modifications are not produced by selection of spontaneous phage variants; they are temporary phage changes due to the intracellular environment in a particular host.

How the host does it, we do not know. It may provide the phage with some special substrate, or it may force the phage to develop differently because of the lack of some substrate, or it may contribute some specific structural patterns to the virus.

LYSIS OF BACTERIA

The mechanism by which phage causes bacterial lysis is unknown. Lysis is not tied to production of infectious phage, since it may take place in the presence of proflavine, which allows formation of incomplete phage particles (175). Phage liberation has been claimed to occur in some cases before visible lysis, possibly as a result of a localized surface damage to the bacterial membranes, which may allow the cell contents to escape. Usually, lysis accompanies phage liberation and appears to be a rather sudden breakage of the cell membranes, which often leaves an empty cell wall that later slowly disintegrates (see figures 30–31).

Nothing is known as to the chemical or physicochemical mechanisms of lysis; these may involve the action of bacterial enzymes, of phage enzymes, or of both. On the one hand, the occurrence of bacteriolytic substances produced by bacteria under stimuli other than phage, and also upon lysis by phage (270), seems to favor a role of bacterial enzymes in the lytic process. On the other hand, the specific duration of the latent period between infection and lysis, which for the same bacterium may vary from 13 to 50 minutes or longer depending on the phage, suggests a role of phage in determining the course of lysis. The latent period remains constant even when the bacterial generation time is varied five-fold, by changes in medium composition. This indicates its independence of the rate of bacterial syntheses. In mixed infection, with a long-latent-period phage like T2 excluding a short-latent-period phage like T1, lysis and liberation of T2 occur after the latent period characteristic of the excluding phage.

Bacteriolytic substances have been obtained from heavily irradiated or osmotically disrupted bacteriophage particles, but their role in the normal process of bacterial lysis is unknown. In some cases the lytic action is due to the isolated skin or "ghost" of a disrupted phage particle (308). Upon lysis by phage, bacteria often release lytic substances acting upon other strains, but there is little evidence that these "lysines" are phage specific (270).

LYSOGENIC BACTERIA

The prophage and its maturation. Cell-free filtrates of bacterial cultures often contain phages that lyse other strains of the same bacterial species or of related species. Such phage-bacterium associations sometimes represent accidental associations of a phage with a resistant

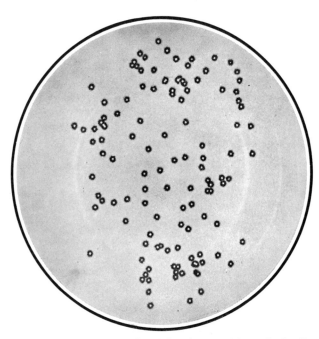

Figure 69. Centered plaques produced by plating a few washed cells of a lysogenic strain with an excess of a sensitive strain. The sensitive bacteria are lysed by the phage liberated by the lysogenic colonies.

bacterium that throws off enough sensitive mutants to maintain phage propagation in mass cultures; it is then possible to free the bacteria from phage by single-cell isolations. In a majority of the phage-bacterium associations, however, this is impossible; *every cell is a potential source of phage* (true lysogenesis). Plating washed lysogenic cells with a layer of phage-sensitive bacteria (indicator bacteria) leads to formation of plaques, each plaque being centered by a colony of lysogenic bacteria (figure 69). In platings of unwashed whole cultures of lysogenic bacteria we also observe noncentered plaques, which originate from free phage particles present in the lysogenic culture.

The phages that establish lysogenic relations with their hosts are called temperate.

There is no doubt that each cell of a lysogenic strain is a phage carrier (453). Phage liberation occurs by occasional lysis of a cell. The frequency of such spontaneous phage liberation was found to be 1:200 cells per generation in one case, 1:50,000 in another. When frequent, the lysis of individual cells can actually be observed under the microscope and is found to be accompanied by liberation of phage, which occurs only at this time. A lysing bacterium liberates an amount of phage of the same order as the yield from a sensitive bacterium lysed by the same phage. Sometimes the lysogenic bacteria cannot adsorb the phage they carry; in most cases they can. They are generally not lysed by such reinfection with their own phage, to which they are, therefore, *immune*.

Inside the lysogenic bacteria the temperate phage is as undetectable as a virulent phage is in the early part of the latent period in the lytic cycle. No infectious phage can be recovered by artificial breaking of the lysogenic cells. In some lysogenic bacteria, mass lysis with phage liberation can be produced artificially, after a latent period of 30–60 minutes, by such means as irradiation, treatment with certain sulfhydryl compounds, nitrogen mustard, H_2O_2, and ion-chelating agents (452; 454). This process is called *induction*. Even in the "induced" bacteria, premature lysis or breakage reveals infectious phage in the last third of the latent period only.

Thus we have reason to believe that phage is present in the cell in a form, the so-called *prophage*, which is different from the infectious particles, and which before liberation must undergo a process of maturation. Inside the cell, the phage shares the fate and properties of all other cell constituents. For example, in spore-forming bacteria the prophage survives temperatures much higher than the free phage could, just as cell proteins in the spore withstand heat treatment much better than in vegetative cells (188). Apparently the prophage reproduces without upsetting the cell economy, and only occasionally does a new situation arise which leads both to phage maturation and to cell lysis. Prophage and bacterial protoplasm are synthesized side by side; the maturation process, instead, is bound to events that preclude bacterial survival. Even in bacteria in which lysis is induced by irradiation, the synthesis of bacterial components (RNA, enzymes) continues during the latent period before lysis.

Is the interdependence between maturation and lysis valid for phage-bacterium relations in general? If so, the difference between the lysogenic and the lytic situations would reside only in the frequency with which the presence of phage sets in motion the unknown series of events leading, on the one hand, to phage maturation, on the other hand, to bacterial disintegration and lysis.

Experiments on mutual exclusion between a prophage and a super-infecting, virulent phage are compatible with this point of view (669). In lysogenic bacteria induced by UV, infection with a phage unrelated to the carried prophage can exclude the carried phage from the yield (i.e., can preclude its maturation). This exclusion can take place even when the virulent phage is added only a few minutes before the appearance of mature particles of the carried phage. We are led to believe that induction does what the prophage is unable to do, that is, eliminates the functional integrity of the cell and allows the prophage to proceed toward maturation; this process can be stopped by infection with another phage.

We may, thus, visualize a series of alternative rulers of cell destiny—the bacterial nucleus, the prophage, and the exogenous phage. The prophage of a temperate phage cannot displace the bacterial pattern without help from inducing agents. In induced bacteria the latent prophage captures the lead, not immediately upon induction but after an interval, during which it can still be displaced by an exogenous phage.

The situation in multiple lysogenesis with unrelated phages fits this hypothesis. Each cell carries the various prophage types; but, when spontaneous phage liberation occurs, only one phage type matures in any one cell (74). Mutual exclusion of maturation among unrelated prophages may indicate that the conditions that allow the cellular controls to be overwhelmed permit a competition among prophage types for control of the maturation mechanism, always leading to total victory of one of the competitors. Mutual exclusion may also indicate, however, that the factors that permit maturation act specifically on one or the other of the prophage types. Related prophages may mature together (359a).

A prophage may prevent multiplication of some unrelated phages and not to others (see table 23). The mechanism of this interference is unknown.

The condition of the prophage in the lysogenic cell. If there were only one prophage copy per cell, some mechanism should be present for its orderly reduplication and segregation along with other cell components. If the prophage were present in multiple copies, these could be assorted at cell division, like other nonnuclear components of the host cells. Nonlysogenic cells are exceedingly rare or altogether absent in lysogenic strains. Therefore, either the prophages are many or they are not assorted at random. The evidence given below seems to support the idea that prophage is present in single copy, at least in permanent lysogenicity, and may be transmitted by a mechanism connected with chromosomal reproduction.

The ability of a phage to be carried lysogenically, that is, its temperate or virulent nature, is genetically controlled. A temperate phage, upon infecting a sensitive host, produces lysis or lysogenesis in comparable proportions of cells. This relation explains why the temperate phages produce a type of plaque consisting of a partially lysed area covered with lysogenic growth. Virulent mutants can be obtained from temperate phages (100). They give clear plaques and induce no lysogenesis.

After infection of bacteria with a temperate phage, the cells that do not lyse may for several generations segregate into lysogenic and sensitive, noncarrier offspring (424). Later, no more sensitive offspring are produced, and every cell derived from a lysogenic parent is lysogenic.

Interesting results are obtained when these stably lysogenic bacteria are infected with related phages, which they generally adsorb (75). Some typical results are shown in table 23. Infection of a lysogenic bacterium with a temperate mutant of its prophage gives rise to a temporary mixed lysogenesis; for several cell generations the few cells that lyse give mixed yields. But after a few generations the prophages segregate, and ultimately either one or the other prophage remains in each cell. Double lysogeny occasionally results.

Reinfection of a lysogenic bacterium with a virulent mutant of its prophage also leads to temporary mixed lysogenesis. This is followed, however, by return to the original condition of lysogenesis for the temperate phage. An exceptional finding of a return to sensitivity suggests that segregation of prophages has occurred, but that the virulent prophage, being inherently unable to establish permanent lysogenesis, becomes eliminated. Altogether, the segregation of related prophages and their mutual elimination are easily interpreted if we assume that permanent lysogenesis requires the fixation of a prophage to some site, which exists in single copy and which segregates in an orderly manner at cell division, for example, a specific chromosomal location. The "anchored" prophage can be removed or replaced, completely or in part, by another prophage of the same type. A weakly virulent mutant cannot establish itself as prophage, nor can it overcome the immunity

Table 23.   The relations among bacteria, temperate phages, and virulent phages

Data supplied by Dr. G. Bertani

Bacterium	Infecting Phage		
	Temperate	Weakly Virulent	Strongly Virulent
Sensitive Sh	Sh + P2 → or ⇒ Sh(P2) P2	Sh + P2rir → P2rir	Sh + P2$\underline{rir}$ ⇒ P2$\underline{rir}$
Lysogenic Sh(P2)	Sh(P2) + P2m → Sh(P2)[P2m] or Sh(P2) Sh(P2m) ⇢ Sh(P2, P2m)	Sh(P2) + P2rir → Sh(P2)[P2rir] or ⇒ Sh(P2) P2rir	Sh(P2) + P2$\underline{rir}$ ⇒ P2$\underline{rir}$
Lysogenic Sh(P2) (prophage unrelated to superinfecting phage)	Sh(P2) + P1 → or ⇒ Sh(P2)(P1) P1		Sh(P2) + P1$\underline{rir}$ ⇒ P1$\underline{rir}$ Sh(P2) + T2 (or T4, T5, T6) †

m = A temperate mutant of a temperate phage.
rir = A weakly virulent mutant of a temperate phage. $\underline{rir}$ = A strongly virulent mutant of a temperate phage.
Sh(P2) = Strain lysogenic for phage P2; sporadic liberation of P2.
Sh(P2m) = Strain lysogenic for phage P2m; sporadic liberation of P2m.
Sh(P2)(P1) = Strain lysogenic for two unrelated phages; sporadic liberation of one phage type at a time (not both together).
Sh(P2, P2m) = Strain lysogenic for two related phages; sporadic liberation of both phages in mixed yield.
Sh(P2)[P2m] = Strain lysogenic for a phage, temporarily carrying also a related phage; sporadic phage liberation with mixed yield. Same for Sh(P2)[P2rir].

† = Death of bacterium without phage production.   → = Change in lysogenicity.   ⇢ = Rare change in lysogenicity.
⇒ = Lysis of bacterium with phage production.

caused by a related prophage. Strongly virulent mutants, however, can overcome the immunity, reproduce, and mature as though the prophage were not present (see table 23).

Genetic experiments on lysogenic bacteria agree with the above conclusion (409). The sexual strain K-12 of *Escherichia coli* (412) may exist in either a lysogenic or a sensitive, noncarrier form with respect to phage lambda. In crosses of lysogenic by sensitive bacteria, lysogenesis behaves as a single segregating factor, whose position in the chromosomal map of the bacterium can be located with proper linkage tests. This observation agrees with the idea of a chromosomal location of the prophage, although it does not exclude that what segregates is not the prophage itself but a genetic determinant responsible for ability to carry the prophage.

Although the prophage may be intimately bound to the reproductive mechanism of the cell, it is not irreversibly bound. It can be lost either by substitution with related prophages, as shown in table 23, or occasionally by growing the bacteria under special nutritional conditions apparently specific for each case, such as low Ca^{++} concentration (135) or presence of glucose (202).

If the prophage is carried in single copy in the host's nucleus, then the process leading to spontaneous or induced production of mature phage from a lysogenic bacterium must involve more than maturation. It must consist also of the transformation of the prophage into vegetative phage and of the proliferation of the latter. Thus, the lysogenic and the lytic types of phage-host relation seem to have in common the full series of events (vegetative reproduction and maturation) that lead to the production of many infectious phage particles from an initial noninfectious element.

The nature of the relation of the prophage to its host cell. The production of lysogenicity by controlled infection with temperate phages makes it unnecessary to consider the prophage of a lysogenic cell as a "normal" cell constituent that becomes a "new virus" upon accidental liberation. Yet the possibility of an intimate relation of the prophage with the reproductive system of the host bacterium suggests a degree of integration that goes beyond the metabolic level and reaches to the genetic constitution of the cell. Once a prophage is established in a cell, it behaves like a cell constituent. This constituent, however, may behave as a rebellious and destructive element and proceed to mature and to lyse the cell. If even more complete integration were to occur, resulting in a carrier state never followed by maturation, we might never suspect the presence of a prophage.

Observations on the genetics of bacteria of the genus *Salmonella* are of interest in this connection (*695*). Most strains of *Salmonella typhimurium* are lysogenic for one or more temperate phages that can infect other strains (*99*). Certain strains produce a filtrable agent FA (identical with a phage) that can transmit or *transduce* individual characteristics of the strain of origin to other strains, which are thereby stably changed and act in turn as sources of FA. The transducing agent, limited in activity range to salmonella cultures having in common the somatic antigen XII, can transfer to other strains individual traits of the strain that has last liberated it. The transduced traits include nutritional properties, fermentative abilities, drug resistance, and specific antigens. Only one trait is transduced at a time. Presumably, during maturation, the *Salmonella* phage may incorporate in its particle not only the phage nucleus but also some genetic elements of the host, possibly from the disrupted bacterial nucleus. These genetic elements are delivered into new host cells, which, if not lysed, may accept the new genetic elements in replacement of their own. This phenomenon brings the phage one step closer to a sort of sexual form of bacterial cell.

There are other instances of host properties (other than phage sensitivity or resistance) that are changed upon acquisition of lysogenicity. In certain nontoxigenic strains of *Corynebacterium diphtheriae* the few cells that upon phage infection become lysogenic acquire the ability to produce the diphtherial exotoxin (*236*). These observations indicate a role of a lysogenically carried virus (or of something "transduced" with it) in the biochemical activities of the lysogenic cell. Nutritional differences occur between lysogenic and sensitive derivatives of other bacteria, for example, in *Bacillus megatherium* (*164a*).

Lysogenicity, phage susceptibility and phage modification. A remarkable situation observed with some of the Vi-phages of *Salmonella typhosa* illustrates a role of lysogenically carried prophages not only in altering the susceptibility of bacteria to other phages but also in impressing upon these phages certain specific transformations. The original Vi-phage II, upon being plated with individual Vi-positive bacterial strains, gives a few plaques. These plaques yield "adapted" phages, which attack a common host strain A plus one or a few of the other Vi-positive strains (*157a*). By this means, 31 adapted Vi-phages have been secured, by means of which 31 strains of Vi-positive typhoid bacilli can be "typed" (*157, 213a*).

The adapted Vi-phages are not (or at least not all) host-range mutants of the original Vi-phage II. Upon a single transfer on the common host strain A many of them revert to Vi-phage A, similar to the original, nonadapted Vi-phage II. The reverted Vi-phage A can then again be adapted by a single passage on a different Vi-strain of bacteria (13a). Thus, at least some of the adapted Vi-phages are not host-range mutants, but *phenotypically modified phage variants* (446; see pages 197 and 295).

The discovery was made that the differences in Vi-type among many Vi-strains of S. *typhosa* are due to specific bacteriophages carried lysogenically within them (13b). These latent, type-determining phages are completely distinct from the Vi-phages derived from Vi-phage II. The most remarkable element of this situation is that the latent pro-phages determine not only the host's susceptibility to unrelated phages but also the host's ability to modify phenotypically in a specific manner the Vi-phages that succeed in infecting it. The implications of these discoveries in relation to lysogenicity and host-controlled variation in viruses are not yet fully understood. The situation in *Salmonella typhosa* is certainly not unique, as shown by observations on lysogenicity and phage susceptibility in other salmonellas (213b). It may indeed be an example of a widespread mechanism for control of virus susceptibility, not only in bacteria, but in other organisms as well.

Coli-phages and colicines. Another observation of interest concerns the relation of lysogenic phage to the so-called *colicines,* substances produced by certain strains of E. *coli* and lethal for other strains (235). The colicines are not viruses, in the sense that they are not reproduced in the cell they kill. Yet most colicines are related, by similarity of host range, to specific coli-phages. Some colicine-producing E. *coli* strains undergo mass lysis, with production of colicine (and no phage), upon treatment with the same agents that "induce" phage maturation in lysogenic strains (360). We get the impression that the colicine may be a nonreproductive maturation form of some lysogenically carried phages. They might be phage skins without nucleus or without the ability to release their nucleus into the host cell.

The observations on temperate phages and on their lysogenic hosts have carried us far from the picture of a virus entering a host cell, reproducing in it, and becoming active and free again. Before our eyes the virus has become more and more a part of the host cell. The free, infectious form has been reduced to an incidental aspect of the life history of the phage. There is no denying the deep insight that these observations promise to give us into the nature of host-virus relationship and even into the genetic structure of the host. As we shall discuss in chapter 18, the facts of lysogenesis do not solve the question of the origin of bacteriophage. The lysogenic condition may include examples of virus origin, or it may simply be the ultimate development of parasitism.

Lysogenicity and phage ecology. The symbiotic relation between prophage and lysogenic bacteria, with occasional liberation, is much more favorable to the maintenance of the virus in nature than the lytic relation. The lytic relation is more frequently observed by superficial observation because of the dramatic occurrence of mass lysis, but is more likely to lead to virus extinction through rapid destruction of its hosts. Most phages probably exist in nature in some lysogenic bacterial reservoir, their occasional liberation providing them with a means for finding new hosts, which the phage may either lyse or render lysogenic. Virulent mutants will have little chances for survival, except under the artificial conditions of their selection and maintenance in the laboratory. The lysogenic condition is extremely frequent. In certain bacterial groups, for example, in *Salmonella typhimurium,* all strains are lysogenic for one or more phages that lyse other salmonellas (99). Indeed, one wonders if every bacterium may not be lysogenic, carrying phages most of which we have no means to recognize. It might even be that every portion of the genetic material of a bacterium has some potentiality to mature into a transmissible agent, that is, to become a phage.

The Interaction of Plant Viruses with Their Host Plants

The information available on the interaction between host and virus is less extensive and less quantitative for plant viruses than for bacteriophage. This is due mainly to the complexity of the hosts, to the difficulties involved in precise quantitative work with plant viruses, and also to the different interest of plant pathologists, whose main practical problems are diagnostic and prophylactic. We shall consider the growth of virus in infected plants, the changes that take place in infected cells, the spread of virus in the host plant, and the alterations of plant metabolism that accompany the manifestations of virus diseases.

GROWTH OF VIRUS

After tobacco leaves are infected with tobacco mosaic virus, it is possible to follow the amount of virus and its increase in the plant sap (334). If the inoculated leaves are excluded from the material extracted for sap, the results represent amounts of new virus formed in the plant. Such data, of course, describe the mass growth of virus in the plant as a whole and not its pattern of growth in individual cells. The results depend on the methodology employed.

It had been reported that tobacco mosaic virus protein, detected by chemical isolation in sap from frozen plants, appeared several days after infection and reached the maximum after 5 to 6 weeks (623). With an improved method for extraction of the leaves and using electrophoretic determination of virus protein (which appears as an abnormal component in the electrophoretic pattern of the cytoplasmic protein fraction), virus protein could be detected 3 days after infection and reached a maximum after about 2 weeks (675). This early appearance of virus protein in the cytoplasmic protein fraction, as distinct from the chloroplast fraction, is accompanied by a decrease in one of the major protein constituents of the same sap fraction, probably a nucleoprotein. It was suggested (*675*) that the virus originates by direct transformation of the normal nucleoprotein into virus protein, without intermediate breakdown to nonspecific building blocks. Direct evidence for this conclusion is lacking. It was, however, noted that the total amount of cytoplasmic protein remains constant, whereas the proportion of virus protein increases from 0 to 40%. Moreover, virus is known to be formed in detached and darkened leaves, where syntheses are slower (*640*). The results are compatible with the idea that virus synthesis is accomplished from nonspecific blocks and that the decrease in normal components is simply due to their normal breakdown with reduced replacement. In tobacco plants, as much as 10% of the dry weight of the plant may finally be represented by tobacco mosaic virus.

Measurements of the relative radioactivity of plant nucleoprotein and of tobacco mosaic virus nucleoprotein (*94*) extracted from infected plants fed with radioactive phosphorus indicated that the virus nucleic acid is synthesized anew from freshly assimilated material, and not by transformation of plant nucleoprotein. In agreement with this conclusion is the observation of inhibition of tobacco mosaic virus production by various purine and pyrimidine derivatives (*151; 477*). The inhibition can be relieved by normal purines or pyrimidines. Apparently, interference with utilization of purines and pyrimidines may block virus synthesis. This is more easily visualized in terms of synthesis of new nucleotides and nucleic acid than of transformation of plant nucleic acid into virus nucleic acid.

Studies with heavy nitrogen ($N^{15}H_4Cl$) as a tracer element in infected tobacco leaves (*479*), as well as analytical study on nitrogen metabolism (*150a*), indicate that virus formation proceeds directly from materials supplied by the medium and not from breakdown products of cell proteins. They also indicate that the virus protein, once formed, is not further broken down and resynthesized, since no incorporation of N^{15} into the virus protein takes place after this protein stops increasing in amount.

A microchemical technique for the isolation and determination of virus protein in small samples of leaf tissue (a few square millimeters) has been applied to the study of tobacco mosaic virus growth (*152*). Isolated leaves are inoculated by rubbing, and samples are cut from the leaves and incubated in liquid medium. Measurable amounts of virus are found about 72 hours after inoculation, and the maximum is reached after 8–10 days, when as much as 0.5 μg of virus protein per square mm of leaf can be obtained (figure 70). The increase is regular and more or less exponential. This is to be expected, whatever the rate of synthesis in individual cells, since what is measured is the total rate of virus production in a tissue infected in one or a few spots, and the rate of virus production reflects mainly the rate of centrifugal spread and invasion of new cells, a process essentially exponential in character.

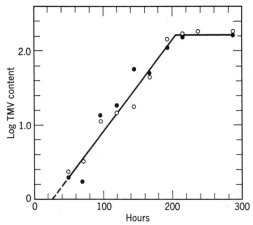

Figure 70. The amount of tobacco mosaic virus, as determined chemically, in samples removed from infected tobacco leaves at various times after inoculation. The TMV content is given in micrograms of virus protein per 302 mm^2 of leaf area. From: Commoner et al. (*152*).

An accurate method of following virus increase in infected plants consists in extracting the sap from measured areas of inoculated leaves, clarifying it, and examining it directly in the electron microscope by the calibrated droplet method, by which one can count the particles of virus protein (*33*). By this method, an increase in the number of virus particles is observed after 18 hours, and the maximum is reached after 4 to 5 days, with a doubling time of about 4 hours (*625;* figure 71). Exposure to 38° C suppresses virus increase rather abruptly. At the point of maximum growth, at least 11% of the dry weight of the plant is represented by virus protein. The growth curve for tomato bushy stunt virus is quite similar to that of tobacco mosaic virus.

More recently, a study by infectivity measurements of the early phases of infection of tobacco plants with tobacco mosaic virus and of bean plants with tobacco necrosis virus (*690b*) has indicated a latent period of 8 to 12 hours, followed by a rapid increase in the amount of infectious virus, corresponding to a doubling time of about 1 hour. The reasons for the difference between these results and those of previous studies (*152; 625*) are unknown. It seems possible

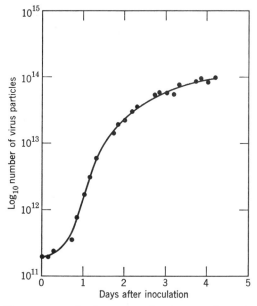

Figure 71. The amount of tobacco mosaic virus, as determined by electron-microscope counts, in areas removed at intervals from infected tobacco leaves. The ordinate represents the number of virus particles per gram of leaf tissue (green weight). From: Steere (*625*).

that the infectivity measurements may permit a study of the earliest parts of virus growth. The other methods may observe later, slower phases of virus production and miss the early phases of virus production because of the presence, in all samples, of an excess of virus particles left over from the inoculum and not participating in reproduction.

There is no evidence in any of the above studies for or against a sequence of virus reproduction in uninfectious form followed by maturation. There is some evidence, however, for a reduction in recoverable virus activity soon after inoculation, suggesting an eclipse period similar to that observed for bacteriophage. A partial disruption of the infecting virus particles is evidenced by the appearance of nonviral P³² in plants infected with P³²-labeled tobacco mosaic virus (48).

INTRACELLULAR MANIFESTATIONS OF PLANT VIRUSES

In electron micrographs of infected leaf tissue, tobacco mosaic virus is seen in the cytoplasm, not in the nuclei (86; figure 72). It often appears to be intimately associated with chloroplasts. This may be due to a secondary invasion of these bodies.

Figure 72. Tobacco mosaic virus demonstrated by electron microscopy of a thin section of an infected cell. Note the absence of virus in the nucleus. Unpublished photograph, courtesy Dr. L. M. Black, University of Illinois, Urbana. Photographs from the same study were published by Black, Morgan and Wyckoff (86).

Changes in the chromoprotein of the green chloroplasts have been correlated with virus production (191; 686). Suppression of chloroplast formation and destruction of existing chloroplasts were observed if the infected plants were kept under conditions of nitrogen starvation, whereas little or no damage to the chloroplasts resulted if ample nitrogen supply was available. It was suggested that the chromoprotein of the plastids had a precursor in common with the virus. During nitrogen starvation, not only would the virus compete with the plastids for the precursor, but also the protein of plastids could be utilized for virus formation, possibly after returning to the precursor stage. This suggestion is hard to reconcile with the evidence for virus synthesis from nonspecific building blocks (479).

In cases of spontaneous variegations—nonvirus diseases that cause localized reduction in chlorophyll—many cells have colorless or shrunk chloroplasts, or have no plastids at all, resembling cells infected with tobacco mosaic virus (191; 686). Cytological observations showed that chloroplast destruction was less and less pronounced toward the periphery of the variegated areas. The suggestion was made, therefore, that the variegation could be considered as somewhat "invasive," and that the plastids could become transformed into spreading, viruslike entities. Plastids are supposed to be related to mitochondria, and the possible origin of viruses from mitochondria has been suggested in connection with plant viruses as well as with some animal viruses. It is hard to see how these speculations receive any specific support from the experiments described above.

Cells infected with a plant virus may or may not show pathological changes, depending on the virus and on the cell function (211). Diminution of the number and size of chloroplasts is observed in the "yellows" diseases. It is uncertain whether a decrease in the yellow pigments (carotenes, xanthophyll) is also involved.

The most direct morphological manifestation of virus infection inside a host cell is the production of intracellular inclusions, abnormal bodies whose presence is strictly limited to the cells of areas showing disease symptoms. In the tobacco mosaic group, two types of inclusions have been described, the ameboid or X-bodies and the crystalline plates (359). The X-bodies appear early in infected cells and are formed by agglomeration of particles visible at first as minute granules streaming along with the cytoplasm. When fully developed, the X-bodies may be 5 to 40 μ in diameter and often enclose mitochondria and oil globules. They have been extracted by micromanipulation; after being washed and crushed they release infectious virus (595). If the cell that contains X-bodies is mechanically damaged, the bodies often disintegrate. It had previously been supposed that the X-bodies represented the result of a nonspecific cell reaction to the virus, but their infectivity suggests that they contain virus in amounts greater than present in an equal volume of cytoplasm. The virus in the X-bodies may be combined with other cell components; tobacco mosaic virus, for example, has a well-established tendency to form complexes with a variety of proteins.

The high virus concentration in the X-bodies is confirmed by the fact that in ageing cells these inclusions are often transformed into the other type of inclusion, the *crystalline plates*, whose high content in infectious virus is well substantiated (see frontispiece). Crystalline plates may be formed directly without deriving from X-bodies; they are variable in shape, but often show a perfect crystalline symmetry. They are strongly birefringent if viewed edgewise. Upon treatment of the cells with acids, the plates are suddenly transformed into a striate material, closely resembling the needles formed by crystallization of purified tobacco mosaic virus (54). Crystalline plates extracted by micromanipulation and dissolved in water yield characteristic virus particles.

Cytoplasmic inclusions are formed in many plant virus diseases, although they are not found in some well-investigated cases, for example, in plants infected with cucumber mosaic virus. This may be due to some peculiarity of the cucumber plant sap (43). Inclusions are never formed in the sap of the vacuole of infected cells. This sap probably does not contain virus.

Intranuclear inclusions have only been observed with certainty in a few virus diseases (367), among which the best known are those of the severe and mild etch viruses of solanaceous plants. Many nuclei of cells infected with etch virus contain regular plates and other crystalline forms. Some of these inclusion-containing nuclei can be seen to divide, even in nonproliferating cells. Tobacco plants simultaneously infected with tobacco mosaic and mild etch viruses show, within the same cell, intracytoplasmic crystalline plates of the mosaic and intranuclear plates of the etch virus. This shows that two unrelated plant viruses can multiply in the same cell (462).

It is clear that an understanding of virus production in the plant cells would be helped by studies on single intracellular cycles of growth, as described for bacteriophage (see chapter 8). Suitable techniques for similar experiments on plant viruses are not yet available. It would also be desirable to correlate the course of virus synthesis with the formation of noninfectious materials serologically related to the virus (49; 473). Growth of viruses could be studied advantageously in plant tissues cultivated in vitro, but the techniques for plant tissue cultures are in certain respects not as developed as for animal tissues. Virus inoculation into tissues cultivated in vitro presents serious difficulties. Tobacco mosaic virus has been cultivated in cultures of root tips derived from virus-infected plants.

The relation of virus infection to cell proliferation is not well understood and is probably different from case to case. On the one hand, certain viruses that infect cells of the reproductive tissues inhibit or completely suppress cell reproduction, with stunting and eventual death of the plant. On the other hand, virus-infected cells often multiply. Some of the infected cells may be stimulated to excessive proliferation, with the production of abnormal outgrowths called *enations,* stemming from the leaf veins. Certain virus strains are particularly apt to cause this type of reaction, for example, the enation strain of tobacco mosaic virus.

Some viruses produce true tumors in plants. The best investigated one (*83*) causes the infected plants to react to wounds by the formation of woody tumor tissue (figure 7). In this case the tumor response varies remarkably with the heredity of the plant. Another tumor virus is responsible for the gall-producing Fiji disease of sugar cane (*503*). The possible role of a virus in the induction of crown gall disease by bacteria (*178a*) is still a matter of speculation.

SPREAD OF VIRUSES IN THE PLANT

The way in which plant viruses spread through infected host tissues depends on the tissues and on the portal of infection (see *43*). Viruses transmitted mechanically, by rubbing leaves, penetrate into a few cells through small wounds. Movement to neighboring cells is slow, of the order of a few microns per hour (*654*) or at most 1 or 2 mm per day (*61a*), and depends upon virus multiplication within each cell, followed by transmission to neighboring cells. Transmission is believed to take place mainly through the intercellular connections or plasmadesmata. When the virus reaches the vascular tissues (phloem and xylem) is spreads rapidly within them (*335; 336*).

The spread occurs mostly through the phloem, although spread through the xylem is observed, for example, with phony peach virus. In the phloem, the virus is carried with the food circulation, without necessarily multiplying in each of the sieve tube cells that it crosses. The rate of spreading may be as high as an inch per minute, as, for example, for curly top virus in the sugar beet. By way of the phloem, the virus may reach the roots and then the whole plant. Actively growing parts of a plant are generally invaded before older, mature parts.

Fast spread starts immediately when viruses are inoculated directly into the vascular tissue by insect vectors. Direct infection of the roots with some viruses, for example, tobacco mosaic, fails to result in generalized spread.

The transport of virus along with the food circulation has been proved by a number of experiments. If the movement of food away from a shoot of an infected plant is retarded because of reduced photosynthesis, either by darkness or by defoliation, the virus reaches the shoot faster in the ascending food current. An experiment on sugar beet curly top virus (60) shows this very clearly. One shoot of a beet plant was placed in the dark, while two other shoots were exposed to light. When one of the illuminated shoots was infected with curly top virus by means of infected insects, the shoot that was kept in the dark (and in which photosynthesis and, therefore, the centripetal food transport were suppressed) became infected in a few days, much sooner than the other noninoculated shoot that was exposed to light.

Although the virus can pass through vascular tissue without reproducing in all its cells, many cells become infected and undergo necrotic changes. Phloem necrosis is often widespread. It probably accounts for most of the circulatory disturbances in infected plants; it is sometimes an important factor in causing their death. As a general rule, virus is unable to propagate across dead tissue, whether in the leaves or in the stem. This is shown experimentally by killing portions of the stem tissues through application of steam; the virus fails to go through the steamed regions.

The inability of viruses to propagate through dead cells is partly responsible for the virus-localizing effects of the necrotic reactions produced in the leaves of some plants by certain virus diseases. Apparently, some cells die before transmitting the virus to neighboring cells, and the result is a protection of the plant against virus spread. Localization of virus in areas of leaf tissue may also occur without visible necrosis (340). In some cases a necrotic reaction is produced in the stem of a plant following graft with a virus-infected scion, and the plant dies. Certain potato varieties, when infected by grafting with certain strains of potato virus X, respond with a "top necrosis," in which the virus spreads to the stem tip and kills it.

An interesting limitation to virus spread is evidenced by the rarity of virus transmission from one plant generation to the next through the reproductive cells. Seed transmission is rare, but has been substantiated for several viruses, among them bean mosaic and lettuce mosaic. Pollen transmission, if it occurs at all, is extremely rare. Prevention of seed transmission may be due either to failure of the virus to penetrate the seed embryo or to the presence of virus-inhibiting substances in the seed; the presence of such substances has actually been verified (368). Seed transmission is more frequent in legumes than in other plants. It is possible that in these plants the modalities of oogenesis favor virus infection of the egg cell. The rarity of gamete transmission of viruses is, of course, of great significance for the survival of the plant in nature, since it protects the progeny of infected plants from infection. Indeed, virus diseases are very important economically in plants that are propagated vegetatively, by means of tubers, rhizomes, bulbs, and cuttings (potatoes, fruit trees, etc.).

VIRUSES AND PLANT METABOLISM

Out of the great wealth of information concerning the symptomatology and the metabolic alterations of virus-infected plants (43; 690), surprisingly little can be utilized for an understanding of the processes involved in virus reproduction or of the direct effect of virus on the metabolism of the host cell. In some cases, such as those of color variegation (breaking) of flowers, effects on specific enzyme systems are probably present, but there is no evidence as to how directly the virus acts on the enzymes, or by what mechanism.

It has been claimed that two main metabolic groups of virus diseases can be distinguished: the mosaic type, in which the nitrogen content of the plant is increased and the carbohydrate content diminished; and the yellows type, in which the opposite changes are observed. But many exceptions are reported. In several cases there is an increase in the starch content of the leaves, but it is difficult to say whether this is due to increased production, reduced utilization, or reduced transfer of starch. Reduction of photosynthesis is accompanied, in potato leaf roll, by an accumulation of starch and a reduced transportation of sugar as compared with the normal plant (40). It is not known whether the initial lesion responsible for this is an alteration of photosynthesis, or a lesion of the phloem, or possibly an alteration of cell enzymes indirectly concerned with starch metabolism. The accumulation of starch often results in increased cell respiration. The changes in nitrogen metabolism in tissues infected with tobacco mosaic virus seem to be due to the actual process of virus synthesis, rather than to an alteration of the nitrogen metabolism of the host (150a).

The effects of the nitrogen and phosphorus content of soil on tobacco mosaic virus synthesis seem to be exerted mainly through effects on plant growth (45). Attempts to curb plant virus infections with anti-biotics effective against bacterial diseases of man and animals have yielded, as expected, negative results (55).

Increased photosynthesis immediately before mechanical inoculation of leaves with various viruses reduces the incidence of infection (51). It is not known whether this effect is exerted through the host metabolism or simply through changes in turgor and vulnerability of the cells, which have to be wounded for the virus to penetrate.

The Interaction of Animal Viruses with Their Hosts—Tissue Cultures— Intracellular Inclusions

VIRUS INFECTIONS IN ANIMAL HOSTS

The study of the interaction of animal viruses with their hosts is complicated by the high degree of host differentiation. Structurally, an animal consists of highly specialized organs and tissues. The external layers consist of modified cells impenetrable to most parasites. The spread of a virus in the tissues is dependent on complex systems of circulation and also, sometimes, on propagation along differentiated channels such as nerve fibers. Serological mechanisms of immunity add to the complexity of the virus-host interaction in animals.

As a rule, manifestations of virus infection at the cellular level can be traced more directly in systems such as tissue cultures, which contain cells of more or less similar genetic and developmental make-up, or in simple, accessible tissues such as the corneal epithelium. More complicated systems, such as the fertilized chicken egg, also provide highly reproducible systems for the study of virus reproduction in single layers of living cells.

It should be the goal of a sound biological approach to interpret the complex situations that arise in virus infections of man and animals in terms of the elementary virus-cell interactions analyzed in simpler situations. This goal can seldom be reached in a satisfactory manner. Yet, the careful analysis of the course of infection in the adult animal body and of the virus spread in animal populations may throw some light on basic virus properties (see *215*). For example, the rather precise incubation time or death time of certain virus infections, and the dependence of these times on the amount of virus inoculated in experimental infections, suggest that the response that is observed requires the presence of a fairly precise concentration of virus (*248*). From survival data, therefore, it may be possible to estimate the rate of virus multiplication in the animal independently of any information as to virus localization.

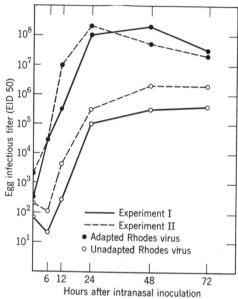

Figure 73. The amount of influenza virus A in ground lungs of mice after intranasal inoculation. The greater reproduction of a mouse-adapted strain is compared with the less extensive multiplication of a strain passaged in ferrets and eggs. The infectious titer is given in EID_{50}'s ($1 \ EID_{50}$ = dose infecting 50% of inoculated eggs). From: Davenport and Francis (*163*).

Growth of viruses in the animal host. Many authors have reported growth curves of viruses in the intact animal, for example, for influenza viruses in the mouse lung (*163*). Groups of animals are sacrificed at intervals, and the lungs are pooled, ground, and titrated. The growth curves are of the type shown in figure 73. The generation times can be calculated; figure 73 gives a generation time of the order of 1 hour. These results and others of the same type, however, are probably a rather distant picture of the process of virus reproduction at the cell level. Rather, they reflect complex cycles of virus infection, reproduction, liberation, reinfection, combination with inhibitors, and so on.

An example of a more direct approach is provided by experiments on pneumonia virus of mice in the mouse lung. These experiments were directly aimed at testing the existence of a growth cycle similar to that of phage in sensitive bacteria and the relation of this cycle to the development of pulmonary lesions (254; 255; 347). Recoverable virus infectivity decreased to almost zero a few minutes after inocu-

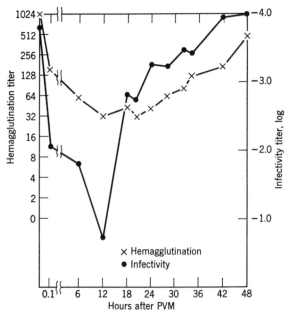

Figure 74. The amount of pneumonia virus of mice (PVM) in mice lungs ground at intervals after intranasal inoculation of virus. From: Ginsberg and Horsfall (255).

lation (*eclipse period*) and remained low for 12–18 hours. Then, a rise by a factor of 10–20 occurred in 10–15 hours, followed by a plateau and by further rises (figure 74). Thus, one cycle of latent period and liberation would take about 30 hours. Of course, the apparent yield in such a cycle is bound to be a minimum estimate, since readsorption of the new virus, with new eclipses, must occur immediately upon liberation. The development of pneumonic lesions closely parallels the rise in virus titer. The degree of suppression of the pneumonic symptoms by the capsular polysaccharide of *Klebsiella pneumoniae*, a specific inhibitor for pneumonia virus of mice, is also in direct proportion to the suppression of viral multiplication. When, in the second week of infection, the virus titer begins to decrease in the lung, no further development of lung lesions takes place.

At least one feature of the pattern of virus production just described, the eclipse period, seems to be of general occurrence in virus infections (550). Nonrecoverability of virus soon after inoculation has been reported for rabies virus, poliomyelitis, St. Louis encephalitis, yellow fever, influenza, and several others.

Factors influencing animal virus infections. A set of empirical observations of great potential significance concerns the influence of the diet of the host on the course of viral infections, particularly with neurotropic viruses (134). A variety of vitamin, amino acid, and mineral deficiencies have been found to result in milder infections, with delayed or reduced lethality or with changes in symptomatology. The mechanisms of these effects are unknown. One may speculate on specific requirements for the deficient substances by different synthetic systems, so that in deficient animals virus synthesis may be interfered with, in the absence of irreparable damage to the tissues. An interesting observation is that eggs from riboflavine-deficient hens support growth of a virus (blue tongue of sheep) which fails to grow in normal eggs (476).

Suppression of virus growth in animals by chemicals has been reported repeatedly. Many of the reports concern mainly the therapeutic or preventive effect of chemicals on virus diseases. Among the few examples of successful virus chemotherapy, we have the action of sulfonamides, penicillin, chloromycetin, and aureomycin on viruses of the psittacosis-lymphogranuloma group (162). A naphthoquinine derivative protects mice against the neurotropic virus Col SK (586). Certain pyrimidine analogues can suppress vaccinia virus in mice (648a). Helenine, a fungal product, protects mice against some viruses (602a). In all these cases, the mechanism of action is unknown, and we have no information as to what phase of virus production is affected.

Toxic manifestations, which are observed too early after virus inoculation to be attributed to virus proliferation, have been described for viruses of the lymphogranuloma (544) and of the influenza groups (162a; 298). The lymphogranuloma-type toxins may be of the nature of endotoxins, since they are not readily separable from the virus particles. For influenza, there is evidence that the toxic reaction is due to an abortive infection of cells in which virus fails to reproduce to maturity, for example, in the cells of adult mouse brain (582). Toxic symptoms are also produced by intravenous or intraperitoneal inoculation of influenza viruses and by inoculation of Newcastle virus in mouse lung, where this virus does not multiply, at least in infectious form (*162a*).

VIRUSES IN TISSUE CULTURE

Tissue-culture techniques. The principle of tissue cultures is based on the classic observations made in 1907 by Harrison. If fragments of tissues from a living host are isolated with sterile precautions and placed in a nutrient solution, the cells not only continue to metabolize but often divide, particularly if the cultivated tissue fragment came from an embryo (generally, 7–10-day-old chick embryos are used). The reduced geometrical and chemical interaction among tissues in cultures may actually produce an increase in the rate of cell growth, a return to reproducing habits in cells that had stopped multiplying, and a loss of some of the characteristics of the cells, which tend to manifest more embryonal characters than they did when still in the animal.

All the microscopical culture methods, introduced mainly by Harrison, Carrel, and Fisher (see *287; 577; 655*), involve the cultivation of small fragments of tissue in balanced salt solutions (Tyrode [1] or others) to which sugar, blood plasma and extracts of fresh chick embryos are added. Serum or serum ultrafiltrate from the same animal species that provides the tissue is generally added. The plasma coagulates and immobilizes the fragments on a cover slip. Proliferation of cells takes place in the thin layer of coagulated plasma and the growing cells migrate along the surface of the cover slip, so that direct microscopic observation is possible. The cover slip can be coated with a collodion layer. This can later be lifted off with a thin layer of cells and mounted for observation in the electron microscope.

Harrison's original method, using hanging-drop cultures in a depression slide (figure 75), requires the transfer of the fragments of tissue to a new culture every 2 or 3 days to insure continued development. The whole procedure must be carried out under rigorous sterile precautions, since bacterial contamination would quickly cause complete disintegration of the culture. Antibiotics may be added to the cultures to suppress bacterial contaminants. Carrel's method avoids some of the difficulties of the slide technique by the use of a special flask (figure 75), one wall of which can be made of cover slip thickness, in

[1] Tyrode's solution: NaCl, 8 grams; $CaCl_2$, 0.2 gram; $MgCl_2$, 0.2 gram; KCl, 0.2 gram; Na_2CO_3, 1 gram; NaH_2PO_4, 0.05 gram; water, 1000 ml. Adjust to pH 7.4 using H_3PO_4 and Na_2CO_3. Sterilize by filtration.

which relatively larger amounts of tissue can be cultivated for a long time with frequent changes of nutrient medium.

Virus infection in cultures of this type can be produced either by infecting the tissue prior to setting up the culture or by addition of virus to the culture fluid. A useful modification of the flask technique

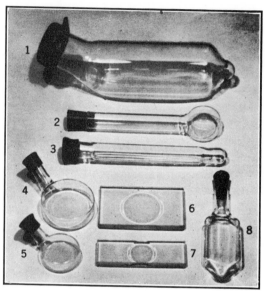

Figure 75. Containers used for tissue cultures. 1. Grand's flask. 2. Porter's roller flask. 3. Roller tube with flattened surfaces. 4, 5, Carrel's flasks. 6, 7. Depression slides, on which cultures on coverslips are inverted. 8. Earle's flask. From: Cameron, *Tissue Culture Technique*, 2nd Ed., Academic Press, New York. Courtesy, Dr. G. Cameron, Medical Research Foundation of Dade County, Miami, Fla.

is the "roller-tube" method (282), in which the tissue fragments are immobilized by plasma on the walls of test tubes. These receive a nutrient solution and are slowly rotated in a drum, so that oxygenation of the fluid can be kept at a high level. Thus, longer intervals of growth without transfer are made possible. An agar-slant technique for tissue culture has also been used for virus cultivation (508). Chemically defined media for the cultivation of tissues have been developed (508b).

For the specific purpose of virus culture, simplified techniques have been developed, which involve the cultivation of tissue fragments floating freely in a thin layer of nutrient fluid (423; 469). This type of culture can best be used for quantitative studies of virus growth, but does not allow for microscopical observation of the cells in the living state. It is really a tissue-survival rather than a tissue-cultivation method, since hardly any cell reproduction takes place, at least for most tissues, and the viruses reproduce in the metabolizing but nondividing cells.

The tissues employed in cultures to be used for virus cultivation vary according to the virus and to the purpose of the experiment; practically all kinds of tissues have been used. It should be recalled that certain tissues, such as differentiated nerve tissue, muscular tissue, and many glandular epithelia, fail to reproduce in tissue culture of any type, although their cells may remain alive and metabolize actively for long periods.

Pure cultures of certain cell types can be set up either by isolating layers of similar cells before placing them in the culture vessel (mainly feasible for surface epithelia) or by utilizing the differential proliferation rate of different types of cells in slide or roller-tube cultures (124). For example, if a slide culture of connective tissue is allowed to grow for a few days, the fibroblasts may move into the peripheral region faster than, for example, the macrophages. After several transfers, it often becomes possible to isolate a group of cells of one type and to transfer them to a new culture, which will then contain cells of one type only.

A recently developed method (196; see figure 4) allows the study of local lesions or plaques formed by some viruses on a layer that consists essentially of a homogeneous type of cell. Many fine fragments of strained embryonal tissue are grown on a layer of culture fluid. The fibroblasts, which are the fastest-growing cells, rapidly form a continuous layer. The fluid is removed, the cell layer is washed, and virus is applied. Then a layer of nutrient agar is added. This immobilizes the fibroblast layer and allows the virus to form localized lesions, easily recognizable by naked eye or with low magnification.

Growth of viruses in tissue culture. The possibility of obtaining virus reproduction in tissue cultures was quickly recognized. The technique became quite common for the preparation of relatively large amounts of viruses in a relatively simple medium. For example, a small inoculum of vaccinia virus in a flask culture will yield up to 10^5 times as much virus within 48 hours. This virus is free from bacterial contamination and is very convenient for the preparation of vaccines.

The need for actual contact of the virus with the tissue as a prerequisite for virus growth was shown clearly by experiments in which the virus was separated from the tissue by collodion membranes that prevented the passage of virus particles; no virus reproduction took place (495). Killed cells fail to support virus growth. In general, the virus grows in cultures in which conditions are favorable for the proliferation of host cells. This can be tested in slide cultures, by comparing the extent of virus production either with the number of mitotic figures present in the culture or with the extent of tissue growth, as judged by the size of the zone of cellular migration. Virus growth is not always tied up with cell proliferation, however. For example, fowl-plague virus grows well at a temperature of 30° C in chick embryo tissue, which at this temperature shows very few mitotic figures (523).

Host and tissue specificities can be studied in cultures of different tissues from different animals. The specificities are not always identical with those manifest in the animal body, but the causes of difference are often trivial. For example, virus III of rabbits grows only in cultures of rabbit testicle (24), although in the animal it grows in other tissues, whose cells, however, survive and proliferate less well in tissue cultures. Several viruses can grow in cultures of tissues from animals that do not generally support their growth. Thus, vaccinia, yellow fever, influenza, and many other viruses reproduce in tissues from the chick embryo, although they fail to grow in adult chickens. In some instances the difference is easily explained; influenza, for example, is unable to grow at the high temperature of the bird's body (207), but grows both in embryonated eggs at 37–38° C and in cultures of chick embryo tissues.

Tissue specificity, as well as host specificity, is often preserved in tissue cultures. Thus, foot-and-mouth virus reproduces only in epithelial cultures from horse and cattle. Rous sarcoma virus grows in cultures of macrophages better than in fibroblasts (124). In macrophage cultures it can induce a true cancerization. Poliomyelitis virus can be grown in cultures of extraneural tissues, especially fibroblasts, a fact that agrees with evidence for the multiplication of this virus in extraneural tissues in the infected animal host (577a; 672). Different strains of host cells cultivated in vitro may show a variety of different types of response to the same virus (37a).

The new host-range potentialities revealed by tissue cultures are probably due to the use of embryonal tissue. The changed specificity relations between host and virus in embryonal tissues is one of the most interesting problems of virology, but one that still needs clarification. It would seem likely that one of two factors is involved: (*a*) the lack in the embryo of inhibitory substances that appear late in the course of development; (*b*) the presence in embryonal tissues of certain enzyme systems or substrates needed for virus growth and lacking or inoperative in adult tissues.

Next to the problem of specificity, we must consider what tissue cultures tell us concerning the mode of virus reproduction. Information of two kinds is available, the first derived from virus titration, the other from direct microscopic observation of abnormal manifestations in infected cells. Unfortunately, little quantitative evidence on virus multiplication can be obtained by either of these methods, particularly because the relation between the amount of tissue present in a culture and the extent of virus multiplication is complicated by innumerable factors. From separate titrations of virus in the fluid and in the tissue fragments in flask cultures infected with psittacosis (455), foot-and-mouth, and other viruses, we have learned that the virus introduced in the culture disappears from the liquid phase and is taken up by the tissue. After 1 or 2 days, during which the amount of recoverable virus activity increases in the tissue without being liberated, virus reappears in the fluid phase and is later taken up again by the tissue. The obvious similarity of these stages with the cycles of growth of bacteriophage in a bacterial culture suggests similar cycles of intracellular growth and liberation. After virus production is completed, virus may remain active in a culture for various lengths of time, up to several months (214).

Tissue-culture experiments have provided evidence for the actual penetration of a virus inside host cells. Rous and his coworkers (567) prepared suspensions of macrophages taken from slide tissue cultures by tryptic digestion of the coagulated plasma. Vaccinia or fibroma virus, mixed with the cell suspensions, was quickly taken up by the cells and apparently penetrated inside them. If the infected cells were mixed with antivirus serum and the mixture was injected into a susceptible animal, virus infection followed, which proved that the virus had been protected against the action of the antiserum. These experiments, using suspensions of animal cells prepared from tissue cultures, illustrate the potential applications of such a technique, which, unfortunately, has long been neglected in the analysis of host-virus interaction. A new application of this method to the cultivation and diagnosis of poliomyelitis virus, using cells from cultures of a human cancer, promises very interesting results (577*b*).

Viruses have been found to grow in cultures of tissues from animals immunized against them (24). This shows that acquired immunity is essentially due to antibodies and not to any intrinsic changes in the cells of the host. Protection of tissue cultures by antivirus serum given before the virus or together with it seems to be of rather general occurrence (288), although it is not always as complete or as permanent as in the inoculation of virus-antiserum mixtures into an animal, where the virus is probably destroyed rapidly if prevented from growing (226). Viruses that are susceptible to drugs—for example, lymphogranuloma to sulfonamides—may be suppressed by drug treatment in tissue cultures as well as in the animal body (283).

Tissue cultures have been used for some studies on the relation of virus growth to the level of host metabolism. Zinsser and Schoenbach (697) found that in cultures of chick-embryo brain the increase in equine encephalomyelitis virus occurred mainly in the first days of culture, when the oxygen uptake was highest. Later, oxygen consumption and virus reproduction diminished in parallel. In contrast, typhus rickettsiae multiplied most actively after the oxygen uptake had ceased and when presumably the cells were no longer viable. This and other observations (468) indicate that animal viruses, just as bacteriophage, utilize for their reproduction the enzymatic machinery of the host cell, rather than simply using preformed substrates.

Observations on the effect of various chemicals on virus growth in tissue cultures are in agreement with this general viewpoint. Metabolic poisons (such as cyanide, dinitrophenol, malonate) interfere with the formation of new virus, probably by preventing the flow of energy through the proper cellular channels (1). A variety of other chemicals also suppress or reduce virus growth. In screening for compounds of potential chemotherapeutic value in virus infections, tissue cultures are widely employed. Even compounds that only reduce or retard virus growth in tissue cultures are worth considering as possible chemotherapeutic agents, since in the intact animal body a reduction of virus growth will increase the chances for successful body defense by means of antibodies and other defense mechanisms. Substances that reduce virus production when administered *after* the virus are considered especially worthy of study.

From the standpoint of interpreting the effect of chemicals in terms of the mechanism of virus growth, few studies on tissue culture have yielded information of interest. Virus production has generally been determined only by the final virus titer, rather than by series of measurements of virus in the tissue and in the surrounding fluid. The most interesting results concern the effect of analogues of amino acids and of nucleic acid constituents. For example, DL-ethionine, an analogue of methionine, inhibits the growth of influenza virus in cultures of chorioallantoic membrane of chick embryo (2). Purine analogues, such as 2,6-diaminopurine, suppress production of vaccinia virus in minced-tissue cultures (648). The effect of these chemicals can be counteracted by the corresponding metabolites (for example, methionine for ethionine; adenine for 2,6-diaminopurine). How direct the action of these inhibitors on virus production is, we cannot say. It is, however, a reasonable hypothesis that they interfere with virus production by blocking the utilization of the corresponding normal metabolites for the synthesis of virus protein or virus nucleic acid. This would then indicate that production of animal viruses involves the synthesis of new protein and nucleic acid from simple building blocks rather than the transformation of large molecules of cell protoplasm into virus material. The reasons for the suppressive effect of certain basic amino acids on some viruses (200) remain obscure.

INTRACELLULAR VIRUS INCLUSIONS

Microscopic study of viruses in tissue cultures cannot always provide evidence as to the extent of infection. Some viruses, like equine encephalomyelitis, cause extensive death of cells; others may multiply abundantly without visible cell destruction, probably because of the ability of infected cells to divide repeatedly, transmitting virus to their daughter cells.

Microscopic examination often allows us to recognize, inside the infected cells, the elementary bodies of those viruses whose particles can be visualized either by staining methods or in the dark field (see chapter 4). The major worth of microscopic observation of virus-infected animal tissues resides in the study of the so-called *virus inclusions* (217; 220).

It was noticed early by pathologists that the cells of tissues infected with several diseases, now known to be caused by viruses, showed rather characteristic bodies (inclusion bodies) not visible in uninfected cells. As early as 1869 such bodies were observed by Rivolta in tissues of chickens suffering from fowl pox. In 1892 Guarnieri discovered typical inclusions in cells infected with vaccinia or smallpox virus, and in 1903 the Negri bodies were discovered in the brains of rabid dogs.

These inclusions are much larger than the elementary bodies of the corresponding viruses. They are easily recognizable microscopically (figures 76–78) and can grow to the extent of occupying most of the host cells and of pushing cell structures aside (see figure 76). Such inclusions can be found almost without exception in tissues infected with a given virus, no matter in what tissue the virus is growing. They are formed either in the cytoplasm or in the nucleus of infected cells, and their location is generally specific for a given virus.

At first, the inclusions were mistaken for protozoa. This mistake gave rise to the term *Chlamydozoa* (mantle animals) to designate these agents of disease (Von Prowazek). As the viral nature of the agents of the diseases became firmly established, the relation of the intracellular inclusions to the virus elements that carry the infectivity in the extracellular state became a matter of debate. Some authors considered the inclusions as products of the reaction of the infected cell to the virus; others considered them as actual virus colonies. In spite of the support apparently given to the first hypothesis by the occasional presence in uninfected tissues of inclusions similar to those associated with virus diseases, most workers today agree that most or all inclusions result directly from the reproduction of virus and contain elements which after isolation can be shown to carry virus activity. It has not yet been possible, however, to decide how the inclusions are formed in each individual case.

Some inclusions are compact enough to permit extraction from the cells by micromanipulation, followed by washing, crushing, and testing for virus activity. In this manner, the inclusions of molluscum contagiosum (which are surrounded by a tough membrane, probably a reaction product of the infected cells) and those of fowl pox (Bollinger bodies) were shown to contain several thousand infectious elementary bodies (262). The bodies appear to be embedded in a matrix, probably containing ribonucleic acid.

Some cytoplasmic inclusions are of great diagnostic importance. For example, the diagnosis of rabies in dogs is made by the finding of intracellular inclusions (Negri bodies) in the cells of Ammon's horn of the brain. The Negri bodies are also found in epithelial cells of the infected rabbit cornea. Cells containing Negri bodies can go through the mitotic process.

Development of virus inclusions. If the inclusions contain the virus and result from its growth, it becomes particularly interesting to follow the process of their formation. Interesting observations have been made by tissue-culture methods, supplemented by observations on tissues of infected animals.

The virus of psittacosis has been thoroughly investigated in tissue cultures of fibroblasts and of lung epithelium (*89; 418*). A first phase without identifiable virus is followed after 12 to 24 hours by the appearance of "homogeneous plaques," larger than elementary bodies. These plaques increase in size and assume a more granular appearance, leading to the formation of large colonies of elementary bodies; the cells are then ruptured and the elementary bodies are dispersed out-

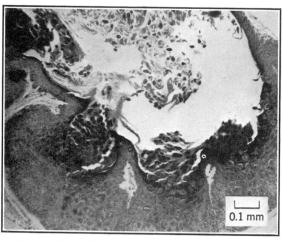

Figure 76. Section of a molluscum contagiosum lesion from human skin. Note the almost complete transformation of the cells into inclusion bodies and amorphous debris. Courtesy Dr. H. Blank, University of Pennsylvania, Philadelphia.

side. As a counterpart to these appearances, we may notice that the agents of mouse pneumonitis and feline pneumonitis, two viruses belonging to the psittacosis group, have been reported to possess a stage of extracellular reproduction (*671*). This claim is open to serious question.

Elementary bodies of vaccinia were already seen by Buist, Paschen, and other workers inside infected cells before their identity with the virus agent was proved by studies on isolated and purified bodies. Borrel (*96*) made his classic studies of the elementary bodies of mammalian and fowl-pox viruses in the fluid from pox blisters, which contain many cells loaded with elementary bodies. Several workers analyzed the appearance and numbers of these bodies from infected tissues, using all sorts of staining methods. More fruitful were studies in which the fate of elementary bodies and the development of inclusions were studied by direct observations in tissue cultures. Bland and Robinow (90) described in detail the development of inclusions at various intervals after accurately timed infection with washed vaccinia particles. At first, the particles were seen unchanged in the cells; a few hours later, the elementary bodies were no longer visible, and in their place larger bodies appeared. Still later, these gave place to less compact and less stainable bodies, the "networks," which, like the elementary bodies, gave a positive Feulgen reaction. The networks

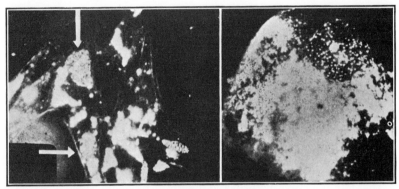

Figure 77 (left). Intracellular inclusions of psittacosis virus in tissue cultures of chick-embryo fibroblasts. Dark-field microscope. The arrows indicate two virus inclusions containing elementary bodies. From: Bland and Canti (89).

Figure 78 (right). Vaccinia virus inclusion in a corneal cell of rabbit. Dark-field microscope. Note the elementary bodies. From: Eisenberg-Merling, *J. Path. Bact.*, **50**:279, 1940.

increased in size and after 1 or 2 days often split up into a number of small granules, which were scattered around in the cytoplasm, thus apparently returning to the stage of elementary bodies. A direct morphological continuity between the infecting elementary bodies and the networks is not proved, and it is possible that a phase without microscopically recognizable virus elements intervenes.

A number of other descriptions of the microscopic events in cells infected with vaccinia virus concur in showing that the inclusions are related to the infecting elementary bodies by a series of complex morphological transformations, which suggest a life cycle. Ultimately, this gives rise to a great many elementary bodies. In some cases, however, the elementary bodies were reported to be present as such throughout the process (321; 322; 643). They simply increased in number and underwent slight morphological changes, ultimately filling the cell completely and causing it to burst and to release the virus particles. The different results may in part have been due to differences in tissue, since different observations were made on the corneal and the chorioallantoic epithelia. The differences might depend on the mode of infection, on the amount of virus inoculated, or on some other unknown factor. The healthy or damaged conditions of individual cells may also play a role.

The electron microscope provides some evidence on the formation of virus inclusions. Virus-infected cells from tissue cultures were used first for electron microscopy; the thin layers of cytoplasm of the periphery of cells that spread over the cover slip in slide cultures (528) were used. These thinly spread cells can be fixed, lifted on a collodion membrane, and observed in the electron microscope. Particles of some viruses could easily be observed because of their high electron scattering power, as shown in figure 79. Virus particles in these thin layers of cytoplasm were often found in pairs. This may simply reflect the tendency of spherical particles to run together when drying in a thin layer of semifluid medium. Destructive viruses such as equine encephalomyelitis may transform cells into practically pure masses of virus particles (figure 80).

The introduction of perfected sectioning techniques has made it possible to cut tissues into slices thin enough for direct electron microscopy. Several virus inclusions have been studied by this method, but the observations are not yet fully interpreted. Chorioallantoic membranes of chick embryo infected with fowl pox show all stages between clusters of elementary bodies and large inclusions in which elementary bodies are not recognizable as such (490). In tissue cultures infected with fowl plague virus (225) the electron microscope shows nuclear damage, especially in the nucleoli, accompanied by formation of extranuclear filaments, which seem to split into elementary bodies.

Examination of vaccinia virus in the chick-embryo membrane shows the formation of elementary bodies, in a more or less homogeneous matrix, with transition forms between the homogeneous stage and the differentiated, fully formed elementary bodies. The latter are observed in practically pure form in the most advanced stages of cell infection (689).

Rather similar observations have been reported on molluscum contagiosum (36). Here, the typical inclusions seem to evolve by the formation of a nucleic acid-containing matrix, within which new virus particles are formed by a stagewise process from large, barely recognizable condensations of material in the homogeneous matrix to the fully developed virus particles (figure 81). Some of the particles, when sectioned by the microtome knife, appear to be hollow.

These observations on the formation of intracellular inclusions, taken

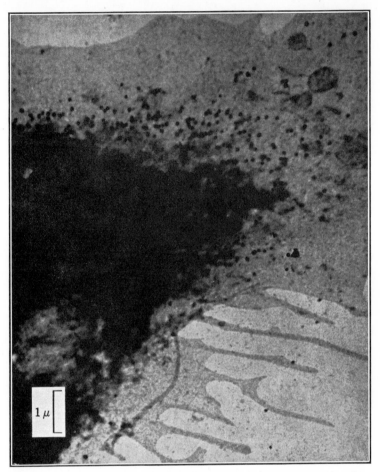

Figure 79. A portion of a cell of chicken tumor I (Rous sarcoma) cultivated in vitro. Note the virus particles about 70–85 mμ in diameter in the thin layer of protoplasm. From: Claude, Porter, and Pickels, *Cancer Res.* 7:421, 1947. Courtesy Dr. K. R. Porter, Rockefeller Institute, New York.

as a whole, support the idea that reproduction of virus material takes place by a process in which mature virus particles are not recognizable. The mature particles appear to be formed as a terminal stage in virus production. Thus there seems to be a further analogy with bacteriophage reproduction, besides the occurrence of the eclipse of infectious

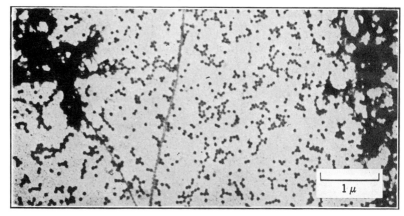

Figure 80. Eastern equine encephalomyelitis virus in a disintegrating cell of chick-embryo tissue culture. From: Bang, *Ann. N. Y. Acad. Sci.,* **54**:892, 1952. Courtesy Dr. F. B. Bang, Johns Hopkins University, Baltimore.

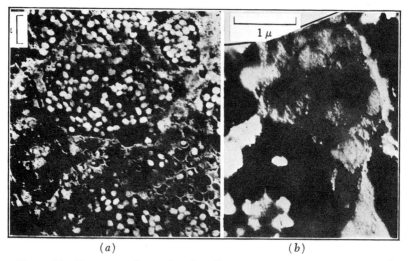

(a)　　　　　　　　　　　　　　　　(b)

Figure 81. Formation of particles of molluscum contagiosum virus in an inclusion body. (a) Virus particles in locules surrounded by a cytoplasmic matrix, in which the particles appear to be formed. (b) A detail from a similar section, showing what may be immature virus particles in the matrix. From: Melnick et al., *Ann. N. Y. Acad. Sci.,* **54**:1214, 1952. Courtesy Dr. J. L. Melnick, Yale University, New Haven.

virus following infection. Eclipse of infectivity and late formation of mature virus particles would be two aspects of the series of transformations of the viruses in their intracellular life cycle.

Intranuclear inclusions. In a number of virus infections, such as yellow fever, herpes, chicken pox and infectious warts, inclusions are found inside the cell nucleus rather than in the cytoplasm. Intranuclear inclusions are present in tissue cultures as well as in the tissues of diseased animals. These inclusions, which are more acidophilic than the nuclear material, have been divided into type A and type B. Type A is accompanied by a greater disruption of nuclear chromatin, type B by less destruction. No observation of mitosis in cells with intranuclear inclusions seems to have been reported.

The relation between intranuclear inclusions and virus particles has not been investigated thoroughly. The inclusions in the nuclei of cells infected with herpes virus contain basophilic granules, which may represent the virus particles themselves. Virus has been demonstrated in herpes inclusions isolated by micromanipulation (42). Yet the nuclei do not seem to contain more virus than the rest of the cell (232). Relatively large amounts of herpes virus are found, instead, in the mitochondrial fractions of the cells (4). Virus might be produced first in the nucleus and then migrate into the cytoplasm. It has been reported (159) that the Feulgen-positive inclusions of herpes in the chorioallantoic cells of chick embryo become progressively less stainable as the infection proceeds, and the nuclei become poorer in nucleoprotein.

Some virus-induced papillomas of man contain characteristic intranuclear inclusions and yield virus particles with a tendency to form regular, crystallike patterns (633). The presence of these particles in the intranuclear inclusions has not yet been established.

A particular group of intranuclear inclusions are the "polyhedra" found in a number of infectious diseases of insect larvae. These crystallike inclusions contain both the virus, in the form of rod-shaped particles and their presumptive precursors (68a), and a noninfectious protein serologically related to the virus (see chapter 5). The nuclear chromatin is destroyed, and the nuclei become completely full of polyhedra.

In tissue cultures of ovarian tissue of silkworm infected with silkworm jaundice (649), polyhedra appear 3 hours after inoculation in the cells that line the ovarian tubules; these are the cells that proliferate best in the cultures. It is interesting that the adult moth, whose tissues are derived in part from just these cells, is quite resistant to the virus.

Multiple inclusions. Inclusions have been found to occur in the nucleus and in the cytoplasm of the same cell in mixed infection with two unrelated viruses, one of which gives intranuclear, the other cytoplasmic, inclusions (*14; 637*). Evidently, a cell already infected with one virus may become infected with a second one. Either a nuclear dysfunction is not necessarily present in intranuclear infection, or, if present, it is not incompatible with the development of another virus in the cytoplasm of the same cell. This in turn may suggest that growth of a virus may not require the functions of the nuclear material of the host cell, but only the functions of the enzymatic machinery, in the same way as was suggested for phage growth (see chapter 8). We must remember, however, that most cells of animal or plant tissues are more complex in organization than bacterial cells, and that the machinery needed by a virus or disrupted by it may only be a small part of the available cell machinery. It would be quite important to clarify the conditions that make some viruses grow in the cytoplasm and others in the nucleus of the host cells; this might also throw light on specific biochemical functions of these cell constituents.

Swedish workers have analyzed by cytochemical procedures (see *127*) the amount and localization of protein and nucleic acids in virus-infected cells (*357*). Viruses that contain DNA cause an increase of protein synthesis and an accumulation of DNA, either in the cytoplasm (molluscum) or in the nucleus (infectious warts), wherever the virus produces inclusions. Neurotropic viruses which supposedly contain RNA (poliomyelitis, louping ill) cause the appearance of intranuclear granules containing protein and RNA (see also *540*). The hypothesis was put forward that viruses which contain RNA are genetically less complex and consist of a single type of nucleoprotein, resembling cytoplasmic nucleoproteins, whereas the DNA viruses are genetically more complex and more similar to chromosomal material.

This hypothesis seems to go beyond the evidence. In the first place, the localization of virus particles or inclusions in the same cells on which the cytochemical analyses were carried out was inadequate. In the second place, there are no grounds for the supposed difference in genetic complexity of DNA- and RNA-containing viruses. Finally, the presence of RNA in some of the viruses used in the experimental work is doubtful.

An increase in the amount of nucleic acid in tissues of chick embryo infected with herpes virus has been reported (*3*), together with specific changes in certain enzymatic activities. We do not know how directly these changes are brought about by the virus.

Growth of Viruses
in the Chick Embryo

A very convenient host for the experimental study of virus infection, introduced in 1931 by Woodruff and Goodpasture (*685*), is the fertilized chicken egg. It is no exaggeration to say that the use of chick embryos has opened a new era in the study of animal viruses for both theoretical and practical purposes (*77*). If anything, one may regret that the quick realization of the great potentialities of egg-culture methods has for many years caused a certain neglect of the more refined types of tissue cultures, which can contribute much to the analysis of virus growth in the host cell.

The chick embryo offers numerous advantages as an experimental host in virus work: ready availability and low cost; absence of latent viruses (see, however, *107*); absence of antibodies; presence of a variety of extraembryonal organs, well-known from embryological studies and suitable for the study of the behavior of many viruses in single layers of cells.

Embryological notes.[1]   When a fertilized hen egg is incubated at 38–39° C, the embryo develops and the chick hatches after 21 days. The embryo develops from the fertilized egg nucleus, which is situated between yolk and albumen under the vitelline membrane. By cleavage, the fertilized nucleus gives rise to a primitive disc of cells. This disc becomes differentiated into an inner cell layer, the *entoderm,* and an outer layer or *ectoderm.* Between these a thickening appears in the central area (primitive streak), due to a deep crowding of cells that give rise to the middle layer or *mesoderm* (figure 82). The three primitive layers—ectoderm, mesoderm, and entoderm—give rise to all tissues

---

[1] The student should familiarize himself more thoroughly with this subject by study of a standard textbook of embryology. Most such textbooks have a chapter devoted to the development of the chick embryo.

and organs of the body. The ectoderm gives rise mainly to the skin, the central nervous system, and some endocrine glands; the mesoderm gives rise to connective and muscular tissues and to the circulatory system; the entoderm, to the intestinal mucosa and its related secretory glands. In addition, the primitive layers develop beyond the area of the body of the embryo proper and form the embryonal membranes, which surround the embryo in the egg and which are of great interest to virus workers.

The mesoderm soon splits into two layers separated by the *coelomic cavity*. While the development of the embryo proceeds, the membrane constituted jointly by entoderm and mesoderm (*spanchnopleure*) extends around the yolk and, inside the embryo, lines the intestine. The membrane constituted jointly by the ectoderm and the outer mesoderm (*somatopleure*) rises in folds all around the embryo body proper. As the folds close over the embryo, they form a sac, the *amniotic cavity*, in which the embryo becomes suspended. The folds dig deeper and deeper around the body of the embryo, leaving only a narrow opening on the ventral side—the primitive umbilicus—through which the intestine of the embryo communicates with the yolk sac, its main source of food. The closure of the amniotic sac over the embryo separates the *amnion* from the outer part of the ectoderm, which lines most of the inner surface of the egg immediately under the shell membrane and forms the *serosa* or *chorion* (figure 82).

Late in the third day of incubation, the entoderm from the hind part of the primitive intestine gives rise to a new sac, the *allantois*, which pushes its way out of the body of the embryo, between the yolk sac (now surrounded by the spanchnopleure) and the amnion. The allantois ultimately fills the whole space under the chorion. Inside the allantoic cavity a clear fluid is secreted. As a result of the increasing size of the allantoic cavity, the embryo at the age of 8 to 12 days, when it is generally used for virus work, presents the following structure. Under the shell we find the shell membrane; at the wide end of the egg the shell membrane is divided into two layers, which delimit the "air space." Under the shell membrane there is a layer of epithelium, representing the ectodermal layer of the chorion. Beneath this we find a mesodermal layer derived from the fusion of the mesoderm of the chorion with the mesoderm surrounding the allantoic sac. Next, we find the entodermal epithelium lining the allantoic cavity. Together, the chorion and the external lining of the allantoic cavity form the *chorioallantoic membrane*.

Across the allantoic cavity, which is filled with allantoic fluid, the allantoic epithelium rests over a mesodermal layer, which lies in contact with the amnion and the yolk sac. The amnion itself is lined by an ectodermal epithelium, in direct continuity with the skin of the embryo around the umbilicus, and contains a limpid fluid. After the twelfth day of incubation, the amniotic fluid begins to receive some of the albumen through a newly established communication between the egg white and the amnion. The yolk sac is lined by an entodermal layer.

The mesoderm surrounding the allantoic cavity is rich in blood vessels, which receive blood from the embryo, circulate it into a rich network of capillaries, and return it to the body. The allantoic membrane constitutes the respiratory organ of the embryo; gaseous exchanges take place between the blood in the capillaries and the atmosphere, separated only by the thin chorionic epithelium, the shell membrane, and the porous egg shell. The presence of blood-filled allantoic vessels, easily seen by "candling" a fertilized egg, represents the best sign of viability of the embryo. The blood vessels become indistinct soon after circulation stops.

Techniques in virus work (77; 655). All parts of the chick embryo have been used for growing viruses: the allantoic cavity, the amniotic cavity, the yolk sac, and various organs of the embryo itself. Growth of the viruses takes place in the cells that line the various cavities. Inocula should, of course, be bacteria-free. If the material to be inoculated cannot be made bacteria-free (as, for example, in first isolations of some viruses from throat washings, whose filtration might remove the virus) bacterial infection may be prevented by the addition of antibiotics. Eggs are incubated at about 38–39° C until they reach the desired age. They are candled before use to check their viability and to mark on the shell certain structures, such as the limits of the air sac, as a guide in the following operations.

Inoculation into the *allantoic cavity* can be done in two ways. After drilling a small hole over a well-vascularized area in the shell, we can introduce the inoculum with a needle or a fine pipette through the shell membrane and the chorioallantoic membrane. Or we can drill a hole over the air sac near its edge and introduce a needle into the allantoic cavity through the hole. In drilling the egg shell over the allantois, it is important to avoid damaging the chorioallantoic membrane; hemorrhage in the membrane often results in death of the embryo.

Inoculation can be made onto the outer surface of the *chorioallantoic membrane*. First, a triangle or rectangle of shell is drilled and lifted

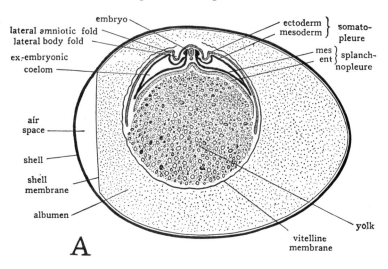

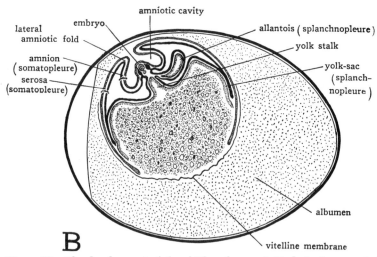

Figure 82. The development of the chick embryo. *A,* Early in the second day of incubation. *B,* Early in the third day of incubation. *C,* Fifth day. *D,* Ninth day. From: Patten: *Embryology of the Chick,* 4th Ed., Blakiston, New York.

out. A small drop of saline solution is deposited on the shell membrane, which is then gently slit with a blunt needle. Suction, applied through a small hole drilled over the air sac, causes the chorioallantoic membrane to drop, that is, to pull away from the shell membrane. This creates a *false air space,* into which the inoculum can be deposited.

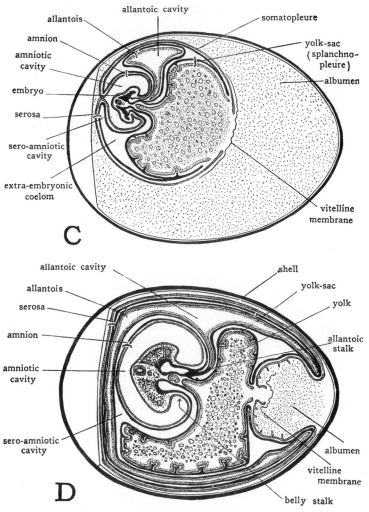

Figure 82 (continued).

For better visualization, the exposed shell membrane can be removed and replaced by a sterile cover slip, which is sealed to the shell with paraffin (figure 83).

Amniotic inoculation can be done either by reaching the amnion through a false air space, or, more speedily but with lower chance of success, by sending a needle through the natural air sac toward the embryo's body while candling the egg. When the tip of the needle touches the embryo, the needle's opening is in the amniotic cavity.

Yolk-sac inoculation, for most routine purposes, is done by introducing the needle to a depth of about 1 to 1½ inches vertically into

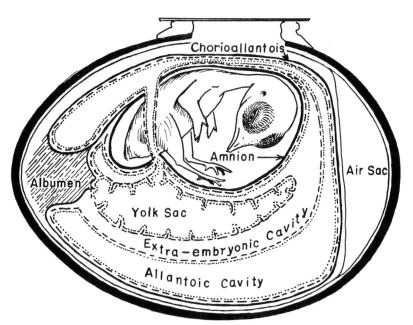

Figure 83. False air space for inoculation of the chorioallantoic membrane of a chick embryo. From: Buddingh. In: Rivers, *Viral and Rickettsial Infections of Man,* Lippincott, Philadelphia. Courtesy Dr. G. J. Buddingh, Louisiana State University, New Orleans.

the blunt end of the egg. Intravenous inoculation and direct introduction into various organs of the embryo have also been described.

After inoculation, the eggs are returned to an incubator (generally at a temperature of around 35° C, more favorable for several viruses than 39° C) and examined after a period of time determined by experience, generally 2 to 4 days. The presence, growth, and effects of viruses are detected by a variety of criteria, depending on the virus and on the route of inoculation. Death of the embryo occurs regularly with such viruses as equine encephalomyelitis or Newcastle disease. In some diseases, specific pathological lesions appear in the body of the embryo or in the extraembryonal membranes. An increase in virus titer either in the extraembryonal fluids or in ground embryonal or extraembryonal tissues is a valid sign of infection. Serological tests on the allantoic or amniotic fluids or on emulsions of the yolk sac or of the whole embryo may be used to demonstrate virus antigens. In some cases, elementary bodies may be stained and counted in the infected fluids.

FACTORS INFLUENCING VIRUS CULTURE IN EGGS

A majority of the animal viruses can reproduce in the chick embryo. Reports on cultivation of trachoma and dengue viruses are doubtful. Some viruses will grow only if inoculated by a given route, for example, the rabies virus only if injected into the brain or on the chorioallantoic membrane, from which it spreads to the central nervous system (72). Successful inoculation may depend on the age of the egg. Influenza virus inoculated in the amniotic cavity gives a higher proportion of positive inoculations in 13-day-old eggs than in younger ones (329); this has been attributed to the active swallowing of amniotic fluid by the older embryo, which brings the virus in contact with the lungs. Thus, the older eggs are used for diagnostic inoculation of throat washings, where the goal is to obtain the highest possible proportion of positive results. Other viruses, for example, mumps (670), grow better or at least reach higher titers in younger eggs.

Living cells are necessary for virus growth, although the embryo itself need not be viable. Influenza virus has been grown in the allantoic cavity of eggs previously kept for several days in the refrigerator and returned to 35° C; the lining cells are still viable, as shown by their continuing metabolism and by their ability to reproduce if transferred to tissue cultures. Chilling the eggs at $-30°$ C, a treatment that kills all cells, also suppresses their ability to support virus reproduction (394).

Little is known of the mechanisms that underlie the specific ability of the cells that line different cavities in the chicken egg to act as hosts for given viruses. Certain regularities are apparent; for example, the viruses of the psittacosis-lymphogranuloma group grow well in the yolk sac, and so do rickettsiae. The fact that the ability of a virus to grow in various locations varies with the age of the embryo suggests that developmental changes in physiological conditions are of importance. It should be remembered that the conclusion as to whether a virus grows or not has generally been reached from tests of recovery of virus in the various fluids. This must depend in part on the release of virus from the cells and not only on its ability to grow.

A number of viruses retain their tissue specificity in the chick embryo, even though they are able to grow in the undifferentiated cells of the extraembryonal membranes. Thus, the Rous sarcoma virus infects both ectodermal and mesodermal cells of the chorioallantoic membrane, but tumors only arise through proliferation of mesodermal cells (369). The rabies virus maintains its affinity for the central nervous system (72), whereas influenza viruses spread from the chorioallantoic membrane to give typical lung diseases.

New affinities, of great practical and theoretical interest, are revealed in the chick embryo. Thus, influenza virus A, inoculated into 2-day-old eggs under the vitelline membrane directly over the embryos, kills them with typical developmental abnormalities which affect mainly the central nervous system; 4-day embryos are also killed, but no evident brain malformations appear (289). These observations, on the one hand, point to a potential neurotropism of the influenza virus, which has recently been confirmed by other observations (582). On the other hand, they illustrate the role of developmental changes in determining the pattern of infection. A striking case in man is that of the virus of German measles, which causes a mild disease in children or adults, but produces severe birth defects in children of mothers who have contracted German measles in early pregnancy (277).

Goodpasture and his collaborators have introduced an elegant refinement for the study of virus specificity in the chick embryo. This consists in grafting pieces of foreign tissues on the chorioallantoic membrane, which is then inoculated with the viruses. In a series of experiments (261), the epithelium from human skin or human placenta was grafted and inoculated either with fowl pox virus or with a typical mammalian virus, the causative agent of mare abortion. The first virus failed to grow on the human graft, but gave typical lesions on the surrounding membrane, whereas the mammalian virus only grew on the graft. Another experiment (260) was made to test whether immunity to fowl pox, acquired as a result of a previous infection, was due to immunity of the individual cells or to humoral mechanisms. The skin from either susceptible or immunized chickens was grafted onto the chorioallantoic membrane, and fowl pox virus was added; both grafts became infected with equal ease. A technique has been described that permits the transplantation of whole corneas from man or rabbit onto the chorioallantoic membrane for study of viruses with strictly mammalian host range (374).

GROWTH OF VIRUSES IN THE CHICK EMBRYO

The embryonated egg has provided a convenient host system for the study of the process of reproduction of animal viruses. Although these studies have not yet reached the stage of detailed analysis of virus growth obtained with bacteriophage, they have provided much information of value.

Cytologically, the growth process has been followed by observations of embryonal membranes at intervals after infection. The chorio-allantoic membrane, inoculated through a false air space, has been used mainly for vaccinia and other mammalian pox viruses (321; 322); and the yolk sac has been used for the psittacosis-lymphogranuloma group (544). Moreover, extensive studies on the histology of early infection have been made on the chorioallantoic membrane with a number of viruses (see 77).

This membrane, after infection with vaccinia or mouse-pox (ectromelia), was observed directly in vivo by the ingenious device of lifting the membrane against a sterile cover slip sealed onto a window in the shell over the false air space. When pressure is applied through a hole in the air-sac shell, the membrane rises against the cover slip and can be observed microscopically under oblique illumination from above ("ultropak" system; 322). The infected cells show elementary bodies undergoing a series of modifications, similar to those observed, for example, in infected cells of the rabbit cornea. The resulting inclusions resemble typical Guarnieri bodies. Results of the same type have been described from histological observations on fixed chorioallantoic membranes (321).

A detailed study of the histology of yolk sac infected with lymphogranuloma venereum (544) showed a more complex cycle, with enlarged elementary bodies giving rise to large homogeneous bodies or "plaques." The plaques are later transformed again into several elementary bodies, which escape and infect other cells. This process is very similar to observations on the related viruses of the psittacosis group in tissue cultures or in the corneal epithelium (89; 418; see page 232).

Quantitative analyses of growth in egg cultures have been published by various authors, and the influence of a number of factors on rate and total amount of virus increase have been studied. For example, growth curves have been published for influenza and for mumps viruses in the allantoic cavity, showing the faster rate of growth of the influenza virus (10^6-fold increase in 18 hours instead of several days; *461; 670*). The effect of a variety of chemicals on virus growth in the allantois has been described, and screening of antibiotics against viruses by such technique has become a routine procedure. The practical results, however, have been limited, and the main successes have been scored in the study of the growth cycle of influenza viruses in the allantoic cavity and of the effect of various agents on this cycle.

Since these studies have derived their main impetus and in part also their interpretation from the discovery and analysis of the peculiar phenomenon of the agglutination of red blood cells by certain viruses (hemagglutination), we shall defer their discussion to chapter 13, in which we describe the hemagglutination phenomenon.

PRACTICAL APPLICATIONS OF EGG CULTURES

Allantoic inoculation, and in some cases yolk-sac inoculation, are commonly used to obtain certain viruses in large amounts for vaccine production. Virus produced in this way is free of bacterial contaminations. Before it can be used as a vaccine, it must be separated from components of the allantoic fluid that may cause allergic reactions in the vaccinated subjects. Partial purification of the virus can be done by differential centrifugation, since the normal allantoic fluid has been found not to contain any component that sediments as fast as most viruses; the largest normal components of allantoic fluid have sizes of the order of 30 to 40 mμ. In viruses of the influenza group, purification is easily performed by letting the virus be adsorbed in the cold by red cells from the allantoic blood vessels, then causing the virus to be eluted from the cells by incubation at 37° C (see chapter 13). Yellow fever vaccine is a desiccated homogenate of whole embryos inoculated at 7 days of age with strain 17D and incubated for 4 days (*292*).

Embryonated eggs are frequently used for the direct isolation of viruses from patients, as a diagnostic procedure. Some viruses will grow best in the allantoic cavity, others in the amniotic cavity or on the chorioallantoic membrane. It is important to remember, however, that the affinities of a virus for different organs of the embryo often vary upon subculture, so that the route of inoculation to be used for primary isolation from a patient is often different from the one that gives the best growth response with egg-adapted viruses. For example, influenza virus, according to several authors, can best be detected by direct inoculation of washings from the human throat into the amniotic cavity, although it will later grow as well or better by allantoic inoculation (329). This is probably due to modifications in the growth habits of the virus in the course of egg passage; variants become established, which grow better than the original type in the new environment.

Radioactive influenza virus, containing P^{32}, was obtained by introducing labeled phosphate in the allantoic cavity either before or shortly after inoculation with the virus (266).

The chorioallantoic membrane has been used for the titration of several viruses (77). Small aliquots of suspensions of viruses such as vaccinia, herpes, ectromelia, fowl pox, myxoma, laryngotracheitis, and many others cause the formation of discrete, localized lesions or *pocks*, whose appearance, both macroscopic and microscopic, is more or less characteristic for each virus infection (figure 3). Under controlled conditions of inoculation, the number of these lesions is a linear function of the amount of virus inoculated, provided the amount of virus is not so great that the lesions become confluent. For different viruses the maximum countable number of lesions varies between 20 and 100. Titers obtained by this method are in good agreement with titers obtained by end-point methods. The chorioallantoic titration has been used in determining virus survival in the titration of virus-neutralizing antibodies. Mixtures of virus and antibody are compared with virus alone for the number of pocks produced, and the neutralizing potency of the antibody is estimated.

The allantoic sac inoculation provides a convenient method for titration of certain viruses by the end-point method, for example, in the measurement of the neutralizing power of antibodies and of the effect of drugs on virus reproduction. The presence of infectious virus can be detected as an all-or-none response from the presence or absence of large amounts of virus after 2 or 3 days of incubation, provided the new virus can be detected directly by some in vitro test. This is true, for example, of viruses that agglutinate red blood cells or that fix complement readily. This procedure eliminates the need for animal inoculation in detecting the virus. Thus, by replacing the use of animals with that of eggs, such procedures have greatly reduced the cost of virus work.

Hemagglutination Phenomena
and Virus Growth
Summary on Virus Reproduction

HEMAGGLUTINATION BY VIRUSES

A fortunate discovery by Hirst in 1941 (*323; 324*) has made possible a remarkable progress in the study of the relation of certain animal viruses to animal cells. In harvesting the allantoic fluid of eggs infected with influenza virus, Hirst observed that if blood was shed into virus-containing fluid the erythrocytes quickly became agglutinated. No such agglutination occurred in uninfected fluids. The agent responsible for this "hemagglutination" is the virus particle itself. The particles are taken up by the red blood cells; this can be shown either by titration of free virus or by observation in the electron microscope of virus adsorbed on the red blood cells (*296*). Antivirus serum inhibits hemagglutination. The inhibitory titer of a serum is related, although not strictly proportional, to its virus-neutralizing titer.

Hemagglutination is detected either by an increase in the rate of sedimentation of a suspension of red blood cells measured by the residual turbidity of the supernatant (figure 84), or by the so-called "pattern test" (*575*). Nonagglutinated cells sediment into a round, solid pellet at the bottom of a test tube, whereas agglutinated cells give rise to a characteristic, scattered pattern of sedimentation (figure 85). A hemagglutination test can be read within an hour or less and represents a convenient method for the detection of viruses with the hemagglutinating property.

Hemagglutination has been observed with three groups of viruses. One group includes the influenza, mumps, and Newcastle disease viruses. A second group consists of vaccinia, smallpox, and ectromelia viruses. A third group includes a variety of other viruses: Japanese,

St. Louis, and Russian encephalitis; mouse encephalomyelitis (Theiler's GD-VII); West Nile fever; encephalomyocarditis group; pneumonia virus of mice and fowl plague.

Different groups of viruses cause different types of agglutination. Those of the vaccinia group (vaccinia-variola-ectromelia) cause an agglutination that is readily reversible by heating, by treatment with antivirus serum, and by changes in pH and in salt concentration. The properties of the resuspended red blood cells are unchanged and the

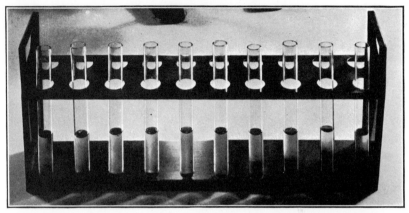

Figure 84. Hemagglutination by influenza virus. Successive 1:2 dilutions of virus. Complete agglutination in tubes 1–5. From: *Research Today,* 8:26, 1952. Courtesy Dr. O. K. Behrens, Lilly Research Laboratories, Indianapolis.

cells are reagglutinable (*133*). The vaccinia hemagglutinin can be separated from the virus particles themselves, and appears to combine in a rather unspecific way with the red cell surface. Red cells from only about 50% of chickens are agglutinated. Red cells from most other animals are not.

The agglutination produced by viruses belonging to the so-called MNI group (mumps, Newcastle, and influenza) is more interesting from a biological standpoint. In the following section we shall mainly be concerned with the viruses of this group. Hemagglutination by most viruses of the third group has several similarities with that produced by the MNI group, but without elution phenomena or any other signs of enzymatic activity by the viruses.

The MNI viruses agglutinate red blood cells of a variety of different animals, for example, chicken, guinea pig, and man. The correlation between the ability of an animal to act as host for a virus and the

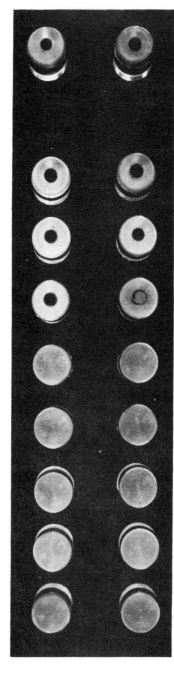

Figure 85. Hemagglutination test by the "Salk pattern" method. Bottom view of tubes, with increasing dilutions of virus suspension from left to right. Top row, dilutions 1:160, 1:32), 1:640···; bottom row, 1:120, 1:240, 1:480···. Dilutions 1:120 to 1:2560 give positive reactions (scattered sedimentation patterns). Dilution 1:3840 gives a partially positive reaction. Higher dilutions are negative (solid pellets of red blood cells). From: Salk (575). Courtesy Dr. J. E. Salk, University of Pittsburgh, and Dr. T. Francis, Jr., University of Michigan, Ann Arbor.

agglutinability of its red blood cells by that virus is good for some viruses, for example, pneumonia virus of mice, but poor for most others. Moreover, there are variations among red blood cells of individual animals and among strains of the same virus. For example, strains of influenza A, when first isolated from man, are in the O (original) form; upon transfers in the chick embryo a variant form, D, appears. This differs from the O form in giving a higher ratio between the agglutinating titer for chicken red cells and that for guinea pig red cells (*116; 118*).

The optimum virus concentration for agglutination of red blood cells (at a concentration of approximately 100,000 cells per ml) is about 10^4–10^5 virus particles per cell. With purified influenza virus, it has been calculated that hemagglutination can occur with equal numbers of cells and virus particles (*242*). Electron micrographs suggest that the agglutination is due to the formation of a lattice, in which red blood cells are held together by multivalent virus particles (*296*). Hemagglutination provides a rapid titration method, which is 100,000 to 1,000,000 times less sensitive than titration of infectivity, but which is advantageous in a variety of tests.

Elution of viruses. The adsorption of virus particles to red cells is not necessarily permanent. If a virus-cell mixture, in which agglutination has occurred, is incubated at 37° C, the virus is soon released more or less completely. The elution of virus is slow or absent at 0° C. The red cells that have released an excess of virus become inagglutinable either by the same virus or by newly added virus of the same strain. The eluted virus, however, is unchanged and capable of agglutinating other cells; the agglutination and release cycle can be repeated indefinitely with successive batches of cells (*324*).

These observations were interpreted by Hirst as indicating that the release phenomenon resulted from an enzymatic activity of the virus particles on a substrate located on the surface of the red cells and needed for stable combination. Thus, the virus particles combine with specific receptors on the cell surface, destroy enzymatically the receptors or some essential portion of them, and render the cells nonagglutinable. All evidence accumulated since Hirst's discovery has confirmed this viewpoint.

The changes produced by the virus are evidenced by a variety of alterations in the red blood cells. New antigenically reactive groups are revealed; these are the T-agglutinogens, responsible for the so-called "panagglutinability" of such cells by a variety of sera (*115*). The electrophoretic mobility of the red cells is altered in a way that is more or less specific for each virus (*631*). Electrophoretic tests with red blood cells, whose receptors have been destroyed by various viruses of the MNI group, suggest that the respective receptors partially overlap. Hemolysis has been observed with mumps and Newcastle disease virus (*119; 132*); cells from which receptors for hemagglutination have been removed are not lysed by the viruses.

Definite evidence for the relation among red blood cell receptors for various MNI viruses is found in studies of the agglutinability of cells from which a virus has been eluted. Elution of mumps virus leaves the cells still agglutinable by Newcastle and influenza; elution of Newcastle leaves the cells agglutinable by influenza only; influenza A leaves red cells still agglutinable by some B strains, and so on. On this basis a *receptor gradient* (see *115*) can be constructed (table 24). The viruses are supposed to destroy a certain fraction of a population of receptors possessing different, specific affinities for other viruses. Each virus would appear to destroy its own receptors, which include the receptors for the viruses that precede it in the receptor gradient scale.

This picture, however, is probably an oversimplification. In fact, every virus of the MNI group is capable of completely destroying the receptors for all other viruses, provided a sufficient amount of virus is allowed to act for a long enough time (*330*). The most likely explanation is that the different viruses are adsorbed, with different affinities, by common or overlapping receptor areas, which contain substrates for the virus enzymes (*332*). Some viruses, once attached, may not elute until they have digested all or most of the substrate (and the receptor ability with it), whereas others may leave behind enough undigested substrate to permit virus strains possessing greater affinity to combine with the receptor. Virus 1233 (influenza virus C), however, apparently has an independent system of receptors in the red cells of some animals. No mutual destruction of chicken red cell receptors is observed between influenza C and the viruses of the MNI group (*331*).

Hemagglutination and the relation of viruses to host cells. The discovery that a group of viruses possessed an enzymatic activity for substrates located on the surfaces of red blood cells was enough in itself to stimulate the analysis of the enzymes and of the substrates involved, even though the red blood cells are not host cells, in the sense that they cannot support virus reproduction. Another discovery by Hirst, however, indicated that the hemagglutination phenomenon had a direct bearing on the process of virus infection (*325*). Excised lungs from ferrets were perfused to eliminate blood, then filled through the

Table 24. The receptor gradient in human red blood cells

From Burnet, McCrea, and Stone, *Br. J. Exp. Path.* **27**:228, 1946

Cells Treated with	\[Tested with 5–10 Agglutinating Doses of\]														Saline Control
	1 MU	2 NDV	3 MEL	4 MIL-AO	5 WS	6 BEL-D	7 IAN-O	8 MIL-AD	9 LEE	10 BEL-D	11 IAN-D	12 SWINE	13 HUT-B	14 MIL-B	
Saline	+	+	+	+	+	+	+	+	+	+	+	+	+	+	−
2. NDV	−	−	±	+	+	+	+	+	+	+	+	+	+	+	−
5. WS	−	−	−	−	−	±	+	±	+	+	+	+	+	+	−
7. IAN-O	−	−	−	−	−	−	−	±	+	+	+	+	+	+	−
10. BEL-D	−	−	−	−	−	−	−	−	−	−	±	+	+	+	−
12. SWINE 1 hr	−	−	−	−	−	−	−	−	−	−	−	±	+	+	−
SWINE 5 hr	−	−	−	−	−	−	−	−	−	−	−	−	−	+	−

+ Agglutination essentially equivalent to that with normal cells.   ± Agglutination less complete than control.   − No agglutination.
Strain 1 = Mumps virus.   Strain 2 = Newcastle disease virus.   Strains 3, 4, 5, 6, 7, 8, 10, 11 = Influenza A viruses.
Strain 12 = Swine influenza virus.   Strains 9, 13, 14 = Influenza B viruses.

bronchi with influenza virus suspensions. The virus was quickly taken up by the cells of the lungs and then, upon incubation at 37° C, became eluted. If the lungs of a living ferret were flooded with virus, the virus was likewise taken up, but soon became nonelutable and infection followed. Similar experiments have been made, with identical results, using mouse lung or allantoic membrane of chick embryo.

These observations indicated the similarity between the adsorption of influenza viruses onto red blood cells and onto host cells. Hirst suggested that the enzymatic activity of the virus on the host cell receptors may be a fundamental stage of the virus attack on the susceptible host cell. Two questions, thus, became preeminent. First, what are the properties of the virus enzyme and of its cellular substrates? Second, can this knowledge be used to investigate the mechanism of cell-virus interaction, and possibly to devise means that would prevent infection? With such perspectives, work on hemagglutination and allied phenomena has progressed rapidly.

A variety of treatments, when properly administered, preserve the agglutinating ability of the virus particles but suppress their ability to elute from red blood cells (enzymatic activity). Heat, ultraviolet light, and various chemicals act in this way (327). The eluting ability is more resistant to various treatments, such as formalin or ultraviolet, than the reproductive ability of the virus, but is much less resistant than the agglutinating ability.

The viruses of the MNI group differ in their resistance to various agents. It has been widely maintained that the suppression of eluting ability results from inactivation of the enzymatic function without suppression of the affinity of the enzyme for its substrate, so that a stable combination results. An alternate possibility is that the combination between virus and cell is mediated by chemical configurations that are different or more inclusive than the enzyme itself; the enzyme, when active, would act to destroy the cell receptors without itself being fully responsible for attachment to the receptors. Evidently, more information about the nature of enzyme, substrate, and receptors is needed to provide an answer to these questions.

The receptor-destroying enzyme. The timely introduction of a model system has helped further progress. Having noticed the similarities between red cells modified by virus elution and red cells altered by certain bacterial filtrates, particularly from *Vibrio cholerae,* Burnet and his coworkers succeeded in demonstrating in such filtrates a "receptor-destroying enzyme" (RDE), which duplicates most of the virus effects on red blood cells (see 115). Exposure of red blood cells to

RDE progressively destroys their susceptibility to agglutination by viruses of the MNI group. The order in which agglutinability by different viruses is lost closely parallels the position of the viruses in the receptor gradient; agglutinability by mumps is lost more readily than that by Newcastle virus, and so on.

The RDE, as well as active virus (328), can remove from red cells virus particles that have become unable to elute themselves. This suggests a more complex basis for virus-cell combination than a direct, 1:1 combination between enzyme and substrate molecules. Since another enzyme (RDE or active virus) can reverse the combination, it seems possible that the cell receptor contains some substrate groups, uncombined with the virus enzyme and available to other enzymes, which are operative in holding virus and cell together. RDE can remove virus receptors from the cells of host tissues, such as mouse lung or allantoic sac epithelium. The allantoic membrane, after treatment with sufficient RDE, remains unable to adsorb virus for as long as 24 hours; if the RDE is removed from the allantoic cavity, the epithelium can regenerate its adsorbing capacity (630). Even active virus already attached to host cells may still be removed by RDE if the RDE is introduced soon after the virus. Trypsin inactivates RDE and reportedly also the virus enzyme. The receptor-destroying activity of RDE requires calcium ions and is suppressed by citrate, a behavior that is shared by the enzyme activity of some of the MNI viruses.

Virus substrates. The RDE provides a convenient model system for virus enzymes. The next question concerns the substrates for these enzymes. A suitable method for the detection of virus substrates is the use of agglutination-inhibition tests.

Heat treatment or other manipulations can, as we have seen, render a virus agglutinating but not elutable. It was observed that a variety of animal fluids and tissue extracts—including urine (642), blood serum (230), allantoic fluid (636), and egg white (398)—can inhibit hemagglutination by the nonelutable virus. Hemagglutination by unmodified virus is inhibited to a very slight extent, if at all. The normal virus, supposedly, is not subject to inhibition because it can destroy the inhibitors enzymatically, whereas the modified virus, which has lost its enzymatic activity, combines with the inhibitors and is thereby prevented from combining with red blood cells. Thus, the inhibitors are revealed by their ability to prevent hemagglutination by modified virus, which acts as *indicator* for the inhibitors.

A variety of inhibitors has been reported. Some occur free, like the so-called Francis inhibitor in blood serum (230); others can be extracted from red blood cells (164) or other cells. A common property of all these inhibitors appears to be their content of polysaccharides. Their activity is suppressed by reagents such as periodates, which are known to affect polysaccharides fairly specifically. It is now generally believed that most inhibitors belong to the class of mucins or mucoproteins, a rather ill-defined group of proteins conjugated with carbohydrates (16). Most materials rich in mucin, such as the fluid from ovarian cysts and from mucous secretions, exhibit inhibitory activity. Usually the inhibitory activity can be destroyed not only by active virus but also by preparations of RDE. The most thoroughly analyzed inhibitor, that from egg white, has been partially purified and obtained in the form of a highly viscous material, consisting of filamentous particles, about 8×10^6 mol. wt. (400).

It seems altogether reasonable to view the combination between virus and cell receptors and that between virus and inhibitors as enzyme-substrate combinations. The inhibitors compete with the cell receptors for the virus enzymes, which, if active, can digest them. This viewpoint can account for most of the known facts. Supplementary hypotheses will probably be necessary to account for specific phenomena observed with modified viruses and with various inhibitors. A kinetic analysis of the inhibition of heated swine influenza virus by egg-white inhibitor (399) has led to a rather simple picture of competition between inhibitor and red blood cells for the active groups on bivalent virus particles, the combinations being practically irreversible. Apparently, each collision between virus and inhibitor or red blood cell is effective in producing combination. This suggests that electrostatic forces play a role in the attachment reaction.

Not all inhibitors are related to the cell receptors for MNI viruses. Thus, allantoic fluid contains two inhibitors: one is not destroyed by virus, is probably lipidic in nature, and acts in a nonspecific way; the other is a specific inhibitor, which is destroyed by virus (636).

According to some workers (15), the picture of virus-receptor and virus-inhibitor combinations as enzyme-substrate combinations is an oversimplification. One objection is that hemagglutination by heated, enzymatically inactive influenza virus is more readily inhibited than the hemagglutination by active virus in the cold, where enzyme activity should be absent. The difference seems hard to explain, if inhibition is simply an enzyme substrate combination without enzyme activity. Since the enzymes are somewhat active even at 0° C, how-ever, this argument is debatable.

Another objection is that a brief treatment of certain inhibitors with periodate increases their inhibitory power; it is pointed out that chemical treatment should not increase the affinity of a substrate for an enzyme. It is possible, however, that the combination between indicator virus and inhibitors is a reversible reaction, which reaches a finite equilibrium (291). Periodate treatment of the inhibitor might simply affect the equilibrium value.

Virus enzymes and infection. The fact that cells which support growth of MNI viruses possess receptors digestible by the viruses or by RDE raises the question of the role of the virus enzymes in infec-tion. Destruction of the receptors in lung or allantoic cells during in-fection with influenza viruses is the rule, and it is an appealing hy-pothesis that the virus, following its uptake by the surface receptors, works its way into the cells by digesting the receptors (332).

It must be admitted that the evidence for this hypothesis is indirect; no proof exists of the role of virus enzyme in penetration. It is possible that the enzyme's main function is the destruction of mucous films on the surface of susceptible tissues.

The recognition of mucoproteins as virus inhibitors and receptors has suggested the use of polysaccharides as competitive inhibitors, which may suppress infection by competing with cell receptors for the virus. Indeed, a number of substances, including pectins, bacterial polysaccharides, and others, interfere both with hemagglutination and with the growth of some of the MNI viruses (273). The capsular polysaccharide from *Klebsiella pneumoniae* (Friedlander's bacillus) is an example (256). It inhibits infection with mumps or with pneu-monia virus of mice, two viruses which interfere with one another in mixed infection, probably at the intracellular level, and which are characterized by rather slow reproductive cycles (252). The growth-inhibiting power is still present if the polysaccharide is introduced as late as 4 days after virus inoculation. It seems possible that this poly-saccharide blocks infection by an intracellular action rather than by interference with virus adsorption. If this is correct, the false lead derived from the study of inhibitors of hemagglutination may have led to a potentially fruitful new approach to antiviral therapy.

Inhibitors and virus purity. The allantoic fluid contains inhibitors of viruses of the MNI group. Not all this inhibitory power is de-stroyed by active virus. Indeed, infected allantoic fluids contain not only free virus but also some in combination with inhibitors (291).

This situation must affect the apparent chemical composition of virus isolated from the allantoic fluid. This is of interest in connection with the cross-reaction that influenza viruses grown in eggs give with anti-serum against normal allantoic fluid, a cross-reaction which has been noted repeatedly (377). This cross-reaction probably reflects the presence of inhibitors or other host materials attached to the virus particles rather than the incorporation of host antigens into the virus protoplasm itself.

A more complex situation is encountered with pneumonia virus of mice (349). Virus extracted by grinding infected mouse lung is in-fectious but does not agglutinate red blood cells. Brief heating of the virus suspension at 80° C renders the virus noninfectious, but confers upon it a hemagglutinating ability for red blood cells from mouse or hamster (not from other species). Addition of ground, unheated, normal lung material again suppresses the hemagglutinating power. Apparently, in the ground lungs the virus is combined with a com-ponent of the host tissue, which, without suppressing infectivity, pre-vents the adsorption of virus on red blood cells. Virus can be ob-tained free of this inhibitor, either by collecting the fluid that seeps out of a sharp cut in the infected lungs, thereby avoiding the grinding of lung cells, or by dissociating the virus-inhibitor combination at low electrolyte concentration. The virus thus obtained is highly infectious, agglutinates red blood cells, and consists of particles about 30–40 mμ in diameter, whereas those obtained by grinding average 140 mμ.

In this case the inhibitor is not destroyed by the virus; there is no evidence that it plays any role either as cell receptor or in virus pene-tration. On the contrary, the inhibitor is found free in the exudate from lung and may be partly responsible for the latency of the virus, since it may limit virus propagation to the transmission from mother to daughter cell and may interfere with its extracellular transfer from infected cell to healthy cell (658).

It should be pointed out that the dissociation of the pneumonia virus of mice from tissue inhibitor at low electrolyte concentration is paral-leled by the nonenzymatic dissociation of this virus from red blood cells at similarly low salt concentrations (658). Influenza virus adsorption on red blood cells can also be prevented, and already adsorbed virus can be removed, by dilution of electrolytes. These phenomena recall the observations on the role of cation concentrations on phage adsorp-tion by bacteria (250; 535).

In summary, Hirst's discovery of hemagglutination by certain viruses has led not only to a remarkable simplification of research methods

with these viruses but also to a certain degree of insight into the interaction between virus and cell surface. It has led to the recognition
of an enzymatic activity in a group of viruses, to the tentative identification of their substrates, and to the recognition of the role of these
substrates in virus adsorption and of their possible involvement in later
stages of cell invasion. Moreover, it has suggested some leads to the
therapy of several viral infections, either employing enzymes similar
to those of the viruses, or using analogues of the substrates for the
virus enzyme. How far this approach will lead remains to be seen;
its fundamental importance cannot be doubted.

THE GROWTH CYCLE OF VIRUSES OF THE INFLUENZA GROUP

The availability of a rapid method for the detection of influenza
viruses, provided by hemagglutination, has made possible detailed
studies of the reproductive cycles of these viruses, especially in the
allantoic sac (299; 305; 353). The situation is somewhat analogous to
that of a phage growth experiment, with the difference that with the
animal viruses the susceptible cells are fixed on the walls of the
allantoic sac.

Titration of infectivity in the allantoic fluid at various intervals after
inoculation reveals at first a reduction in free virus ("adsorption").
The adsorption proceeds at a constant rate up to amounts of virus
corresponding to at least 30 infectious units per host cell (122). There
follows a "latent period" of several hours, during which no increase in
free virus occurs. Then the virus titer suddenly rises in the allantoic
fluid. The interval between infection and rise is rather precise, being
about 5 to 6 hours for strains of influenza A and 8 to 10 hours for
small inocula of influenza B (304). Heavier inocula of influenza B
strains give a shorter latent period, approaching that of influenza A
(427). The latent period decreases with increasing temperatures, between 30° and 39° C (659). The rise continues more or less irregu-
larly until the maximum titer is reached, probably as a result of successive cycles of adsorption and infection of new cells.

One-step growth experiments. To isolate one cycle of growth,
Henle and his coworkers (305) utilized the ability of heterologous
virus (influenza A versus B, and vice versa), after inactivation by
ultraviolet light, to suppress reproduction of active virus and to reduce
materially its adsorption onto susceptible cells. Under the proper
conditions, the heterologous virus does not suppress the growth of
active virus that has already been adsorbed onto the cells.

The experiments are carried out as follows. A first inoculation with active virus (for example, influenza A) is followed after 1 or 2 hours by a second input consisting of a large excess of UV-irradiated heter-

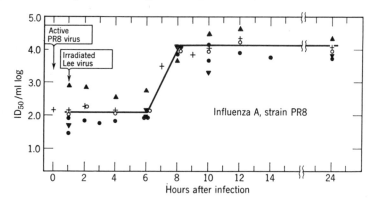

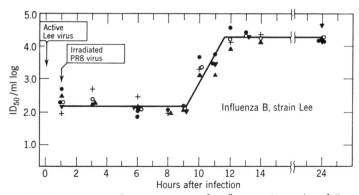

Figure 86. One-step growth experiments with influenza viruses A and B in the allantoic cavity of chick embryos. Heterologous irradiated virus in excess was inoculated 1 hour after the active virus to reduce readsorption of liberated virus. The ordinate gives the log amount of virus in the allantoic fluid in ID_{50} per ml. (ID_{50} = 50% infectious dose.)   From: Henle et al. (*305*).

ologous virus (influenza B). Samples are taken at various times, antiserum against virus B is added, and virus A is titrated. The virus titer rises after the normal constant period (5–6 hours), and a maximum titer is soon reached (figure 86). The rise in virus titer in one such step of growth is about 60- to 80-fold for strains of influenza A and 30- to 40-fold for strains of influenza B.

A somewhat different picture is observed in experiments in which virus readsorption is prevented by the use of RDE instead of heterologous virus and the liberation of virus is followed by taking successive samples of fluid from the same eggs (122). Virus liberation, when started, apparently continues for many hours; the cells continue to excrete virus. The stepwise liberation shown in figure 86 is due to the particular conditions of the experiments. The total yield may be over 1000 per cell.

The process just described resembles in part the growth cycle of virulent bacteriophages, except for the fact that release of virus is a continuous rather than a sudden process. Further similarities to phage growth are actually observed. If allantoic membranes are washed and ground early after inoculation, only 1 to 2% of the initial virus activity is recovered. There is therefore a definite "eclipse" of the infecting virus (299). Most of the residual virus activity is probably due to superficially adsorbed virus since it can be destroyed by the addition of antibody in the allantoic sac.

Active virus is found in allantoic membranes collected and ground late in the latent period. It begins to appear about 1 hour before liberation into the allantoic fluid takes place.

Interesting results are obtained by following not only the infectious virus but also other materials with viral specificity. This is done by measuring, besides the infectious titer, the complement-fixing titer and the hemagglutinin titer of the allantoic fluid and of extracts of ground allantoic membranes. Complement fixation detects both the type-specific soluble antigen, consisting of small particles (sedimentation constant around 30 S), and other, strain-specific antigens, which are found within the virus particles.

In an allantoic sac infected with influenza A virus, the titer of soluble antigen begins to increase in membrane extracts about 3 hours and in the allantoic fluid about 4 to 5 hours after infection (figure 87). In membrane extracts the rise in soluble antigen may be 1000-fold (353). Some time later, the hemagglutinin titer also rises, both in the membrane and in the fluid. The demonstration of the hemagglutinin in membrane extracts requires removal by RDE of a powerful inhibitor of hemagglutination present in the membrane (426).

Thus the complement-fixing antigen and the hemagglutinin appear at a time when the infectious titer is still very low. These noninfectious, virus-specific materials increase in amount before the infectious virus. What are the properties of the noninfectious materials and their relation to the mature, infectious virus?

Noninfectious, immature virus elements. Free, soluble antigen is present in relatively large amounts in all virus preparations. More of it can be extracted from the particles. Noninfectious hemagglutinin has been found to accompany influenza virus and Newcastle virus in crude preparations (242; 267). This hemagglutinin is adsorbed by red cells and can be eluted. It is not proved that the elution is due to the activity of the noninfectious particles themselves, since they have not yet been obtained free of accompanying active virus. A fraction of the noninfectious hemagglutinin can be separated from the virus by

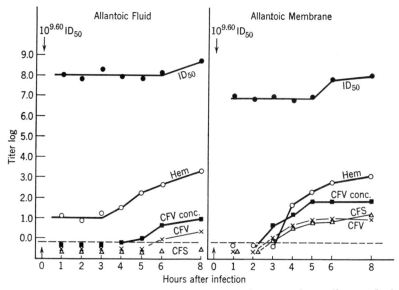

Figure 87. The amounts of various virus-specific materials in allantoic fluids and in ground allantoic membranes of chick embryos inoculated with influenza virus A. ID_{50} = 50% infectious dose titer. Hem = hemagglutinin titer. CFV = complement-fixation titer, viral antigen. CFV conc. = same, after eight-fold concentration. CFS = complement-fixation titer, soluble antigen. Initial inoculum $10^{9.6}$ ID_{50}. From: Henle and Henle (302).

ultracentrifugation, its sedimentation constant being somewhat lower than that of the virus. The hemagglutinin particles contain strain-specific, complement-fixing antigen, as do infectious particles. Altogether, the noninfectious hemagglutinin appears to consist of particles very similar to the mature virus particles, but lacking infectivity.

The hypothesis that the soluble antigen and hemagglutinin, which precede the infectious virus in infected cells, are immature stages of virus synthesis is supported by other observations. In some cases, incomplete virus elements are the only or the main product of infection. Massive transfers of high-titer influenza virus into the allantoic sac result in the production of allantoic fluids with very low infectivity, but with hemagglutinin titer and soluble antigen titer similar to those of highly infectious fluids (the Von Magnus phenomenon; *660*). Most of the hemagglutinin is associated with particles not much smaller than the virus (sedimentation constant about 500 S instead of 600–700 S) (*249; 290*). Successive transfers of the allantoic fluids containing these "incomplete particles," with a minority of active particles, induce further cycles of incomplete reproduction (see table 25). The hemag-

Table 25.   Serial transfers of influenza A virus in undiluted allantoic fluid

Modified from Von Magnus (*660*)

Egg Passage	Inoculum Volume, ml	Incubation Period (hours)	Titer of Allantoic Fluid			Log Ratio $\left(\dfrac{\text{Egg-Infectious Units}}{\text{Hemagglutinin Units}}\right)$
			Log Egg-Infectious Units	Log Mouse Lethal Units	Log Hemagglutinin Units	
Standard	0.1	44	10.5	7.5	3.9	6.6
I	0.1	22	9.8	6.1	3.7	6.1
II	0.1	22	8.5	5.5	3.9	4.6
III	0.1	22	5.5	2.5	3.1	2.4
IV	0.1	22	5.2	2.8	2.3	2.9
V	0.1	22	8.5	5.8	2.8	5.7
VI	0.1	22	7.2	4.8	2.9	4.3
VII	0.1	22	7.5	3.8	2.7	4.8
VIII	0.1	22	9.5	6.1	3.6	5.9
IX	0.1	22	7.5	3.5	3.4	4.1
X	0.1	22	7.5	4.8	2.7	4.8

glutinin titer remains high and the infectious titer low. After several passages, the infectivity titer may suddenly rise again for one or two passages. Similar results are obtained using, instead of the intact eggs, deembryonated eggs, in which the virus grows in the allantoic cells that line the shell cavity (*71*).

Another case of incomplete formation of influenza virus has been observed. Upon heavy inoculation of nonneurotropic strains into the brain of mice (*582*), no increase in infectious titer occurs and the infectivity of the inoculum is lost. But there is a rise in hemagglutinin titer and in complement-fixing antigen. The inhibitor of hemagglutination that is normally present in mouse brain decreases in amount in the course of this abortive growth cycle. The hemagglutinin from mouse brain is not much smaller than the active virus particle and is possibly similar to the noninfectious particles responsible for the Von Magnus phenomenon (290).

It seems reasonable to consider these abnormal growth cycles of influenza as processes in which virus synthesis is arrested at a stage where a hemagglutinating but uninfectious particle has been formed but not yet been transformed into infectious virus. The incomplete growth in the brain suggests that the cells of this organ lack only the ability to carry out one specific step needed for virus maturation. The potential affinity of influenza virus for the brain tissue is shown by other observations: the existence of neurotropic variants, capable of reproducing in infectious form in mouse brain (633a); the neurotropism of influenza virus in the very early chick embryo (289); and finally, the ability of influenza virus to interfere with the growth of neurotropic viruses in mouse brain (656; see chapter 14).

The incomplete reproductive cycle of influenza in mouse brain accounts for the "toxic" symptoms that follow intracerebral injection of virus (298). Damage to brain cells is apparently produced by virus that fails to reproduce beyond the incomplete stage.

The mechanism of influenza virus growth. Hoyle has summarized experiments on the production of the various specific materials of a strain of influenza A in the allantoic sac and has proposed an elaborate theory of virus reproduction (354). According to this author, the two types of complement-fixing antigen of the virus, the strain-specific and the type-specific ones, play distinct and characteristic roles. The type-specific antigen, identified with the soluble antigen, is claimed to increase logarithmically inside the host cells between the second and the fourth hour after inoculation, and to be delayed in growth by dyes acting as metabolic inhibitors. The strain-specific antigen, identified with the hemagglutinin, increases later and less than the soluble antigen. Finally, infectious virus is said to appear in the allantoic fluid in amounts larger than are ever recoverable from the allantoic membrane itself. The interpretation offered by Hoyle is that inside the cell the infecting virus disintegrates and that the soluble antigen, representing the essential viral nucleoprotein, reproduces as such. The agglutinin component increases later in the cells, and the two are then secreted into the allantoic fluid. In passing through the cell membrane, they would produce more agglutinin and acquire a lipoid component derived from the cell, binding the other components into infectious particles.

As arguments in favor of this theory, Hoyle mentions first, that ether treatment of virus particles frees both soluble antigen and hemagglutinin (presumably by removal of the lipoid layer); second, that filamentous forms of virus, when present, are supposedly seen in the allantoic fluid but not in membrane extracts, which suggests that they may be formed upon liberation; and third, that infected allantoic cells removed from the allantoic sac liberate filaments resembling virus materials. This is observed both in the dark field and in the electron microscope (201; 224).

This theory involves many assumptions, the justification for which is rather weak (246; 426). The acquisition of infectivity by the virus upon extrusion from the cells appears plausible, however. The infectious virus may not be released immediately in the allantoic fluid. What we can state with some certainty is that the influenza virus particle, upon infecting the host cell, is transformed into noninfectious materials. These materials reproduce inside the host cells in the form of elements not recognizable as viral particles. The new virus particles (or filaments) are formed by a stagewise process and are preceded by different elements (hemagglutinin, complement-fixing antigens) which ultimately become incorporated into the infectious virus. For an understanding of the relations among the various elements and of their relative role in virus growth, chemical studies of various virus-related materials are greatly desirable.

Genetic recombination. Burnet and his coworkers (118a; 120) have reported experiments that suggest that influenza virus strains may undergo, in mixed infection, phenomena of genetic recombination of the type reported for bacteriophage (314). The strains utilized belonged to the influenza A group. Both laboratory variants and naturally occurring strains were used. Two sets of experiments were first reported. In one set, a neurotropic variant NWS, characterized by lack of enzyme activity on the egg-white inhibitor, was mixed with a serologically different nonneurotropic variant (WSM), characterized by heat-resistant hemagglutinin. The mixture was inoculated intracerebrally into mice. The encephalitic syndrome produced by NWS was more or less completely suppressed by interference on the part of WSM (27; see chapter 14). From the brains of mice with encephalitic symptoms, strains of two new types were obtained. One type, N, is neurotropic but more heat resistant and enzymatically more active than

NWS. The other type, NM, is somewhat neurotropic, heat resistant, and serologically similar to WSM.

The second group of experiments employed mixtures of strain NWS with either MEL or SW, nonneurotropic strains serologically distinct from NWS. From the brains of mice inoculated with the mixtures new strains were isolated which were neurotropic and resembled, serologically and in other properties, the MEL and SW strains. Infection with a mixture of NWS and OcI, a nonneurotropic filament-forming strain, gave rise to neurotropic, nonfilamentous derivatives serologically similar to OcI.

In these and other experiments (118a) the virus isolated from mixed-infected animals showed hereditary characters present in the two strains used as inoculum. By analogy with the phenomena of genetic recombination in bacteriophage, Burnet suggested that genetic recombination takes place with influenza virus in mixed-infected cells. The investigators carefully sought to avoid a possible role of selection and of strain mixtures in these experiments. They used strains that had been made genetically as homogeneous as possible by repeated transfers at limiting dilutions, so that each strain had presumably originated from a single particle.

In experiments of this type, in which mass inoculation of animal brains leads to repeated cycles of virus reproduction in different cells, selection of spontaneous variants cannot be excluded as easily as with bacteriophage, where single cycles of infection can be analyzed. Moreover, the method of transfers at limiting dilutions is not completely reliable in eliminating virus mixtures, especially when strains of different pathogenicity are present. More recent experiments carried out in the chick embryo have confirmed and extended the results obtained in the mouse's brain (120b).

Reactivation phenomena. Henle has reported (303) that ultraviolet-irradiated influenza virus A or B, upon inoculation into the allantoic sac, gives rise to a growth cycle whose characteristics depend on the amount of inoculum. This suggests, according to Henle, a "multiplicity reactivation" similar to that observed in bacteriophage (436). Light inocula of the irradiated virus give a growth cycle similar to the one that would be expected from an inoculum of active virus corresponding to the residual active titer in the irradiated samples. With increasing inocula, however, the amount of virus growth increases more than proportionally to the inoculum, as though some of the inactive virus had been reactivated. It has not yet been shown that this reactivation occurs in cells infected with several inactive particles.

GENERAL CONSIDERATIONS ON VIRUS REPRODUCTION

There are many similarities between the growth cycle of lytic bacteriophages (chapter 8) and that of influenza viruses. We may legitimately ask whether there is a similar pattern in the growth cycles of other viruses as well.

Certain aspects of virus-host interaction are the same for many viruses. Pneumonia virus in mouse lung (254), mumps virus (253), and meningopneumonitis virus in the chick embryo (603) exhibit growth cycles characterized by an initial reduction (eclipse) of the infectious titer below the level of the inoculum, followed by a period in which virus titer remains low. The virus titer then increases and reaches a maximum after a time interval fairly characteristic for each virus.

Similar results have been reported for neurotropic viruses (576a). An interesting feature is presented by Theiler's virus GD-VII of mouse encephalitis. Following peripheral injection in mice, the virus is detected in infectious form as it proceeds along the nerve fibers toward the central nervous system. As the virus reaches the nerve cells, infectivity disappears for 20 to 30 hours. Later it reappears and reaches a maximum around 100 hours after infection, at the time of the onset of symptoms. Virus hemagglutinin titer parallels the virus infectivity. Here, apparently, the virus loses its infectivity only when it reaches the cell body proper, not in the nerve fiber, although the nerve fiber is truly a part of the host cell.

Vaccinia virus, both in rabbit skin and in tissue cultures of the same tissue, exhibits a growth curve characterized by eclipse, followed by rapid growth (101a; 158; figure 88). The measurements of infectivity are closely correlated with the counts of elementary bodies in infected cells.

Electron-microscope and light-microscope observations on virus-infected cells (chapter 11) strongly suggest that the new virus particles represent the culmination of a process of stagewise maturation. These observations reveal no sign of binary fission of the virus particles as such.

The main similarity among all viruses whose growth cycle has been analyzed is the eclipse phenomenon, followed by reappearance of virus. With some phages, the eclipse has been explained by changes in virus organization, especially by the separation of a nucleic acid-containing core from a protein skin. With other viruses, the mechanism of eclipse is as yet unknown. With plant viruses, the limited data in the literature do not prove the occurrence of an eclipse stage.

Concerning the later phases of virus development, it should be remembered that most information available on animal and plant viruses, except that from egg experiments, derives from tests on tissue extracts. The cycles studied in this way resemble experiments on premature lysis of phage-infected bacteria, rather than cycles of infection

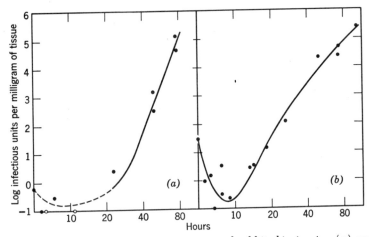

Figure 88. Growth of vaccinia virus in normal rabbit skin in vivo (*a*) and in shavings of skins in vitro (*b*). Unfilled circles: no virus recovered. Modified from: Crawford and Sanders (*158*).

and lysis. Maturation of new virus evidently takes place in the host cells, but we know little about the modalities of the virus release and of the reinfection of other cells. Symptoms often appear when the amount of mature, infectious virus is at a peak; but it is hard to decide whether the cell damage reflects the maturation process itself or the second wave of attack by newly liberated viruses. Indeed, we know that many viruses, and not only the "latent" ones, but some like influenza (*326*), can reproduce to a maximum extent in susceptible tissues without causing any symptom of disease.

The well-established facts of lysogenicity in phage, together with the established similarities between phage infection and infection with animal viruses, justify the question as to whether cell infection by animal and plant viruses may also be followed by a "lysogenic" type of relation, with reproduction of virus in noninfectious form (*provirus*), followed rarely (or even not at all) by maturation and production of active virus particles.

There are numerous observations that suggest a reproduction of virus without maturation. In infections followed by recovery, persistent immunity is frequent. This may be due in part to persistence of antibody, but according to many workers this persistence of antibody is itself evidence for persistence of virus. In plant viruses, where antibodies cannot be invoked, infectious virus persists in recovered plants and is found in their new leaves. It is present, however, in much smaller amounts than in recently diseased plants (see chapter 14). One wonders whether the virus does not reproduce mainly in an immature form, with only occasional maturation. The reproduction in immature form might result from the infection of very young tissues, just as the frequency of lysogenization in bacteria is affected by the physiological conditions of the infected cells.

The data on latent viruses closely recall the facts of lysogenicity. Often, latency simply means absence of symptoms; but there are reasons to suspect that sometimes the virus is not present in infectious form or at least that the infectious virus is only a small proportion of the virus present in noninfectious form. Cases like that of herpes virus (see *114*), which enters the human body in childhood, remains unobserved and undetectable (except by antibody test) for many years, and occasionally produces symptoms and infectious virus, remind us of lysogenic bacteria and of the induction of phage maturation by a variety of stimuli.

It is indeed important to establish whether infection with a virus can produce symptoms of cell damage in the absence of virus maturation. Toxic symptoms of influenza (*298*) are probably related to incomplete maturation. Even in the lung of mice, influenza may cause rapid death, with little virus being recoverable in the lung tissue (*634*), an observation that suggests cell damage without virus maturation.

Transmission of virus from cell to cell may occur either in the noninfectious or in the infectious form. In multicellular organisms, transmission of noninfectious virus from cell to cell generation, with occasional maturation, can provide a relation of relative stability. Egg and sperm transmission of virus diseases, however rare, provides possible instances of such a type of relation.

In summary, we may say that our present knowledge supports the idea that virus multiplication inside the host cell proceeds according to the following pattern. Upon invasion of the host cell (or of some special part of it) the infectious particle is so modified as to become unrecognizable as such. Reproduction of noninfectious virus elements takes place by mechanisms, the nature of which still escapes us, but which are probably on a level with the reproduction of the specific, self-perpetuating elements of the host cell itself (chromosomes, mitochondria, plastids). The role of the preexisting virus in inducing the formation of more virus is completely unknown. The cell may possess a diffuse, nonspecific machinery for such syntheses, and the specific material of the infecting virus may introduce a new model for synthesis.

Reproduction of noninfectious copies of the infecting virus may be followed by maturation, with production of infective particles. In bacteriophage, there is good evidence that the matured particles no longer reproduce in the cell where they have arisen; that is, before reproducing again they must go through the invasion process. The mature particle in a sense is a resting stage, which carries the essential virus material from cell to cell and probably protects it from external injury. For other viruses, the relation of maturation to reproduction is not yet clear, but the concept of mature virus as a resting stage seems to stand on a solid basis (28). Polyhedral viruses of insects reach the infectious rod-shaped form by a process of maturation. Their inclusion into the polyhedral bodies arrests further production of virus. The capsules around the particles of other insect viruses may represent protective coats acquired in maturation.

Reproduction of virus material may lead to a more protracted state of immaturity. Even with virulent phages, it is likely that not all the phage elements that have been produced reach maturation. It is quite conceivable that many viruses, after infecting a host cell, remain in that cell (and in its offspring) in a noninfectious form, reproducing further or sometimes being eliminated. Maturation may take place in some cells only and even in a small minority of the cells. Continued reproduction without maturation and without cell destruction may lead to cases of nonrecognizable viruses. These will be, both semantically and operationally, indistinguishable from the so-called normal cell components; and the problem arises as to the possible origin of certain cell components from elements that may have been viruses. The possible function of such virus remnants, for example, in normal and abnormal development, will be discussed in chapters 17 and 18.

Interference Phenomena
in Virus Infections

In chapters 9 and 13 we have already discussed some of the phenomena observed when a host is infected with two viruses. Interactions in mixed virus infections are of great interest not only for the study of virus-host relationships but also in relation to immunity to viruses. In bacteriophage it has been possible to analyze interactions between viruses in terms of the response of individual host cells. In plant or animal viruses this is more difficult, because of intervening complications: the multicellular nature of the host, the complicated pathways of virus spread in the host, the occurrence of humoral mechanisms of defense against viruses. It is a general observation that particles of two or more virus types do not react directly with one another outside the cells, so that all interactions must have to do with events that take place on the surface of, or inside, the host cells.

INTERFERENCE IN BACTERIOPHAGES

Virulent phages. Infection of bacteria with two virulent bacteriophages leads to different results, depending on the degree of relationship between the two viruses. When the two phages are unrelated (according to serological and morphological criteria) *mutual exclusion* occurs, generally accompanied by a yield-depressing effect (*168; 174*).

When the infecting viruses are related, the result depends on the time between infections. If two related phages infect the same host cells almost simultaneously, they both multiply and mature. The closer their genetic relationship, the greater the number of cells which liberate both phages; for example, all cells mixed infected with a phage and one of its mutants, such as T2 and T2r, liberate both types, whereas only a fraction of the cells infected with T4 and T6 may liberate both

Table 26. Mixed infection with two bacteriophages

The proportion of bacteria that liberate both phage types following simultaneous
infection with equal amounts of two phages.

Phage Pair	Per Cent Mixed Yields
T1–T2	0
T1–T7	0
T1–T5	0
T2–T5	0
T2–T7	0
T2–T4	80
T2–T6	60
T4–T6	20
T2–T2r	100

(table 26). In such "mixed-yielder" cells, each phage does not grow
to the same extent as it would if the other phage were not present;
rather, the two phages share the total yield, which is approximately
the same as if only one virus had infected the cell (309). Recombination phenomena may take place, leading to production of new virus
types (173; 314).

For mixed growth, it is not necessary that two related phages attack
the host cells simultaneously. The same result is observed if the two
phage infections are separated by an interval of time during which the
host cells receive no available nutrient. If, instead, two infections with
related phages are separated by an interval of a few minutes, while
the bacteria are actively metabolizing, a mechanism for the exclusion
of the second phage becomes rapidly established (table 27) (195).
Indeed, part of the phage that comes late is actively broken down outside the infected cell (238); about 50% of its phosphorus appears in
soluble form in the medium.

Temperate phages. A bacterium carrying a phage in lysogenic condition (prophage) is susceptible to lysis by most unrelated phages
(although it may be resistant to some individual phage strains). Even
bacteria in which maturation of the prophage has been induced by
ultraviolet light can still support growth of an unrelated virulent
phage (669). The virulent phage can actually prevent maturation of
the prophage.

Reinfection of a lysogenic bacterium with the phage it already carries, or with mutants of it, gives rise to complex interactions, including

Table 27. Exclusion between two related phages

The fraction of bacteria that liberate both T2r^+ and T2r phage when infection with one phage preceded infection with the other phage by various intervals of time. Only about 50% of the bacteria received both phages. Modified from Dulbecco (195).

	Time Interval Between First and Second Infection	Bacteria That Liberate			Fraction of Mixed Yields	Relative Fraction of Mixed Yields
		both	r^+ only	r only		
T2r^+ first	0	385	223	133	0.51	1.00
	1 min	178	319	137	0.28	0.56
	2 min, 25 sec	53	428	120	0.09	0.18
	5 min, 40 sec	21	491	132	0.03	0.07
	10 min, 40 sec	10	504	139	0.02	0.04
T2r first	0	396	204	233	0.48	1.00
	1 min	147	293	222	0.22	0.47
	2 min, 25 sec	66	364	415	0.09	0.16
	5 min, 40 sec	23	301	400	0.03	0.07
	10 min, 40 sec	22	263	389	0.03	0.07

prophage substitution, prophage elimination, and double lysogenesis (see page 203 and table 23).

In general, bacteria infected with two phages exhibit two distinct categories of phenomena, depending on whether the infection is of the lytic or the lysogenic type. In the lysogenic form, a prophage can prevent maturation of related phages and limit their establishment to the prophage form; the prophage may or may not interfere with unrelated phages. In the lytic condition, instead, there is no prevention of maturation between related phages (provided infection is simultaneous) but there is prevention of maturation between unrelated phages.

INTERFERENCE IN PLANT VIRUSES

Acquired immunity and cross-protection. In discussing interference phenomena among plant viruses, we must consider first what happens in plants that are exposed twice to the same virus. In several diseases, a virus infection, after becoming generalized in a plant, results in an apparent recovery. For example, a tobacco plant infected with tobacco ringspot virus, after the early manifestation of ring patterns on its leaves (acute stage), seems to recover (chronic stage); the new leaves are practically normal in appearance. A second inoculation with the same virus does not result, however, in a disease similar to the one produced by the primary infection; the recovered plant has an *acquired immunity* toward the virus (see 533). In the so-called recovered plant the virus is still present, although in amounts smaller than in actively diseased plants. The ringspot virus in recovered tobacco plants is in one-tenth to one-fifth the amounts that can be extracted during the active infection. In exceptional cases, it is claimed that no active virus can be demonstrated in the recovered, immune plants (251).

Apart from the question whether it is correct to call such plants "recovered," and the lack of symptoms upon reinfection "acquired immunity," there is no doubt that the previous infection with virus prevents the newly introduced virus from reproducing to the same extent as it would if inoculated into a virus-free plant. The establishment of the immune condition has been attributed to the entry of the virus into susceptible cells at a stage of active cell proliferation, so that an equilibrium is established between formation of virus and formation of cell components. The usual type of infection supposedly occurs when the virus penetrates mature cells.

Situations of this type are quite common with plant viruses, and the general observation with plants is that acquired immunity extends not only to reinoculation with the identical virus but also to inoculation with a closely related virus strain. This *cross-protection* between two related viruses holds also for plants that are in the acute stage of the disease. It is particularly clear in the mosaic diseases of tobacco, potato, and other plants. The first observations concerned tobacco mosaic and its yellow mutants (458; 648b); similar findings were made on green and yellow strains of potato virus X. In all these cases, previous infection with a less virulent strain, provided it has become generalized, prevents manifestations of the symptoms of a more virulent virus. The opposite type of interference, in which a less virulent strain is excluded by previous infection with a more virulent one, is more difficult to detect, since the symptoms of the more virulent virus do not permit conclusive observations as to the absence of those of the milder virus.

For protection to occur, the cells exposed to the second virus must actually be infected by the first. Upon successive inoculation of the same leaves with tobacco mosaic virus and with a necrotic variant of this virus, necrosis fails to occur in those areas that have been directly inoculated with the first virus or into which this virus has already spread (figure 89; *386*). Here, as well as with severe and mild strains of potato virus X, the excluded virus actually fails to multiply in the protected area. Protection may sometimes occur upon simultaneous inoculation. A high concentration of the ribgrass strain of tobacco mosaic virus in a mixed inoculum with ordinary tobacco mosaic virus

Figure 89. Leaves of *Nicotiana sylvestris* partly protected against aucuba mosaic by direct inoculation with tobacco mosaic. The areas free of the necrotic aucuba lesions were rubbed with tobacco mosaic virus 5 days before inoculation with the aucuba virus. Courtesy Dr. L. O. Kunkel, Rockefeller Institute, New York.

reduces the number of lesions produced by the ordinary strain on bean leaves (*54a*).

Plant virus studies of this type have been handicapped by the difficulty of detecting a virus in a mixture with another. This test requires indicator hosts susceptible to one virus and resistant to the other, and such hosts are seldom available. Moreover, small amounts of plant viruses are difficult to detect and titrate. Nevertheless, it seems to be well established that in cross-protection the first virus actually interferes with the multiplication of the second.

The acquired-immunity phenomena in plant virus diseases might be compared with the situation observed with bacteriophages in the lysogenic condition (*75*). We may suppose that in the recovered plant the virus is mainly in a condition (*provirus*) similar to the prophage.

This may explain the nonrecoverability of infectious virus in some instances (*251*) and its low concentration in others. Reinfection with a related virus would lead to limited reproduction and to failure to manifest symptoms.

Cross-protection and classification. Cross-protection is a satisfactory criterion of relationship. Plant pathologists have so concluded because they have found cross-protection between virus strains known from other evidence to be closely related. Several virus strains have been classified by this test (see *533*). Although the rule may be generally valid, some reservations may be made (*460*). Cross-protection is not always a clear-cut phenomenon. The suppression of the second virus may be more or less complete, depending on the amount of virus used in the test. A heavier inoculum may simply increase the chances of infecting cells not invaded by the first virus, but may also allow competitive relations between two viruses in individual cells. McKinney has shown that the green tobacco mosaic virus prevents manifestation of yellow mosaic symptoms, but that infection with the yellow strain does not prevent growth of the green strain, which slowly replaces the symptoms caused by the yellow strain with its own (*459*). Thus, even with closely related viruses, cross-protection does not always work both ways. There is actually one virus that offers a complete exception to the cross-protection rule, the sugar beet curly top virus. This virus exists in several strains differing in virulence; there is no protection by the avirulent toward the virulent strains, and even an avirulent strain can be shown to multiply in a plant already infected with a virulent one (*250c*).

In some instances, cross-protection may fail to occur between viruses that are serologically closely related (*46*). On the other hand, there are rare instances of two completely unrelated viruses (for example, severe etch virus and potato virus Y) in which the first virus not only prevents infection with the second but also displaces it when it is already fully established (*44*). Similar displacements have been described for diseases, such as those of peaches, that can only be transmitted by insect vectors or by grafting. Little peach virus displaces the virus of peach yellows from yellows-infected buds grafted on plants carrying little peach (*387*). Altogether, the cross-protection tests, although generally very valuable, cannot be considered as complete evidence for relatedness.

Virus synergism. It is clear from these few examples that interference phenomena in plant virus diseases can take different forms. We have described some in which one virus suppresses or inhibits the multiplication or the manifestations of another. There are instances in which the reverse is true, and two viruses together give more extensive and more destructive manifestations than either one alone; for example, tobacco mosaic virus gives a severe necrotic disease in plants already infected with potato virus X. Sometimes the association of a mild virus with a latent virus may produce a rapidly destructive disease. Some virus synergism is probably due to an actual increase in virus production in doubly infected cells (561a). There might also be a more rapid destruction of cells infected by two viruses, or a cooperation between two viruses infecting different cells in destroying the plant tissue. Mixed infection of individual plant cells has been demonstrated by the presence of the characteristic inclusions of two viruses, one of which gives cytoplasmic, the other intranuclear inclusions (462).

Acquired immunity and "plant antibodies." A peculiar situation has been reported by Wallace for the sugar beet curly top virus in tobacco or tomato (662; 663). This virus is transmissible either by graft or by the leafhopper *Circulifer tenellus*. Infected tobacco plants generally recover and become immune to reinfection with the same strain, whereas tomato plants become severely sick and seldom recover. The recovered plants can always be shown to contain virulent virus, because a leafhopper can transfer the severe disease from recovered plants to healthy tomato. If tomato plants are inoculated by grafting from recovered plants, they manifest only a mild disease and recover regularly. This situation was interpreted by Wallace as suggesting that recovery depends on the production by the plant of a protective substance similar to an antibody. In grafting, the protective substance is supposedly transferred along with the virus, thus producing a passive immunization, whereas the insect transmits only the virus. It is possible to imagine, however, that in the recovered plants there exist two or more mutant forms of the virus (see chapter 15), some more virulent, some less, and that the less virulent protect the plant against the more virulent. In grafting, the mild virus may have an opportunity to spread ahead of the virulent. The insect, instead, may either transmit only the virulent virus or may transmit both viruses in such a way that the virulent one is not hampered by the mild strain.

Apart from these observations, which, incidentally, could not be confirmed by other workers (533a), there is no evidence for humoral mechanisms of immunity in plant virus diseases. Interference phenomena such as acquired immunity and cross-protection are, therefore, especially important, since they seem to be the only mechanisms that may lead to a protection from viruses in intrinsically susceptible plant cells. Apparently, most acquired immunity to plant viruses is due to a persistent, chronic disease and depends on direct cell protection by virus already present within the cells.

INTERFERENCE IN ANIMAL VIRUSES

In the study of the responses of an animal host to double infections with two viruses or with two inputs of the same virus, we find situations more complicated than with plant virus diseases (see *300; 583*). The major complication derives from the occurrence in animals of serological reactions with the production of antiviral antibodies, whose effect on the virus has to be taken into account in interpreting the course of infection. Many nonfatal infections with virus (measles, mumps, yellow fever) leave a permanent, more or less complete, specific immunity, which may or may not be dependent on persistence of virus in the recovered host. Some immunity is transitory, and reinfection is possible even after rather short intervals (common cold, influenza). This may reflect the rapid replacement of the cells of tissues attacked by these viruses (*556*). Usually immunity can be correlated with presence of antibodies in the blood serum of the recovered animal. It is often difficult to establish whether other mechanisms of immunity at the cellular level are also involved.

Acquired tissue immunity. The first point to be considered is the fate of the virus during infection and recovery (*288*). For a number of viruses, for example, for the infection of the central nervous system caused by the herpes virus (*466*), the amount of infectious virus that can be extracted from the infected tissue diminishes after a certain time; finally, no active virus can be recovered. This "autosterilization" precedes either the death of the host or its recovery, and in case of recovery is generally associated with the establishment of immunity to a second infection with the same virus. It is not clear whether the virus need still be present to stimulate antibody production, thereby preventing infection by the second inoculation, or whether a change in the antibody-producing cells has occurred, which causes them to continue antibody production (or at least to retain the ability to produce such antibodies quickly if presented again with the viral antigen).

A phenomenon that illustrates both the relation between actual infection of a group of cells to their immunity upon reinoculation and the speed at which such immunity can be established is the so-called "rail immunization" (*Schienenimmunisierung* of the German authors; see *287*). In herpetic infection of the central nervous system, the virus spreads along the nerve fibers from the periphery to the central nervous system and, within the latter, from the point of entry to other parts of the brain or of the spinal cord. The virus, which if injected directly into the brain would cause a rapid fatal infection, often produces only a mild infection or even a completely latent one, if it spreads along the nerve paths within the nervous system. At the same time, the nerve tissue invaded by the virus acquires a definite degree of immunity to a challenge inoculation that would otherwise be fatal. It can be demonstrated that only those portions of the central nervous system that have actually been invaded by the virus are immune to the second inoculation.

Phenomena of this kind have been observed not only for neurotropic viruses but for other viruses as well. For example, influenza virus inoculated into mice intraperitoneally soon reaches the lungs, where, instead of the usual fatal pneumonia, it causes a mild infection and gives rise to solid immunity against reinoculation by the bronchial route (553).

In cases like this, local immunity apparently becomes established as the virus spreads, before antibodies are detectable in the general circulation. One is therefore tempted to suppose that immunity results from an alteration of the infected cells, following infection by a route that does not lead to their destruction. The nonrecoverability of the virus in these immune tissues might have to do either with actual disappearance of virus, leaving the cells in a modified condition, or with the persistence of the virus inside the cells in such a way that it cannot be extracted in active form.

The possibility of the persistence of modified virus inside cells that have acquired local immunity might be tested by serological methods. For example, we might try to detect virus antigens by the complement-fixation reaction in extracts of immune tissues. Such tests have not yet been made systematically.

Attempts have been made to test whether tissues that would be immune to a virus in the animal body are still able to support virus reproduction if isolated in tissue cultures. The results are somewhat contradictory. Some authors report ability of a virus to grow in cultures of tissues from immune animals, provided antibodies are carefully removed (virus III; 24); others report a suppressed or reduced multiplication of viruses in tissues from immune animals (559). It is not always clear whether the tissue investigated has acquired local immunity of the type described above, as distinguished from the generalized immunity of the animal, which is due mainly to circulating antibodies. In reduced multiplication of virus in cultures of immune tissue, it is also difficult to exclude the presence of some residual antibody in the tissues, since complete removal of antibody is very difficult, even by perfusion of immune tissues and organs.

The theory that local immunity is caused by an alteration of the virus-growing ability of the host cells has been weakened by the demonstration that high concentrations of antibody exist in the very areas where virus activity is greatest. In some neurotropic virus infections, particularly poliomyelitis and equine encephalomyelitis, the distribution of antibodies in the central nervous system closely parallels that of the areas of active multiplication of the virus. This parallelism is not accounted for by a secondary localization of antibody from the circulatory system. The suggestion arises that antibody is produced locally by the infected cells; these local antibodies have the same properties as antibodies found in serum (492; 581). A possible role of local antibody production in local immunity (and in rail immunization) is supported by the rapidity with which this antibody may be produced when mice immunized with the virus of equine encephalomyelitis are reinoculated with the same virus (580). The vaccinated mice often die if given a small challenge dose, but are fully resistant to intracerebral inoculation with high virus doses, presumably because the high doses cause in the vaccinated animal a quick local production of antibodies in amounts sufficient to protect. Immunity may depend, in such cases, on the rate of multiplication of the challenge virus; a rapidly multiplying strain may develop too fast for the local antibody titer to reach an adequate level, whereas a slow-growing strain may be held in check.

These quick local immune responses may explain such paradoxical phenomena as the so-called Magrassi protection phenomenon (467). Intracorneal inoculation of a neurotropic strain of herpes virus, which would normally spread to the brain along the optic nerve and cause a fatal encephalitis, fails to do so if the animal receives, 7 or 8 days *after* the first inoculation, a direct intracerebral inoculation of the same virus. By itself, the intracerebral inoculation would also cause a rapid, fatal disease. Thus, two inoculations, each by itself potentially fatal, mutually protect the animal when the routes of inoculation and the time interval between them are delicately balanced.

We see then that serological mechanisms may be responsible for much local immunity; even where other mechanisms are involved, it is difficult to discriminate between their role and that of antibodies.

Protection by interference. There are instances of acquired resistance to viruses for which serological mechanisms are not responsible. A classic case concerns infection with strains of yellow fever virus. A neurotropic strain, restricted in its affinity to the central nervous system and almost harmless to monkeys, can protect monkeys against the effects of a pantropic strain, which by itself causes a fatal visceral infection (*221; 350*). The neurotropic strain can protect monkeys even if inoculated several hours after the pantropic strain. The neurotropic yellow fever strain also protects the monkeys against Rift Valley fever virus, which is serologically unrelated to yellow fever.

The above observations illustrate some of the typical features of interference between strains of the same virus, and also between serologically unrelated viruses, where serological protection seems excluded. The same is true of interference in the chick embryo, where antibody production is absent.

Interference may be detected by a variety of observations: by survival instead of death; by failure of typical lesions to develop; and, sometimes, by actual demonstration of a reduced or suppressed virus multiplication. Such a suppression can be demonstrated better in interference between unrelated viruses, by titrating them separately, either in selectively susceptible hosts or after suppressing one of the viruses with specific antiserum. Interference between the rapidly fatal, serologically unrelated Western and Eastern equine encephalomyelitis viruses can be demonstrated in animals previously immunized against one virus; injection of a large amount of this virus gives a resistance of short duration against the other virus, due to interference (*585*). The short duration of protection by interference is typical, in contrast with the lasting protection given by serological immunity.

In interference between strains of the same virus, various methods can be used to titrate one virus in the mixtures. For example, neurotropic influenza virus in a mixture with nonneurotropic influenza strains can be titrated in the mouse brain. By this method the suppression of the neurotropic strain by the nonneurotropic one in tissue cultures could be demonstrated (*27*).

It seems certain that interference requires the actual occupation of a cell by the interfering virus (*583*). Thus, a virus inoculated in excess can seldom be suppressed, except by a more rapidly developing virus. The establishment of interference closely parallels the progress of infection with the interfering virus, and it wears off as the infection regresses.

When the interfering virus does not multiply appreciably in a tissue, large amounts of it are required for interference. In general, a virus is only able to interfere with other viruses in those tissues for which it has some affinity. For example, influenza virus can protect the central nervous tissue of mice against Western equine encephalomyelitis (656). Although in the mouse brain the influenza virus does not reproduce in infectious form, it can at least undergo a cycle of incomplete reproduction.

The occurrence of interference between serologically unrelated viruses is not the rule. Double inoculations may lead either to double infection or to interference; the outcome depends on the nature of the viruses, on the mode and amount of inoculation, and on the host. Relevant data are summarized in tables 28 and 29, reproduced from Henle's excellent review (300). In some cases, interference is reciprocal, in others it has been demonstrated in one direction only.

Dual infection rather than interference may occur with potentially interfering viruses if the amounts of viruses inoculated are so small that reproduction can take place in different cells (635). In other situations, interference fails entirely to take place. With mixtures of two viruses, one of which gives intranuclear inclusion, the other intracytoplasmic, cells with dual inclusions have been observed (14; 639). Virus synergism, in which a dual infection leads to more severe lesions than either infection by itself, has also been reported (219).

Interference by inactive virus. Interference among animal viruses has been observed between inactivated and active virus of the same strain, and also between an inactive virus and an unrelated active virus. It is a fairly safe prediction that, given the proper conditions, practically any interfering ability that a virus exhibits when active will also be exhibited by the same virus inactivated by agents such as ultraviolet light. Examples are given in table 30. In influenza viruses, interference has been observed with heat-inactivated virus that had lost its receptor-destroying ability; this indicates that the latter property is not necessary for interference to take place (358). Also, in interference between influenza and Western equine encephalomyelitis virus, the enzymatic activity of influenza virus is not needed for interference (584).

Large inocula of inactive virus are needed for interference to occur. The presumption is that enough virus must be present in the inoculum to invade most of the cells in which interference has to be produced. Thus, in the allantoic sac, which contains about 10^8 cells, we need at least 10^8–10^9 irradiated influenza virus particles to suppress the growth

Table 28.   Reports on interference between antigenically unrelated
active agents

From Henle's review (*300*), which should be consulted for original references

Interfering Agent	Excluded Viruses
Columbia SK and MM	Poliomyelitis; Western equine encephalomyelitis
Equine encephalomyelitis, Eastern	(?) Newcastle disease
Equine encephalomyelitis, Western	Eastern equine encephalomyelitis; vesicular stomatitis; (?) Newcastle disease
Foot-and-mouth disease	Rabies; lymphogranuloma venereum
Herpes simplex	Rabies; (?) vaccinia
Influenza A	Influenza B; Eastern and Western equine encephalomyelitis; Newcastle disease; St. Louis encephalitis; Bwamba
Influenza B	Influenza A; swine influenza; Western equine encephalomyelitis
Swine influenza	Influenza B; Eastern equine encephalomyelitis; Newcastle disease virus
Louping ill	Rabies
Lymphocytic choriomeningitis	Poliomyelitis; Columbia MM
Mumps	Western equine encephalomyelitis
Newcastle disease	Western equine encephalomyelitis; (?) poliomyelitis; influenza A
Poliomyelitis	Columbia MM, lymphocytic choriomeningitis; (?) heterotypic poliomyelitis
Rabbit papilloma	Sheep dermatitis; herpes simplex
Sheep dermatitis	Rabbit papilloma
St. Louis encephalitis	Western equine encephalomyelitis
Theiler's encephalomyelitis	Western equine encephalomyelitis; rabies; poliomyelitis; St. Louis encephalitis; louping ill; lymphocytic choriomeningitis; lymphogranuloma venereum
Vaccinia	Foot-and-mouth; rabies
Virus III	Infectious fibroma
West Nile	Venezuelan equine encephalitis; influenza A
Yellow fever	Rift Valley fever; West Nile; influenza A; Venezuelan equine encephalitis; dengue

(?) denotes questionable instances of interference.

Table 29. Reports of dual infection of a host organism or of failure
of interference

From Henle's review (300), which should be consulted for original references

First Agent	Second Agent
Eastern equine encephalomyelitis	Mumps
Feline pneumonitis	Fowl pox
Fowl pox	Herpes simplex; laryngotracheitis; vaccinia; feline pneumonitis
Herpes simplex	Vaccinia; fowl pox; rabies
Infectious myxomatosis	Rabbit papilloma
Influenza A	Influenza B; mumps; lymphogranuloma venereum; epidemic typhus; yellow fever; rabies; Semliki forest; pneumonia of mice; West Nile
Influenza B	Influenza A; mumps; pneumonia of mice
Laryngotracheitis	Fowl pox
Louping ill	Lymphogranuloma venereum
Lymphocytic choriomeningitis	Distemper
Lymphogranuloma venereum	Influenza A; rabies; louping ill
Mumps	Influenza A; influenza B; Eastern equine encephalomyelitis; Newcastle disease
Newcastle disease	Mumps
Pneumonia of mice	Influenza A; influenza B
Rabbit papilloma	Vaccinia; infectious myxomatosis; virus B; virus III
Poliomyelitis	Heterotypic poliomyelitis; rabies
Rabies	Lymphogranuloma venereum; poliomyelitis; herpes simplex
Epidemic typhus	Influenza A
Vaccinia	Herpes simplex; fowl pox; virus B; rabbit papilloma
Virus B	Vaccinia; rabbit papilloma
Virus III	Rabbit papilloma
Yellow fever	Vaccinia; Venezuelan equine encephalomyelitis; West Nile

of a simultaneous or subsequent inoculum of active virus (300). It
has been calculated that one particle can prevent multiplication of
heterologous virus in a cell (122).

Interference phenomena of this kind must be taken into account in
practical problems, as in testing cross-protection after vaccination or
in assaying inactivated virus preparations for residual active virus. It

Table 30.   Interference between inactivated and active agents

From Henle's review (*300*), which should be consulted for original references

Interfering Agent (inactivated)	Excluded Agent (active)
Ectromelia	Ectromelia
Infectious bronchitis of chickens	Infectious bronchitis of chickens
Influenza A	Epidemic keratoconjunctivitis; influenza A; influenza B; mumps; swine influenza; Western equine encephalomyelitis
Influenza B	Influenza A; influenza B; mumps; swine influenza
Mumps	Influenza A; influenza B; mumps
Columbia SK and MM	Poliomyelitis
Newcastle	Newcastle
Psittacosis	Meningopneumonitis
Swine influenza	Influenza A; influenza B; swine influenza

is clear that the presence of an excess of inactive virus in the test may mask a considerable amount of residual infectious virus.

Mechanism of interference.   Even though the cellular basis of interference among animal viruses is well established, it is seldom possible to interpret the observations in terms of phenomena occurring at the cellular level, such as mutual exclusion, depressor effects, and prevention of maturation, which are recognizable in work with bacteriophage. Some progress has been made, however, in the study of interference between influenza viruses in the allantoic sac of the chick embryo. Simultaneous inoculation with influenza A and B, with one virus in large excess, leads to suppression of the minority virus; suppression also occurs between ultraviolet-inactivated virus and active virus of the same type or of the other type.   Interference may in part be due to enzymatic destruction of the cell receptors for virus adsorption.   But interference at the level of intracellular reproduction also plays a major role; in fact, a second inoculum of inactive virus, whether homologous or heterologous, several hours after the first inoculum can still reduce the yield of active virus by the infected cells.   The second inoculum may prevent maturation of those virus particles whose development had not reached a certain critical stage (*426*).

It is important to realize that interference is observed only when the amounts of virus inoculated are adequate.   For example, influenza viruses A and B can be carried simultaneously in the allantoic sac for at least 9 serial transfers when the inocula are not great enough to cause initial interference (635).

The phenomenon described by Von Magnus (659), consisting of the production of hemagglutinating but noninfectious virus upon inoculation of influenza virus at high concentration in the allantoic sac, may also involve interference. The original virus suspension may contain a large proportion of immature particles, incapable of reproduction but capable of attacking the host cells and of interfering with the maturation of normal virus. Upon heavy inoculation, the interfering, nonreproducing virus elements may prevent the reproduction of most normal virus beyond the stage of the immature particle itself; the cycle can then be repeated.

The interpretation of interference phenomena in animal viruses is not yet clear. Apart from cases in which interference may be due to removal of virus receptors from host cells, one may conceive of a competition for substrates, or of a blockade of the processes leading to virus production at any one of its hypothetical stages. Usually, if interference arrested the development of a virus at the level of the production of intermediate forms, these would not be detected at all.

In view of the increasing support for the idea that reproduction of most viruses involves both a process of reproduction and one of maturation, it is conceivable that either process may be interfered with at any one of its stages. Interference between related viruses may involve mechanisms different from those of interference between unrelated viruses, just as in bacteriophages.

The practical significance of interference phenomena. It is difficult to assess the role of interference phenomena in the immunity of animals to virus diseases. Experimental observations indicate that interference phenomena could provide a protection different from the serological one. It is debatable, however, whether this cellular mechanism of protection plays any important role in the course of natural infections.

The interference phenomenon has been utilized in the therapy of distemper in silver foxes. A ferret-adapted strain of distemper virus protects the animal by interfering with the fox-adapted strain (272). Protection still occurs when the ferret strain is introduced after the virulent strain, provided the virulent strain had been administered by the nasal route, which is presumably the natural way of transmission.

Interference phenomena could be of great significance in virus immunity if viruses remained present in the cells of recovered animals for a long time and thereby protected them from reinfection. On the one hand, since the best evidence, if any, for the long persistence of viruses is based on the lasting presence of antibodies against viruses, it is difficult to discriminate between the role of the antibodies and the role of the virus itself in protecting against related viruses. On the other hand, there is no evidence for lasting immunity against a virus disease resulting from previous infections with unrelated viruses.

15

Variation in Viruses—
Host Variation and
Susceptibility to Viruses

VIRUS VARIATION

Viruses form a very heterogeneous group and must be considered as comprising a number of different and distantly related entities. Great variation is found even within groups of viruses that are considered as related. Variations are even observed within virus populations raised under experimental conditions that make it as certain as possible that the whole population has originated from one individual virus particle within the duration of the experiment. Thus we witness the appearance of new virus properties just as we witness the appearance of variations in any organism, provided populations of sufficient size are observed. Because of this, it has recently become an almost general custom among virologists to interpret the variation of viruses, and therefore also their evolution, along more or less classic genetic lines (*114; 218*).

In the past microbiologists had often assumed that viruses (and also bacteria) exhibited a peculiarly great variability and adaptability. Indeed, it was observed that transfer of a virus to a new host, or even inoculation by a different route, was often followed by permanently inherited changes in the properties of the virus. This adaptability suggested to virus workers a peculiar plasticity of virus heredity.

Adaptability in populations of higher organisms depends on the availability of a variety of hereditary traits, including some that will be favored under new environmental conditions. Virus plasticity, instead, used to be considered as directly dependent on the ability of the virus to change its nature according to the environment in which it grew. A priori, it may indeed seem logical to assume that a strictly intracellular parasite may directly derive some of its heredity from the host cell that produces it.

The belief that most virus variation is directly produced by the host environment is unjustified; we now know enough about variation in viruses to state this with fair confidence. Just as in higher organisms, most (but not all) variation in viruses appears to occur through an essentially random production of mutations. The range of mutability is determined by the intrinsic potentialities of the genetic material of the virus proper. The frequency of such apparently "spontaneous" mutations (*mutation rate*) is not obviously affected by extrinsic factors, although no adequate data are available on the rates of virus mutation in different hosts.

Virus mutants will be selected in environments in which they reproduce faster, or spread faster, or survive longer than the parent types. Microorganisms differ somewhat from higher organisms by the very large size of their populations, which, by making available large numbers of individuals, provides a great variety of mutants. Selection among these can bring to the fore, by selective reproduction, the more favorable phenotypes. To give an example, a heavy virus inoculum, such as is used in the so-called "adaptation procedures" to make a virus grow in a new host, may contain a billion or more virus particles. Most of these may be unable to grow in the new environment, but if one particle in hundreds of millions happens to be a mutant capable of growing, it may produce a population consisting almost entirely of its own offspring.

The situation will not always be so simple. Often, exposure to a new environment may lead to no multiplication at all (failure to adapt). Sometimes, on the contrary, there may be differential multiplication of two or more types of particles, which either were present in the original inoculum or which arose by mutations during growth. The composition of the final population depends on the relative abilities of the different types to proliferate, survive, and spread. All these various types of situations are encountered and play some role in the survival of viruses in nature.

VARIATION IN BACTERIOPHAGE

Plaque-type mutants. Variation in bacteriophage provides us with an almost schematic series of examples on the mode of origin and possible consequences of variation in viruses.

The spontaneous origin of phage mutants is clearly seen in mutations the results of which do not require any special selective environment to manifest themselves. Typically, populations of certain phages (for example, the coli-phages T2, T4, and T6) always contain mutants characterized by plaques larger or smaller than those of the normal, wild-type strain (309). Phage derived from these variant plaques continues to give the modified plaque type. The frequency of such mutants is often of the order of 1 in a 1000 particles. If one searches for mutants in the phage yields from single bacteria infected with wild-type phage, one finds that the mutants, when present, are produced in small groups or clones, along with many nonmutant particles (438). Besides proving the actual production of mutants during growth, the analysis of the clonal distribution of the r mutants, characterized by a larger plaque on agar, provides evidence for the exponential rate of reproduction of phage material (chapter 9). The frequency of spontaneous mutation of phage T2 from the wild type to the r type is about 1 mutation for every 10^4 duplications. This value, however, represents the sum of the frequencies of all mutations that can give rise to the r character; and the number of these is high and as yet undetermined.

In fact, the genetic determination of plaque type in phages of the T2 group is quite complex (see figure 63). The difference in the plaque types reflects differences in the extent to which lysis of the infected bacteria can be inhibited by a second phage infection (181). The least inhibited or r type can arise by any one of a large number of different mutations, which apparently occur in different discrete genetic determinants, since they manifest genetic recombination (see chapter 9). Over 20 strains of T2r, when paired, always gave genetic recombination in mixed infection (314). This situation suggests a great complexity of the genetic apparatus of the bacteriophage, with the presence of a large number of independently mutable elements, all involved in the determination of the response to lysis inhibition.

Host-range mutants. The failure to observe a repeated occurrence of the same r mutation in phage T2 is probably not due to any basic misunderstanding in the interpretation of the experiments on genetic recombination. In fact, similar experiments with other types of mutants of the same bacteriophage yield different results. This is true for mutations affecting the host-range property (*host-range* or h mutants). Most of the independently isolated h mutants of phage T2 do not give genetic recombinants upon mixed infection, and appear therefore to be mutations occurring at the same genetic site.

These host-range mutants provide a typical example of the role of mutation in virus adaptation to new hosts (*434*). By plating a large population of a bacteriophage with a bacterium related to its sensitive host, but resistant to that bacteriophage, we often find a few phage plaques. From each plaque we can isolate a new strain of bacteriophage, similar in most respects to the original one but possessing the permanent ability to attack the resistant bacterium. The frequency of host-range mutants may vary from 1 in 1000 to 1 in 10^9 or more normal phage particles. The mutants may differ from their normal ancestors in heat sensitivity and in some other properties, besides host range.

The host-range mutants of phage illustrate another instructive feature of the play of mutation and selection in determining the make-up of virus populations. If even one host-range mutant particle is present when a suspension of phage is exposed to a resistant bacterium culture that the mutant can attack, the mutant will be the only particle to proliferate and will completely swamp the normal type and quickly eliminate it in successive transfers, since the remaining normal particles will be diluted away.

Mutations may affect any of the phage properties that we can observe. Thus, phages that require certain ions or organic cofactors for adsorption give nonrequiring mutants (*170*). Proflavine-resistant mutants of phage strains have been described (*227*), as well as temperature-resistant mutants (*10*). Mutations can transform a temperate phage into a variety of more virulent forms (*100;* see table 23).

Phage mutations observed to date have not affected either the morphology of the phage particles or the serological specificity of phage types, so that these two groups of characters, which are well correlated between themselves, form the best basis for classification of phage groups. Serological variation with quantitative effects on cross-reactions is observed both among independently isolated phages of a given group and among genetic recombinants (*8*).

Host-range characters are of little value in classifying phage, except in relation to very unrelated bacterial groups. A phage may acquire by one mutation the ability to grow on a strain of a different bacterial species, or even genus or family, from its original host. Host range, therefore, although representing a useful criterion for identification of strains, is too variable a character for taxonomic purposes.

Population analysis of phage variation. With phages, it is possible to carry out interesting analyses of the relative fitness of different mutant types growing on the same host (*309*). Infrequent reverse mutations occur from mutant types to the wild type. If any one mutant is isolated in pure form and carried through a series of sub-cultures, the population tends to revert to the wild type, unless the conditions continue to favor the mutants. For example, an *r* mutant will revert to wild type in 3 or 4 subcultures; rare wild-type particles, originating by mutations, slowly pile up and are favored by a larger yield per bacterium. This is a clear instance of the fact that the virus type found as the majority type in a standard situation is generally the best fitted for reproduction in that situation. The wild type of phage T2 is, of course, the type found in stocks that have been transferred repeatedly in the standard medium. The rate of mutation from a T2*r* to a T2 is only of the order of 10^{-7} per duplication; but although the rate of mutation from T2 to T2*r* is much greater (about 10^{-4}), it is T2 that predominates in a mixture at genetic equilibrium, because of its reproductive advantage. In turn, genetic equilibrium can be reached quickly because of the large size of the bacteriophage popu-lations with which we are dealing. A similar advantage is found for the wild type over the *h* mutants in the presence of bacterial cells in which both *h* and wild types can reproduce; the selective mechanism in this case is unknown.

The reversion of most mutant types to wild type upon subculturing has made possible an analysis for independence of various mutations (*310*). A strain that has undergone two successive mutations is sub-cultured as described above. If reversion to wild type is always pre-ceded by reversion to a single-mutant type, the two mutational steps are considered independent; if reversion occurs in one step, the two mutations were apparently mutually exclusive, as allelic mutations in the same gene would be.

Genetic recombination. The phenomena of genetic recombination in bacteriophage, described in chapter 9, exemplify a type of variation peculiar to mixed populations of related phages. New types arising by recombination are genetically as stable as new types arisen by mu-tation. The role of genetic recombination in phage under natural conditions is unknown; by analogy with higher organisms, we may speculate on a useful role of recombination in increasing the frequency of genetic types within interbreeding phage populations, including the populations of prophages (if any such populations exist) in lyso-genic bacteria.

Nonhereditary variation in phage. There are several interesting cases of phage variation induced by known factors. In all these the variation is nonhereditary, in the sense that the removal of the conditions that provoked the variation causes an immediate return to the original type.

One example of "phenotypic" variation, as distinct from hereditary or "genotypic" ones, is the production of modified phage in bacteria that have received a mixed infection with phages T2 and one of its relatives, T4 or T6 or T2*h* (*500*). For example, cells of *Escherichia coli*, strain B, infected with T2 and T4, liberate part of their phage with T4 host range (active on strain B and an indicator strain B/2, inactive on a strain B/4); but, after one cycle of growth on B or on B/2, some of this phage becomes stable, normal T2. Phenomena of this kind, called *phenotypic mixing*, suggest that some of the phage produced in the mixed-infected bacteria comes out with the genetic material of T2, but coated with a "skin" resembling that of the other phage that was present in the host cells. In the next cycle of growth the new phage comes out with a skin formed under its own control, therefore corresponding to its genotype.

Another type of nonhereditary variation, already mentioned in chapter 9, is a *host-controlled modification of the growth ability* of phage (*446*). For example, phage P2 normally grows in *Shigella dysenteriae* but does not grow in *E. coli*, strain B. Occasionally, a particle of phage P2 succeeds in growing in some exceptional cell of *E. coli* B. The phage that is liberated by B is in a form P2B, which remains capable of successive growth cycles in the *E. coli* strains *as long as it stays with this host* (*76*). It is still fully active on *Shigella*, though, and a single cycle of growth on *Shigella* returns it to the primitive form, which is almost unable to grow on *E. coli*. These relations are illustrated in figure 68 (page 198).

In another typical case (*446*), growth of phage T2 on certain mutant strains of *E. coli* (see table 19) results in the production of phage particles which are unable to reproduce in most cells of the *E. coli* host but remain able to grow on certain strains of *Shigella*. One cycle of growth on *Shigella* restores the normal T2 type, which grows both on *Shigella* and on *E. coli*.

There is no question of mutation and selection in here; the variant character of the phage is directly and strictly determined by the host in which it has grown.

It appears that, by growing in a new host, the phage particles undergo some modification of their physiologically active material (but not of their genetic, hereditary material), which alters their ability to initiate reproduction in some hosts.

There is no clearly adaptive relation in these changes: some new hosts modify the phage so that the phage continues to attack those hosts; some modify the phage so as to prevent it from multiplying further. We have already discussed the role of host-controlled variation in the Vi-phage system of *Salmonella typhosa* (see page 206).

The main interest of these phenomena is that they reveal a new type of plasticity of viruses and a directly governing role of a host on the properties of the virus produced within that host. No definite evidence for or against the occurrence of such host-controlled variation in viruses other than phage has been reported. The relative stability of the best-known virus variants with modified host range, even after return to their original host, suggest that most host adaptation in viruses results from genetic, hereditary changes rather than from host-controlled, phenotypic ones. But the recognition of the phage modifications controlled by the host has opened a new field for the interpretation of a variety of virus transformations whose mechanism and meaning still escape us.

For example, a virus may reproduce extensively in a certain host or in a certain tissue, but apparently only to a limited extent in other hosts or tissues to which it is highly pathogenic. Reproduction of active virus may even fail completely in diseased tissue, as in virus "masking" (see chapter 17). Since the usual tests for virus are made by inoculation of certain hosts, in some of these complex situations the virus may actually be present, but so modified by the host cells that it does not reveal itself in the test host. It seems possible that such phenomena play some role in the course of the transfer of viruses to new hosts and of the spread of viruses from one tissue of the organism to another.

VARIATION IN PLANT VIRUSES

Variation in plant viruses is evidenced by the occurrence in nature of a variety of virus strains for almost every major virus type. These strains may differ in the symptoms produced, in host range, and in many other properties.

Tobacco mosaic virus strains have been found in great numbers; a systematic collection has yielded close to a hundred different types (*362*). Most of these are found accidentally in nature, and their recent common origin must be inferred by similarities in properties (serological cross-reactions; physical similarities between the particles). But some mutants actually appear under the eye of the investigator. Bright yellow patches are occasionally observed in plants infected with a green mosaic virus (figure 6). From these patches one can isolate variants that breed true and give a yellow, more severe type of mosaic (457). The occurrence of yellow mutants in different strains of a virus and in different viruses (tobacco mosaic virus and cucumber mosaic virus; 531) suggests the presence of common genetic determinants with common mutability in these different viruses. Parallel mutants characterized by similarity of symptoms have actually been found to be associated with virus proteins manifesting similar changes in electrophoretic properties from the parental types (243). These viruses with similar mutational patterns are probably more or less related to one another, although they may have become so differentiated that serological cross-reactions may have disappeared. The chemical analysis of several closely related mutants (380) shows differences in the amounts of a few amino acids. The proteins of serologically unrelated viruses differ to a much greater extent (see table 9).

There is no indication that such differences in composition can originate directly as a result of growth in the chemically different environments of different hosts. No valid evidence for chemical similarity between virus protein and host proteins has been obtained. Mutations in plant viruses can reasonably be assumed to arise by the same type of mechanism that causes mutations in hereditary material of all other organisms. The incidence of mutation can be increased by radiation, an agent known to cause gene and chromosomal mutation in plants and animals (264). Most of the procedures used in obtaining variants of plant viruses (passage through different hosts; growth at temperatures above optimum; selection from areas with unusual symptoms or from abnormal local lesions) probably involve simply a selection of spontaneous mutants.

Some interesting conclusions can be derived from ecological observations on the distribution of plant virus strains in nature. It is generally the mild, nondestructive strains that are widely and more or less permanently established in large natural populations of the host. This is only reasonable, since survival and successful propagation are dependent on the ability of the virus to infect as many hosts as possible, allowing them to live and propagate, so that the favorable environment to which the virus is bound will not be exhausted. For a parasite, invasiveness and destructiveness, the two features of virulence, operate in opposition; invasiveness makes for survival of the parasite, destructiveness for self-destruction.

Virulent variants of plant viruses, such as the yellow mutants, are found only in exceptional patches at the place of their origin and are often difficult to maintain without reversion. For all plant viruses there is probably at least one host in which the response is systemic and nonnecrotic. This systemic response is clearly more suitable for virus survival than the necrotic one. The role of latent virus-plant combinations in the survival of virus in nature is actually well established. Many plant viruses are found latent in symptomless hosts.

VARIATION IN ANIMAL VIRUSES

The field of variation in animal viruses includes such an enormous number of observations that it would be impossible to cover it in detail, even by devoting several chapters to it (see 218). Our purpose, however, is to point out the major types of variation, their interpretation, and their practical importance both for virus biology and for the requirements of therapy, prophylaxis, and control of virus diseases. The general principles discussed at the beginning of this chapter make it possible to interpret practically every known observation according to a single pattern.

Natural variation is reflected in the occurrence of groups of viruses, whose relationship to one another is manifested in the morphological similarity of their particles, in serological cross-reactivity, and in common patterns of variability. A typical example of such a group of related viruses is the vaccinia-variola group. Smallpox or variola virus has been known to be the cause of human epidemics for at least 500 years. In man it causes severe smallpox manifestations; a somewhat different strain causes a milder disease (alastrim). Horses, sheep, and cattle are subject to diseases caused by similar viruses; swine-pox is apparently caused by an unrelated virus. Vaccinia virus, the strain used for human vaccination, is derived from smallpox either by transfer through the skin of calves or, more easily, by successive transfers in monkey and rabbit. Other animal pox viruses such as horse-pox also give vaccinia strains, characterized by low virulence for the animal of origin and by frequent failure to produce typical intracellular inclusions (Guarnieri bodies).

The viruses that cause pox diseases in birds, although serologically unrelated to the group of mammalian pox viruses, form a similar group of agents infectious for several domestic and wild birds. Another well-defined group is that of the psittacosis-lymphogranuloma viruses, including several mammalian viruses characterized by similar particles and similar growth cycles, and by the susceptibility of the infections they produce to treatment by various antibacterial drugs (543).

Among groups of naturally occurring related viruses it is interesting to observe the variety of degrees of relationship, as indicated by serological reactions. Let us take, for example, the fibroma and myxoma viruses of rabbits (602). Myxoma virus contains all or almost all the antigenic determinants of fibroma, plus some antigens not present in fibroma; fibroma virus cannot remove all antibodies from serum against myxoma. The relationship between these two viruses is also shown by the fact that both give rise to a similar variant, which produces an inflammatory type of disease instead of a tumoral syndrome.

A more complex situation has been recognized in the influenza viruses. Three major types are known: swine influenza, influenza A, and influenza B, with weak serological cross-reaction between the first two and none between influenza B and the others. A fourth group, influenza C, is represented by one strain, #1233. Each major type occurs in a variety of slightly different serological types; several such types are often isolated from a single outbreak of influenza, suggesting a rapid variation in the course of relatively few transfers. It seems reasonable to suppose that for a virus that is periodically exposed to neutralizing antibodies there will be a selective advantage in a type of mutability providing for great serological variation, and more especially for variants resistant to antibodies that would neutralize the parent type. Thus, hereditary plasticity based on serological variability would afford animal viruses greater chances for successful spread.

Host adaptation and tissue adaptation. Virological literature is full of examples of virus variation arising under the eye of the experimenter. The two most commonly observed types, because of their importance in practical work, are host adaptation and tissue adaptation. A virus pathogenic for man will often give no manifestation, or even not reproduce at all, if injected into a laboratory animal or into the chick embryo; but it may become adapted to do so by repeated transfers, especially by the use of large inocula. This type of adaptation is obtained more or less easily for different viruses and is probably due to the selection of variants which are capable of reproduction in the new host. Typical examples are the adaptation of rabies virus to rabbits, the adaptation of human poliomyelitis virus to mice (something that has occurred only exceptionally, for instance, for the so-called Lansing strain), and the adaptation of a number of viruses to growth in the chick embryo. The adapted variants obtained in this way are generally stable and maintain their new host range even after some transfers through the original host.

Tissue adaptation follows the same pattern and consists of the "training" of a virus to reproduce in a tissue different from the one in which it was found. For example, the viruses of vaccinia, yellow fever, herpes, influenza A, and Newcastle disease give rise to neurotropic variants, which can be revealed by injecting large amounts of the virus directly into the central nervous system of susceptible animals. Examples of host and tissue adaptation could be multiplied at will, a major segment of the experimentation on animal viruses being devoted to finding more suitable hosts for virus cultivation.

Changes associated with adaptation. It is important to keep in mind that, since adaptation probably consists in the selection of spontaneous mutants, the adapted strains may differ from the strain of origin not only in the new host or tissue affinities but also in other properties. This is only natural, because virus mutations are likely to be *pleiotropic*, that is, to affect a number of different characteristics. For example, neurotropic vaccinia is more virulent for the skin and for other organs of rabbit than the dermotropic strain (*190*). Neurotropic strains of yellow fever, on the contrary, after long selection by intracerebral transfer, are almost completely nonvirulent for most organs of monkey and presumably of man. It was a neurotropic strain of yellow fever which, after more than 50 transfers in chick embryo tissue cultures, gave rise to Theiler's strain 17D, which is not pathogenic for man but immunizes against yellow fever. This strain is now used the world over for vaccination (*647*).

Another classic case is that of rabies virus. The virulent virus from rabid dogs ("street" virus) was attenuated by Pasteur by means of successive transfers through the central nervous system of rabbits. This attenuated virus ("fixed" virus), after proper treatments, can be used for human vaccination. Innumerable examples can be found in any book on medical virology. Indeed, the selection of nonvirulent but immunizing virus strains by means of adaptation procedures has provided the best vaccines for the prophylaxis of virus diseases.

A number of interesting changes are associated with the early stages of adaptation of influenza virus to new hosts (*118*). Human strains as first isolated from throat washings or after some transfers in the ferret lung are in the O form, characterized by a low ratio between their hemagglutinating titer for red blood cells of fowl and that for guinea pig red blood cells (low F/G ratio). After several transfers through the allantoic or the amniotic cavity of the chick embryo, the F/G ratio increases. The increase is apparently due to an actual replacement of the O particles by a D mutant, which is better suited for growth in the chick embryo. The virus can be maintained in the O form for several transfers in eggs by using inocula with very little virus. Presumably, the virus population produced in an early egg transfer still consists predominantly of the original type. A light inoculation will generally transfer only this type, and the process of variation and selection of mutants has to start all over again. If, however, the inoculum happens to contain some of the variant virus type, then this type will suddenly take over. In fact, even small inocula can maintain the O form for 5 or 6 transfers only.

The change from O to D form also results in several other changes, affecting pathogenicity, extent of multiplication, and susceptibility to inhibitors of hemagglutination. Other variant forms of influenza viruses appear upon egg transfer (613). Important changes also take place in influenza virus during the first few transfers through mice. Strains isolated from the same epidemic outburst in man, after passage through mice, are often serologically different. If these differences are already present in the original strains from the patients, they have to be taken into consideration in the epidemiological interpretation of such outbursts (231). Since, however, some serological variation accompanies the adaptation of virus to mice, an originally homogeneous group of isolates from a human epidemic may give rise to a serologically heterogeneous group of viruses after mouse adaptation (326).

Virus variation and the evolution of virus diseases. The few examples of variability that we have mentioned give us a lead to the interpretation of the origin of naturally occurring groups of more or less obviously related viruses; each group is probably derived from a common ancestor, which might or might not have been identical with one of the forms currently encountered. Generally, all viruses of a group have morphologically similar particles, in line with the findings on bacteriophages. In looking for the common ancestor of a group of viruses we should expect it to be a virus that produces a mild or fully latent disease of some host, while having opportunities to come into contact with the other hosts now parasitized by the group of viruses. A good example is that of the mammalian pox viruses (117). One member of the group is the virus of ectromelia, a mild endemic disease of mice. The ancestral type of the group may have been either ectromelia itself or some other form of virus well established in some rodent. Rodents are widespread, come in close contact with many other mammals, and are almost ideally fitted to act as virus reservoirs.

The problems of virus evolution and of the survival of viruses between epidemics are among the most fascinating aspects of virology

(*114*). The record is extremely fragmentary, and evidence is often supplemented by guesswork. Even so, a few examples illustrate the principles. Yellow fever as a human disease would have been eradicated by mosquito control had it not been for the occurrence of a jungle form of the disease in wild monkeys and other animals in the tropical forests. Psittacosis, sporadic and very virulent in man, is endemic among parrots and other birds. It is maintained not only in wild birds but also in domesticated ones, because of transmission from mother to young in the nest. Infection of the young is frequently followed by apparent recovery, with return to a stage of active liberation of virus after the animals reach maturity (*483*).

Some instances of variation in animal viruses involve complex situations still unclarified. One such is the fibroma-myxoma virus transformation (*73; 612a*). Fibroma virus causes a mild disease of rabbits, characterized by fibrous tumors, which generally regress; it may be the ancestral form of this virus group. The highly virulent myxoma virus, characterized by a jellylike transformation of connective tissues, is always fatal to rabbits. Injection into the rabbit skin of a mixture of live fibroma virus and heat-killed myxoma virus (which cannot cause myxoma by itself) often gives rise to typical myxoma. This indicates either a transformation of the fibroma into myxoma virus or a reactivation of the inactive myxoma. Successful transformation depends on the relative amounts of live fibroma and heated myxoma virus. The transformation can also be induced by deproteinized extracts of myxoma (*612a*).

We have already discussed in chapter 13 the recent experiments on phenomena resembling genetic recombination in influenza viruses (*120*).

GENETIC AND DEVELOPMENTAL FACTORS IN VIRUS SENSITIVITY

The host range of any virus must reflect not only the genetic properties of the virus, but also those of its hosts. Different tissue affinities must reflect differences arising in the course of development among the cells of an organism. Usually the genetic and developmental factors that determine virus-growing ability are too complicated for analysis in either genetic or biochemical terms. Some simple cases of differences in virus sensitivity or in virus response among closely related organisms offer an opportunity to see some of the basic mechanisms in action.

Sensitivity to bacteriophage. With bacteriophages, the sensitivity of a bacterial host may be suppressed by a single spontaneous mutation (*435*). That the bacterial mutations to phage resistance are spontaneous, that is, not induced by contact with the phage, is shown, for example, by the fact that phage-resistant mutants can sometimes be isolated without previous contact with the phage, either because of peculiarities in colonial morphology or by means of special detection procedures (*411*).

The spontaneous origin of the bacterial mutations to resistance results in a peculiar distribution of mutants in a series of similar bacterial cultures (*442*). The sooner the first mutation to resistance happens to occur in a given culture, the larger will be the number of mutants in that culture, when later tested. If many similar cultures are tested for the proportion of phage-resistant mutants they contain, they show wide fluctuations. These fluctuations are, therefore, an expression of the fact that the mutants are already present in the cultures, in the form of clones of identical sibs, before the cultures have ever come in contact with phage. This forms the basis of the so-called "fluctuation test" for spontaneous bacterial mutations.

The genetic resistance of bacteria involves either complete inability to adsorb phage or only inability to carry out the irreversible stage of phage adsorption (*250*). It has proved valuable material for the study of bacterial genetics (*435*). A bacterium may by one mutation become resistant to one or more of the phages that attack it, and, by successive independent mutations, may acquire resistance to several phages. There seems to be no correlation between the properties of two phages with a common host and the existence of bacterial mutations producing joint resistance to both phages. A mutation to resistance to one phage often modifies several bacterial properties, such as ability to adsorb other phages, ability to synthesize some essential metabolites, or ability to produce other phages in normal form. For example, certain mutants of *Escherichia coli,* strain B, are resistant to phage T4 and, although still sensitive to phage T2, produce a modified form of T2 (*446; see page 295*).

Bacteria with known sexual phenomena of the genetic-recombination type (specifically, *E. coli,* strain K-12) show that each mutation producing phage resistance behaves as a change in a single gene. In diploid races of K-12 heterozygous for resistance and sensitivity to a phage, sensitivity is dominant (*410*). In this bacterial strain, even the alternative characters, lysogenicity or sensitivity for the phage lambda, behave as a pair of allelic differences (*409*).

Plant viruses. Good evidence has been presented for a simple genetic determination of the type and severity of plant response to several plant virus diseases. The best examples are those of genetic control of necrotic response to tobacco mosaic virus in tobacco and in other plants.

The usual tobacco plant, *Nicotiana tabacum,* as well as many other species of *Nicotiana,* respond to tobacco mosaic virus by a systemic chlorotic disease. *Nicotiana glutinosa* responds with necrotic lesions at the points of entry of the virus. This localization of the virus prevents its spread. If present in the commercially valuable *N. tabacum* it could confer a "field immunity" to a tobacco crop. Hybrids of *N. tabacum* × *N. glutinosa* give the necrotic response; this is due to a dominant factor (N) from *N. glutinosa* (*337*). These hybrids are sterile and cannot be used to transfer the N gene to *N. tabacum* by further crosses. Success was obtained (*339a*) by crossing *N. tabacum* with *N. digluta,* a fertile artificial amphidiploid hybrid (carrying both the *tabacum* and the *glutinosa* chromosomes). Some of the progeny plants had the N type of response; unfortunately, this was present in a chromosome derived from *N. glutinosa* (*250a*) and was accompanied by other commercially undesirable *glutinosa* properties. Further crosses have succeeded in reducing the amount of *glutinosa* heredity in the tobacco derivatives and seem to have provided commercially valuable derivatives (*250b; 654b*). The resistance conferred by the necrotic response is not complete, since generalized necrosis may follow heavy inoculation, but is quite adequate under field conditions. The genetic basis of the necrotic type of resistance to tobacco mosaic virus in plants other than tobacco has also been elucidated (*339*).

Another type of resistance has been observed in the variety Ambalema of *N. tabacum.* This variety remains symptomless if inoculated with tobacco mosaic virus (*498a*). The dominant factor for resistance (A) can be introduced in other varieties of tobacco. Its practical usefulness may be limited by the fact that the virus may multiply in the resistant plants.

Single gene differences determine the ability of an insect (*Cicadulina mbila*) to transmit the corn streak virus; the dominant allele of a sex-linked gene determines ability to transmit the virus, apparently by controlling the permeability of the wall of the insect gut for the virus (*632*). Other cases of the same type exist (see chapter 16).

Animal viruses. Genetic work on sensitivity to viruses in higher animals has been limited by the practical difficulties of pure-line work in mammals; until recently there was an inadequate realization of the importance of hereditary factors in resistance to disease (see 265). "High-mortality" and "low-mortality" strains of mice with respect to several viruses (pseudorabies, equine encephalitis) have been reported. Some results of hybridization suggest a single-gene control of susceptibility and resistance; more commonly, control is probably polygenic.

A discovery by Sabin (572) has provided a clear-cut example of genetic determination of sensitivity to animal viruses. An inbred strain of mice (PRI) is 100% resistant to the neurotropic 17D strain of yellow fever, and is also resistant to several other neurotropic viruses (dengue, West Nile fever, encephalitis of the Japanese B, St. Louis, and Russian types; not to poliomyelitis, equine encephalomyelitis, or rabies). In crosses with other inbred mice, the resistance of strain PRI behaves as if controlled by a single dominant gene. Resistance is only complete in the adult mice, not in the newborn. The mechanism of resistance is a reduction in the extent of production of infectious virus in animals with the dominant gene. It is not known whether virus multiplication is altogether suppressed or arrested at some noninfectious stage.

Other studies of this kind have seldom given such clear-cut results. These studies are complicated, in the first place, by intrinsic complexity of the genetic mechanisms involved (multiple-gene characters; genes with incomplete penetrance, that is, with more or less frequent failure to produce their phenotypic effect). In the second place, there are complications due to developmental differences. These manifest themselves both in the various tropisms of viruses, which cause them to reproduce in some tissues of a host and not in others, and in the influence of age on the susceptibility of the organism as a whole.

Thus, even a bacterium may differ in its response to a phage according to the stage in its cultural cycle, from actively reproducing cells to resting cells. In plants, a virus that invades rapidly growing cells may produce a milder infection than in mature cells. The competition of actively synthesized protoplasmic components may be too strong to allow the virus to grow as much as in nongrowing cells.

In animals, the age of the host may affect either the tissue response or the successful operation of immunity mechanisms. Newborn animals are inefficient producers of antibodies; in man this condition lasts about 6 months after birth and is reflected in greater morbidity and mortality, for example, from encephalomyelitis (579). Persistence of antibodies from immune mothers may sometimes play a role in the opposite direction. In mice, the degree of immunity produced by vaccination with Eastern equine encephalomyelitis increases rapidly in the first few days after birth. This age-dependent immunity is strictly peripheral and due to production of antibodies; the susceptibility of the brain to direct inoculation with the virus remains constant (491).

In some cases, the age of an animal determines its receptivity to a virus, which then remains latent for a long time in the animal's tissues. This is so, for example, for the so-called milk factor of mammary carcinoma in mice (see chapter 17). Age and hormonal factors determine the later manifestations of the latent virus.

Viruses and tumoral host cells. An important application of the specific tropism of viruses is their use as tumor-destroying agents (489a). A variety of viruses will attack preferentially the cells of certain tumors and destroy them. For example, a mouse sarcoma may become necrotic and nontransplantable 6 days after the mouse that carries it is inoculated intraperitoneally with encephalitis virus (Russian strain). A virus may even destroy a tumor of an animal in which it produces no sign of disease, for example, encephalitis virus in tumor-bearing chickens (594).

This "oncolytic" (= tumor dissolving) property of viruses obeys definite rules of specificity. Certain viruses destroy only certain tumors, others none. There is no absolute relation between the ability of a virus to destroy a tumor and its ability to reproduce in its cells. Successive transfers of a virus in a tumor may increase its oncolytic ability (489a); the mechanism of this adaptation to a more destructive action on the host cell has not yet been analyzed.

Transmission, Vectors,
and Survival of Viruses

For its successful propagation, a virus must come in contact with susceptible cells. We must now consider how virus propagation is effected in nature. A consideration of virus transmission and survival furnishes the key to an understanding of the epidemiology of virus diseases, hence to a rational prophylaxis.

Transmission presents no special problems for bacteriophages. Chance contact between phage and bacteria is probably the general mechanism of propagation. Lysogenic bacteria are the virus reservoirs, and it is likely that any phage well established in nature exists in lysogenic relation with some bacterial strain.

The situation is more complex for animal and plant viruses. The external surfaces of the host organisms act as barriers to virus penetration. The structural differentiation of the host often buries the susceptible cells in deep tissues and organs. To parasitize successfully an animal or a plant, a virus must penetrate the surface and sometimes also internal barriers, reach the susceptible cells, multiply, and be released in such a way that it can reach another host.

Direct mechanical transmission is possible only through wounds or by contact with poorly protected cells. In animals, the cells lining the respiratory or digestive tract are the most exposed. Often, transmission by mechanical means is inadequate and the virus must be introduced directly beyond the protective cell layers, generally by arthropods or other vectors.

Once penetration has been accomplished, the virus often has a long way to go in order to reach susceptible cells. Success is possible because of the existence of spreading pathways. Plant viruses move along with food in the vascular tissues of plants. Likewise, animal viruses circulate with the blood, the lymph, and possibly the spinal fluid [1] of animals until they reach susceptible cells. Humoral transport is especially successful in the early phases of infection, before circulating antibodies appear.

Some viruses, however, have special ways of spreading. Several of the neurotropic viruses spread along the nerve fibers to the central nervous system (352). This nerve transport appears to occur in the axon rather than along the surrounding sheaths of the nerve fiber. This is the major route of spread for some viruses, which may reach the nerve endings in the mucous membranes or in exposed, wounded tissues (93). Not all neurotropic viruses are restricted to the nerve pathway, however. Poliomyelitis virus apparently multiplies at the point of entry and in other tissues (573), and is found transitorily in the blood circulation. Its spread to the central nervous system may occur either through the blood or along the nerve fibers (91). Spread through the blood before reaching the central nervous system is the rule with equine encephalomyelitis.

Nerve transport occurs both centripetally and centrifugally, as well as from one part of the central nervous system to another. It is doubtful whether viruses such as rabies and poliomyelitis actually multiply in the nerve fibers. The rate of progress of poliomyelitis virus in nerves (2.4 mm per hour; 92) is compatible with the idea of spread without multiplication.

The precision and selectivity of the mechanisms for virus spread in an infected organism may seem extraordinary. We must, however, remember that the possibility of infection exists only when such mechanisms are present. Virus-host relations as we find them in nature are the product of a long process of selection, which continuously perfects these relations by trying the viruses in a variety of anatomical and physiological environments.

Mechanical and graft transmission of plant viruses. Few plant viruses are regularly transmitted by mechanical inoculation. Tobacco mosaic virus can penetrate through the roots, although by this route it often fails to invade the rest of the plant (532). Infection of roots from soil also occurs for tobacco necrosis and wheat mosaic viruses. Some of the potato viruses are perpetuated by the planting of infected tubers. Seed transmission is the exception rather than the rule. Even when tuber and seed transmission can maintain viruses, transmission

---

[1] The spinal fluid probably transmits viruses injected into it to the central nervous system but does not seem to be involved in the natural propagation of neurotropic viruses.

from diseased plants to healthy plants is necessary for virus survival; otherwise the diseased plants would ultimately be displaced by healthy ones and the virus would perish with them. Therefore, all viruses must be transmitted in nature from plant to plant by external mechanisms; most of them are spread by insect vectors.

Practically all plant viruses are transmissible by *grafting* (or *budding*), but this method plays a role only in the natural spread of viruses of domestic fruit trees. Plant viruses can also be transmitted through dodder.

Mechanical transmission of animal viruses. Many animal viruses are regularly transmitted by mechanical transfer. We may mention measles, psittacosis, poliomyelitis, the mammalian pox viruses, and pseudorabies. These viruses are liberated from infected individuals in crusts, droplets, or feces, from which they can easily reach accessible mucous membranes of other individuals. For poliomyelitis, the frequent presence of virus in the feces of infected and carrier persons has incriminated flies (*478*) and cockroaches (*356*) as possible vectors. These insects would be vectors only in the sense of spreading the virus and introducing it into food, not as specific carriers involved in the actual propagation and inoculation of the virus. The inoculation of rabies virus by the bite of rabid animals may be considered as a peculiar instance of mechanical transmission.

Human-disease viruses that are transmitted mechanically will survive if they produce mild diseases that are widespread in the human population. For example, the virus of lymphogranuloma venereum remains in the infected person for a long time, is transmitted almost exclusively by sexual contact, and is very frequent among sexually promiscuous groups in certain localities. Another survival pattern is exemplified by those viruses sporadically causing a serious disease in man, while the virus is endemic in a domestic or readily domesticated animal. For example, lymphocytic choriomeningitis is common in grey mice (*31*), in which it remains active for a long time and causes a symptomless infection transmissible from mother to offspring in the womb (*651*). In such cases, even a high mortality rate in an accidental host, such as man, does not preclude virus survival. The epizootic pseudorabies virus causes a regularly fatal disease in cattle. It persists in nature because of its widespread occurrence in hogs, in which it causes a readily transmitted, extremely mild syndrome (*599*).

Control of human viruses transmitted mechanically is even more difficult than control of insect-transmitted viruses, as evidenced by the persistence of measles and poliomyelitis. Mass vaccination is the only effective measure, provided effective vaccines are available, as for smallpox. (In domestic animals, breeding for immunity is an important possibility.) The futility of many quarantine measures (351) is due to the mild and often symptomless course of the infection in most individuals (subclinical infections).

Poliomyelitis is again pertinent (114; 351). The paralytic disease is apparently the exception, probably representing about 1% of the cases of infection; a genetic factor seems to be involved in its occurrence. Most people have contacts with the virus in childhood, possibly more than once, and become at least partially immune for life. The maximal incidence of primary infections seems to have shifted from infancy to early school age. This may be due to a later average time of first exposure to virus in children, because of a higher proportion of immune adults in the community. In spite of this widespread immunity, there must always be present enough subclinically infected carrier individuals, probably children with primary infections, to give the virus its almost world-wide distribution in the form of small epidemics.

TRANSMISSION BY VECTORS

Many animal viruses and practically all plant viruses are transmitted in nature by arthropod vectors, mainly insects. This mechanism of transmission is favored by the feeding habits of the vectors. Bloodsucking insects such as mosquitoes and lice take up a virus by feeding on infected animals and transmit it to other animals of the same species or of other species. In plants, sucking insects (aphids, leafhoppers, etc.) and some biting ones are continually feeding on plants and moving from one plant to another, thereby transmitting viruses. Some such vector mechanism is usually a necessity (see table 2).

Animal viruses. As examples of vector transmission we may take, first, yellow fever and dengue fever, both of which are transmitted by mosquitoes, particularly by the species *Aedes aegypti*. This is a frequent pest in tropical and subtropical human communities along the coasts of the Atlantic Ocean and the Mediterranean Sea. The proof by Walter Reed and his group (548) of the role of mosquitoes in the transmission of yellow fever has long been part of the saga of medical microbiology.

The equine encephalomyelitis viruses are transmitted by several mosquitoes and other arthropods. The Western form of equine encephalomyelitis (WEE) can be transmitted by a common tick, *Dermacentor andersonii*. The Eastern form (EEE) and a Russian form are also transmitted by ticks, and so are the louping ill virus of sheep and the virus of Colorado fever. Sandfly fever (papataci fever), a mild virus disease common around the Mediterranean, is transmitted by a diminutive fly, *Phlebotomus papatasii*.

The relations among virus, host, and vector are ecologically and biologically complex. Not all arthropods feeding on an infected host can transmit viruses, and different insects transmit different viruses. Moreover, if we find that a given insect can transmit a virus, this does not mean that it is the vector of that virus in nature, or even one of the usual vectors. Ecological factors may completely prevent it from playing a role. For example, although ticks can transmit the Western equine encephalomyelitis virus (*638*), it is doubtful that they play any significant role in its spread.

After feeding on an infected animal, the vector is not always immediately capable of infecting another animal. For example, it takes 8–12 days for *Aedes aegypti* to become "infectious" after engorgement with yellow fever-infected blood (*419*), and 7–10 days after feeding on a dengue patient (see *87*). What is the reason for this delay or "incubation period"? One reason is that the virus finds itself in the gut of the insect and must reach the salivary glands before being injected with the insect's saliva into another susceptible animal. The passage from the gut to the blood and from the blood to the glands may take some time. There is definite evidence that the intestinal wall of an insect may be a barrier to virus penetration. *Aedes aegypti* can transmit WEE virus, but apparently not EEE virus. Merrill and Tenbroeck (*481*), repeating with the EEE virus a classic experiment on a plant virus (see page 315), found that if, after feeding on emulsions of guinea pig brain containing EEE, mosquitoes had their abdomens punctured, so that the ingested virus could penetrate into the body cavity, they became capable of transmitting the virus. In viruliferous mosquitoes the virus is present in practically all tissues and organs (*342*).

Multiplication of animal viruses in vectors. At least some animal viruses multiply in the tissues of the vector. The incubation period represents in part the time needed for multiplication of the virus. Yellow fever virus can be titrated by injecting mice intracerebrally with the pulp of *Aedes aegypti* at various intervals after the insects have fed on a monkey infected with yellow fever. The virus titer decreases at first, then increases and reaches a level that may be 50 times higher than the initial one (*681*). This rise in titer is particularly evident if the mosquitoes are not allowed to ingest too much virus (a mosquito can ingest as much as 10^6 infectious units at one feeding). With the same mosquito, the WEE virus was carried for 17 successive insect-to-insect transfers without loss of titer (481). This virus can be cultivated in cultures of tissues from mosquito (650). The EEE virus also multiplies in the mosquito vectors (482).

Although the virus multiplies in their tissues, the infected mosquitoes do not show any recognizable symptoms of disease. This situation is different from that of typhus rickettsiae in the body louse, which dies because of massive destruction of its intestinal mucosa by the rickettsiae (see chapter 19).

The reproduction of viruses in the insect appears to be the explanation of the long persistence of transmitting ability after a single infective meal. For dengue, transmission by mosquitoes has been obtained as long as 174 days after feeding, (88) the longest period tested. Once infectious, an insect will probably remain so for life. Virus transmission from generation to generation through the egg is exceptional; it is doubtful whether it occurs at all for yellow fever. St. Louis encephalitis virus can be transmitted for two generations through the eggs of the chicken mite, *Dermanyssus gallinae* (612).

The fact that viruses that are generally considered to be parasites of vertebrates multiply in their arthropod vectors raises the problem of the significance of the host-insect cycle in virus reproduction. There is no evidence for a relation similar to that obtaining, for example, for malarial parasites or for rust fungi, in which alternating forms of reproduction take place in different hosts, so that the host cycle reflects the reproductive cycle of the parasite. Viruses that are transmitted by insects in nature can also be transmitted directly from a vertebrate host to another by injection or other means, and, as we have seen, from insect to insect. All available facts can be explained by postulating that the passage of a virus through a vector is not an essential part of the life cycle of the virus and that insect transmission is simply the expression of the ability of one particular virus host to inoculate the virus successfully into another host.

Vectors and ecology of animal viruses. The vector-virus relation should be considered from the standpoint of virus survival and, therefore, of the distribution and the epidemiology of virus diseases. Let us consider WEE (549). This disease is sporadic in man and sporadically epidemic in horses. In horses, it appears in widely scattered herds in the spring and subsides before fall. Mosquitoes, particularly *Culex tarsalis,* can transmit the disease to horses, but infection of mosquitoes by feeding on infected horses has not succeeded, probably because of the low virus titer in the horse blood. It is almost certain that the natural pathway of the disease is not "horse–mosquito–horse." Moreover, adult mosquitoes do not survive the winter and do not transmit the virus through the egg. Instead, several fowl, both domestic and wild, are found to be infected in a symptomless way and can infect mosquitoes that feed on them. The fowl are infested by parasites, particularly mites, which can carry the virus through their eggs and can transmit it from chicken to chicken. The most likely cycle for this virus is, therefore, "fowl–insect–fowl," with horses and man as accidental hosts. This idea is in agreement with the theoretical expectation of a mild, symptomless infection in the most stable reservoir. Some vectors may carry the virus through the winter, but their role does not seem to be important.

An intriguing situation arose in connection with yellow fever when sporadic human cases were first recognized in jungle clearings of the South American interior, away from the usual coastal abodes of *Aedes aegypti* and in the absence of human reservoirs, which by that time had practically been eliminated. This "jungle yellow fever" was traced to infection of monkeys, with transmission from monkey to monkey or to man by mosquitoes other than *Aedes aegypti*. If the jungle yellow fever virus is introduced into an urban community, it can then be spread by *A. aegypti* (*618*).

A similar jungle yellow fever is suspected to exist in central Africa, the presumptive cradle of yellow fever. Yellow fever is rare and mild among African Negroes, even if they are not vaccinated. This fact suggests a certain degree of selection for yellow fever resistance among the African Negroes during the long centuries of exposure to the virus.

The examples given above illustrate the general causes underlying the geographical distribution of animal virus diseases and clarify some of the epidemiological problems in virus control. It is clear that neither human vaccination nor *Aedes* eradication, however successful in eliminating coastal yellow fever, can completely eradicate the disease as maintained in the jungle. Similarly, vaccination of horses against WEE can protect these animals but cannot eliminate the virus harbored in its bird reservoirs. Vector control can go one step further. There is a great difference between these diseases and those caused by ubiquitous, presumably single-host viruses, such as measles. Vaccination, when possible, is the key to the control of the single-host diseases. Serological variation of the virus is probably the main source of complications in such control measures.

Another interesting consequence of the mode of transmission of a virus is its seasonal incidence. For example, in two concurrent summer epidemics of WEE and poliomyelitis (203), the WEE rapidly disappeared with the coming of colder temperatures, which caused rapid death of mosquitoes, whereas the poliomyelitis incidence continued high until late in the fall. This observation speaks against any important role of insects in the spread of poliomyelitis. The causes of the summer incidence of poliomyelitis in man are unknown. We might speculate on a role of the summer vacation habits that bring together children from different areas, whose previous immunizing contacts, if any, may have been with serologically different strains of the poliomyelitis virus (492).

Some complex relations of viruses to multiple hosts can be clarified by brilliant and painstaking work; a classic example is that of swine influenza (601). The disease is caused by a double infection with swine influenza virus and with the bacterium *Hemophilus influenzae suis*. It is epizootic in swine herds, where it appears regularly in the fall, although the virus does not persist long in pigs. Interepidemically, the virus can be preserved for years in the lungworm, a nematode that infests the lungs of the pigs and there becomes infected with the virus. The lungworm retains the virus throughout its complete life cycle, which involves several stages of parasitism in the pig and in the earthworm. The pig becomes parasitized by the lungworms after eating earthworms infested with the lungworms. The adult lungworms develop in the pig and transfer the virus to it. The virus cannot even be detected serologically in the lungworms during large portions of their life cycle ("masked" virus). The only proof of the presence of the virus is the fact that pigs that have ingested lungworms and have been inoculated with *H. influenzae suis* can come down with influenza. The actual outbreak of the disease is generally brought about by any one of a variety of exposures to unfavorable conditions (wet, cold weather; poor hog house conditions, etc.). Prophylaxis may be aimed at controlling one or more of the links in the complex chain of events.

Interestingly enough, swine influenza appeared as a new disease in 1918, coincident with a world-wide outburst of pandemic influenza. It is possible that in pandemic influenza some bacterium may have played a role similar to that of the *Hemophilus* in the swine.

Plant viruses. Insect transmission is the rule in most plant virus diseases. The specificity relations are similar to those observed with animal viruses. Some vectors are biting insects, for example, the vector of turnip yellow mosaic. However, the majority of the insect vectors of plant virus diseases are sucking insects, mostly aphids and leafhoppers, but also white flies, mealy bugs, and tingids. The tiny green aphid *Myzus persicae*, a common plant louse, feeds on a great many plants and transmits at least 50 different viruses of potato, bean, cabbage, onion, tulip, sugar beet, and other plants. The leafhopper *Circulifer tenellus*, the vector of the virus of sugar beet curly top, probably transmits only this virus and is the only species known to transmit it. In one instance, vectors belonging to different related genera are needed to transmit two barely distinguishable virus strains (*81*). Because of such specificities, single virus strains can often be isolated from mixed-infected plants by means of proper insects.

Nonpersistent transmission. Two types of virus transmission by insects are observed in plants. These are the persistent and the nonpersistent types (*667*). In the nonpersistent type, the insect can transmit the virus immediately after feeding and for a relatively short time thereafter (24 hours or less). This is true, for example, for potato virus Y and *Myzus persicae*. It was long supposed that transmission in these cases was simply due to mechanical transfer of virus by the contaminated mouthparts of the insect. The relation is apparently more complex, however (see *43*). Nonpersistent transmission shows certain specificities. Aphids may fail to transmit viruses such as tobacco mosaic virus that are readily transferred mechanically, yet may transmit other viruses from the same host plant. Successful transmission depends on the physiological condition of the insects, such as the degree of previous starvation. Viruses transmitted in a nonpersistent way probably do not have to be deposited into the plant phloem, whereas some viruses transmitted by the persistent mechanism probably do.

Persistent transmission. In the persistent form of transmission, the insect is usually not immediately infectious after feeding. The incubation period, which lasts from a few hours to several weeks, includes the time for passage of virus through the wall of the gut, into the blood, and into the salivary glands. For some viruses at least, there is actual multiplication of the virus in the vector. The viruses reach the new host with material injected by the insect's stylets. The stylets find their way, by an intercellular or intracellular path, through the epidermis and often reach the phloem tissue of the vascular bundles (figure 90).

The passage of viruses through the wall of the gut has been demonstrated by Storey's classic experiments (*632*) on *Cicadulina mbila*, the leafhopper that transmits the corn streak disease. This leafhopper exists in two strains, one that can transmit the virus, the other that cannot. The transmitting strain carries the dominant allele of a gene pair, whereas the nontransmitting strain is homozygous recessive.

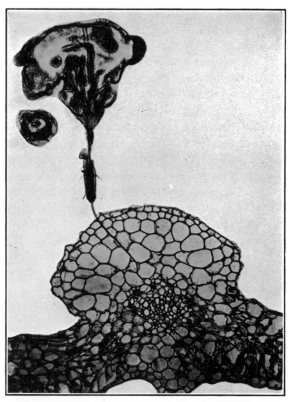

Figure 90. Section through a potato leaf and an aphid (*Myzus pseudosolani*) showing the path of the insect's stylet reaching into the phloem. From: Dykstra and Whitaker, *J. Agr. Res.* **57**:319, 1938.

Storey showed that the nontransmitting insects can transmit the disease if, after they have fed on infected plants, their abdomens are punctured. The puncture permits the passage of the contents of the gut into the blood. Thus the effect of the genetic difference appears to be at least in part a difference in gut permeability to the virus.

The presence of virus in insect's saliva has been demonstrated by allowing leafhoppers infected with sugar beet curly top virus to feed on droplets of a sugar solution. The sugar solution receives virus and can give it to a new batch of uninfected insects that are later fed on the same droplets (124a; 609). The salivary glands of insects, however, often contain less virus than the blood (63).

The deposition of viruses into the vascular tissue by their vectors cannot be the whole explanation of the success of insect transmission of plant viruses. Many viruses cannot be transmitted by needle inoculation into the phloem, for example, aster yellows virus. It is possible that the insect's stylets are less damaging than needles to plant cells, or that sometimes the virus may be combined with some inhibitor present in the plant sap but not in the saliva. In some cases, a virus that affects the plant xylem is inoculated by its vector into this tissue (350b).

Multiplication of plant viruses in their insect vectors. Several plant viruses transmitted by leafhoppers actually multiply in the body of their insect vectors, just as yellow fever virus multiplies in *Aedes aegypti*. The incubation period, especially when long, represents in part the time needed for virus reproduction. The evidence in favor of the multiplication of plant viruses in their insect vectors is now beyond question.

Multiplication had long been postulated, for such virus as aster yellows, on the basis of the following observations (82; 389; 390): 1. Insects fed on infected plants may remain viruliferous for a very long time, presumably for their whole life. 2. After feeding, the amount of virus recoverable from an insect decreases at first, then increases again. 3. This process can be exaggerated by heating the insects, a treatment that can render them nonviruliferous. If the heat treatment is properly administered, the insects may later become viruliferous again, supposedly because of multiplication of residual virus.

More direct and convincing evidence has come from experiments in which the viruses have been carried from insect to insect for such long series of passages that multiplication must have occurred for any virus to be present. At least two viruses can pass from mother to progeny through the egg. Rice stunt virus was transmitted through the eggs of its vector for 6 generations (245), and clover club-leaf virus for 21 generations (84). Had the clover club-leaf virus not multiplied, it would have been diluted by a factor of at least 10^{26} between the initial insect and the last batch of eggs tested. This result is clearly incompatible with the hypothesis of dilution and can only be explained by multiplication of the virus in the insect.

The discovery that some plant viruses can be transferred directly from insect to insect by injection of extract of viruliferous insects into nonviruliferous ones (*632*) has made possible another proof of virus multiplication. Aster yellows virus has been transmitted for 10 passages, corresponding to a dilution factor of 10^{40}, in the leafhopper *Macrosteles divisus* (*470*), and the wound tumor virus has been transmitted for 7 transfers in the vector *Agallia constricta* (dilution factor 10^{18}; *85*). In these experiments, reinfection through the plants on which the insects fed was excluded by using plants that do not support multiplication of the virus under investigation. Particles of the wound tumor virus isolated either from plant tissue or from insect tissue have the same morphology (*100c*).

Although multiplication of plant viruses in their insect vectors has been proved for several viruses, it is not certain whether it occurs in many others. For example, curly top virus presumably does not multiply in its vector, or at least does not multiply enough to maintain itself in insects that have acquired small amounts of virus.

Whether many plant viruses multiply in the insects or not, there is no evidence for an obligatory alternation of plant and insect parasitism. Both insect-to-insect transmission and plant-to-plant transmission appear to be possible in all instances that have been investigated.

VECTORS, HOST RANGE, AND EVOLUTION OF VIRUSES

Virus multiplication in the insect vectors of viruses parasitic on vertebrates and on plants raises a number of interesting problems. We must ask whether these viruses should be considered as plant viruses, insect viruses, or vertebrate viruses. It is clearly a matter of choice whether we call aster yellows virus a plant virus or an insect virus. The real problem concerns the origin of these viruses and their natural history. The primary host of a virus, that is, the host which is essential to its survival, is probably the one in which the virus produces the least damage and can best maintain itself alive from generation to generation. Thus, insects in which a virus can be transmitted through the eggs, and which show no harmful effect of the virus, may be the most important reservoir.

We know that virus reproduction requires a host possessing a specific pattern of synthetic mechanisms, whose suitability for the virus is genetically determined. If a virus can grow in two hosts widely separated taxonomically (such as a plant and an insect, or a mammal and a mite), it must find suitable conditions for growth in both hosts.

In turn, this suggests that similar synthetic mechanisms have arisen, probably by different genetic evolution, in the two hosts.

It is unlikely that an insect-transmitted virus, for example, aster yellows, could have remained parasitic on a long evolutionary series of plants and of insects feeding on them. It is reasonable to assume that the virus was originally restricted to one of the hosts only, the plant or the insect. The same may be said of insect-transmitted animal viruses. Suppose we started with a virus parasitic in an insect that feeds regularly on a plant, for example, the aster. Virus will regularly be inoculated into the plant, in which we assume it does not reproduce. If the virus happens to produce variants that can multiply in the plant tissue, whenever such a variant particle even by an extremely rare chance enters the plant, its chances of invading other insect individuals or even other insect species feeding on that plant are enormously increased. Such a variant will soon become the predominant type. A mutant of a mammalian virus able to reproduce in (and reach the saliva of) one of the many types of mosquitoes that suck the blood of the mammalian host (particularly if the mosquito is not itself damaged by the virus) might spread so much better than the parent virus strain as to displace it or to occupy successfully many new ecological niches.

Thus we may visualize the ability of a virus to multiply in two hosts, one feeding upon the other, as an adaptation, by natural selection, to a mode of life more favorable for survival. The survival of an insect virus will be greatly favored by introduction into a longer-lived host, rendering it less dependent on egg transmission. In turn, the survival of a plant virus will be enormously favored by multiplication in an insect that feeds on plants.

Although the paths of evolution of viruses are as yet difficult to trace, the above considerations suggest some of the possible features of the process. Another source of information is provided by epidemiological data, as we have mentioned in connection with Western equine encephalomyelitis. Ecological considerations are also useful. They have been employed, for example, in attempts to trace the origin and evolution of tobacco mosaic virus and of the response of various species of *Nicotiana* to this virus (*341a; 654c*); in support of the origin of pox viruses of man and the domestic animals from an ancestor pathogenic for rodents; and of poliomyelitis from viruses of the mouse encephalitis group (*114*). Rodents, in view of their widespread distribution, their high fertility, and the continuous contacts between wild rodents and their man-surrounding relatives, are probably excellent reservoirs for many viruses of human diseases.

In speculating along these lines we must remember that we are not only observing virus evolution but the evolution of virus susceptibility in the host populations as well. For example, the virus of measles causes a mild disease in human populations that have long been exposed to it, but it produced a highly fatal disease (with over 25% mortality) when first introduced among the inhabitants of South Sea islands. This suggests that the present virulence relation in the "civilized" world is due to the selection of resistant human hosts rather than to changes in virus properties.

Let us state once again that the changes in host and virus populations that are most favorable for virus survival are those that encourage widespread and asymptomatic infection. Herpes virus infects about 90% of humans within their first 5 years of life and generally remains in the body in a symptomless relation. Other viruses related to herpes (pseudorabies, virus B) also have a tendency to produce asymptomatic infections. The virus of silkworm jaundice, which can probably be transmitted through the insect egg, is carried in latent form by most silkworm colonies. A variety of stimuli can provoke the appearance of the disease (654a; 690a).

A man-made experiment in virus ecology is the artificial introduction of myxoma virus in Australia as a means of controlling rabbits which have multiplied to enormous numbers in some parts of that continent. After several years of slow spread among the rodents, the myxoma virus, disseminated by contacts and with the help of some insects (215a) has suddenly spread widely in epidemic waves since 1951, destroying enormous numbers of rabbits (545a).

Viruses and Tumors

Tumors and cancers. The tendency of virus-infected cells to disintegrate, as for example in the lysis of phage-infected bacteria, is by no means general. Frequently, cells continue to divide after virus infection, as proved by the presence of mitotic figures in inclusion-bearing cells. The major manifestation of a virus infection may even be an abnormal proliferation of the host cells, which may lead to the formation of tumors.

A variety of abnormal growths in multicellular organisms (animals or plants), in which a group of cells reproduces beyond its place in the organism, are called *tumors* or *neoplasms*. The cells that constitute a tumor are generally not different in any obvious gross way from those of normal tissues. Yet, the tumors are distinguished from pathological hyperplasia (an exaggerated growth of normal cells, as in the formation of excessive bone tissue in the callus around a bone fracture) by their lack of functional coordination with the rest of the body. This autonomy makes tumors truly parasitic on the rest of the organism. For example, a tumor of fat tissue or lipoma will not lose fat when the rest of the organism loses almost all its fat because of starvation or disease.

The degree of parasitism upon the organism varies from tumor to tumor. *Benign* neoplasms are those that grow without actively destroying neighboring organs or disrupting the metabolism of the organisms, and with no tendency to produce *metastases*, that is, secondary tumors caused by transfer and implantation of tumoral cells into other organs. A typically benign tumor, such as a lipoma or a fibroma, is mainly a mechanical nuisance, as in growing it pushes aside other organs. The transition is almost continuous from benign to *malignant* tumors, the *cancers* of current speech. Cancers are neoplasms that grow very rapidly, whose cells exhibit frequent and often abnormal mitoses, infiltrate and destroy normal tissues and organs, and produce metastases.

The changes that make cells neoplastic and, more especially, malignant are not yet understood. Usually tumor cells are related to normal cells and may perform some of the specific activities, secretory or otherwise, of the tissues from which they derive, although without coordination with the normal body constituents. Thus, we distinguish epithelial and connective tumors. Among the epithelial we find, for example, papillomas or epidermal tumors (warts), adenomas or glandular tumors; among the connective, we find chondromas or cartilaginous tumors, osteomas or bony tumors, and many others. Even in the most atypical cancer, the tissue organization often bears some resemblance to that of a normal tissue. This is evident both in epithelial cancers or *carcinomas* (in which the tumoral epithelial cells are accompanied by a nontumoral connective stroma), and in connective tissue cancers or *sarcomas*. The tumoral quality of the cells is an intrinsic property. In tissue cultures, a line of tumor cells maintains its tumoral properties and, if the cultivated cells are properly reimplanted by graft into a suitable host, they will "take" and produce a tumor.

Transplantability by *graft* is one of the major techniques of experimental tumor research. Tumor grafting is subject in animals such as mammals to the same type of limitations as the grafting of normal tissues. Genetic factors prevent the "taking" of heterologous grafts, partly because of immediate toxic reactions, partly because of the formation of antibodies against the foreign tissues. Heterologous grafts, even beyond the borders of the species and the genus, may succeed in places, such as the brain and the anterior chamber of the eye (275), or in chick embryos (497), where antibody production and penetration are restricted and other resistance mechanisms are probably less effective.

Graft experiments with tumors in laboratory animals generally require highly inbred stocks obtained by repeated brother-to-sister matings (pure lines). An interesting manifestation of the relative autonomy of tumor tissues is that the genetic conditions for successful implantations are often somewhat less stringent than for most normal tissues; for example, some mouse tumors can be propagated by graft in many individuals of noninbred colonies (see 425). Moreover, extrachromosomal factors appear to play a role in determining susceptibility to tumor grafting (141; 406).

In typical instances of tumor graft, it is the transplanted cells that give rise to the tumor in the new location, without neoplastic transformation of host cells. Following heterologous grafts, serological tests indicate that the transplanted tumor cells still possess the specificity of the donor. There is usually no reason to suspect a tumoral transformation of the cells of the recipient host by the material in the graft. The frequent appearance of sarcomas in the stroma of transplanted carcinomas or even of benign adenomas is unexplained, however; it may be due to a tumoral nature of some of the connective cells already included in the first transfer, although the spread of cancer-producing agents from one type of cell to another cannot be excluded (502).

ETIOLOGY OF TUMORS

Carcinogenic agents. What causes a cell or group of cells to assume the neoplastic habit of growth and to become a tumor? Generally, the cause is unknown; we speak of "spontaneous tumors." Within recent years, however, it has become clear that a number of agents can induce the formation of neoplasms. Notable among them is a group of cyclic hydrocarbons (for example, methylcholanthrene, 3,4-benzo-pyrene, 1,2,5,6-dibenzanthracene; see 276), whose application to normal tissues provokes a high incidence of tumors. These chemically induced tumors include most varieties that occur spontaneously and also some that would not be observed otherwise, possibly because their spontaneous incidence is too low. Following inoculation into a rat, for example, of one of these carcinogenic substances, a series of tissue disorders occur, which at first are not very dissimilar from a chronic inflammation, but which lead more or less rapidly to the formation of a true neoplasm, often a cancer. In the neoplasm the carcinogen is no longer present, but the cells have become permanently modified.

The carcinogenic hydrocarbons are the best example of a variety of agents, including radiations (615), parasites (see 161), and many chemicals, that act as *provocative* causes of cancer, by inducing or favoring a more-or-less irreversible neoplastic transformation of the cells, after which the agent appears to play no further role.

Virus tumors. There are some carcinogenic agents, however, that remain present in the tumors they induce and apparently continue to play a role in the development of the neoplastic cells, accompanying them, so to speak, in their growth career. These *persistent and actuating carcinogens* (563) are viruses.

In 1903 Borrel (95) put forward the suggestion of a possible virus origin of cancer. His evidence was mainly a comparison of the properties of carcinomas with those of a series of virus diseases of epithelial cells (*infectious epithelioses,* such as pox diseases and foot-and-mouth), in which cell proliferation was observed side by side with cell necrosis. Borrel pointed out that the causes of tumors were probably multiple. Valid proof of the viral etiology of a tumor would require the demonstration of the successful production of tumors by inoculation of cell-free extracts of other tumors into normal hosts (97). In 1911 Rous produced such proof.[1]

Fowl tumors. Rous succeeded in reproducing indefinitely by serial inoculations of cell-free, bacteria-free filtrates of tumor extracts a sarcoma that had appeared spontaneously in a Plymouth Rock hen and had been transplanted into several hens of the same race (562). The agent in the extracts gave rise to tumors similar to the one of origin; they appeared very fast, from 7 to 10 days after inoculation. This is a much shorter time than is required for the action of chemical carcinogens. The agent of Rous sarcoma was also present in the blood of tumor-carrying chickens. It was shown later that the active agent is in the form of particles, about 70 mμ in diameter, with a ratio of particles to infectious units of about 2000 in the best preparations (139). Tumors could be induced by injecting filtrates either into the connective tissue of chickens or into the blood. The agent was indeed a virus in the accepted sense of the word.

Following Rous' discovery and an almost simultaneous similar one (244), several viruses were isolated from a variety of tumors of chickens, ducks, and other birds and from cases of fowl leukemia (228). Although no viruses have as yet been isolated from fowl carcinomas, it seems possible (229) that for every fowl tumor there will ultimately be found an etiologically responsible virus. Often a virus can be obtained by extraction from the original tumor, without previous transplantation (285).

Individual viruses of fowl tumors differ from each other; some of them are apparently as little related to one another as any two animal viruses taken at random. In general, each virus gives rise to tumors with the same histopathological features as the tumor from which it has been isolated, and only if introduced in the proper tissue. This discriminating, directional carcinogenesis clearly differentiates these

---

[1] Transmission of fowl leukemia by cell-free extracts and blood serum had been reported in 1908 (204a), but the neoplastic nature of this disease had not yet been recognized clearly.

viruses from the chemical carcinogens, which bring out the neoplastic potentialities of a variety of tissues in a variety of hosts. Clearly, the specificity relations observed with tumor viruses resemble the relations of specificity between viruses and host cells in general.

Most fowl tumors, in spite of their inducibility by viral agents, are not contagious under natural conditions. Animals kept in the same cage with cancer-bearing individuals do not show any higher incidence of tumors than control animals. No insect vectors have been found, and the problem of the normal transmission of these viruses remains unsolved. The agent responsible for fowl lymphomatosis is transmitted from hen to chick through the egg and possibly also through the sperm (107).

There was initially a great resistance among cancer workers against recognizing the virus tumors of fowl as true tumors, or their agents as true viruses. The suggestion was put forward that the virus provided only the stimulus for the tumoral transformations of the cells. The virus, however, continues to reproduce and to play a role in the neoplastic development of the cell line derived from the initially infected cell. Many of the arguments whether the Rous agent and other tumor agents of fowl are true viruses or transmissible inducers of cell transformations (transmissible mutagens; 140) are in reality applicable to viruses in general. They do not set aside the fowl tumor agents, which at any rate qualify for inclusion among viruses according to the definition of virus adopted in this book. The arguments have rather to do with the mode of action of viruses in their host cells and with their relation to other cell components.

Other virus tumors. The fowl tumors did not long remain the only known examples of tumors produced by viruses, and we now recognize virus tumors in insects (78a), in amphibia, in mammals, and in plants.

A frequent carcinoma of the kidney of leopard frogs is caused by a viruslike agent (429; 560). Its cells contain peculiar intranuclear inclusions such as many viruses produce.

In mammals, viruses have been isolated from tumors of man, rabbit, and mouse. Human warts (skin and laryngeal papillomas) and the genital papillomas (condyloma acuminatum) are caused by a virus or a group of closely related viruses (216). The role of the virus in the occasional cancerization of genital warts is unknown (see 563).

In rabbits, there occurs a group of virus diseases (fibroma-myxoma) intermediate between inflammations and tumors. The fibroma (597) is a mild proliferative disease of the subcutaneous tissue, endemic in wild rabbits, which regularly undergoes spontaneous regression. The myxoma (576) is a highly fatal, more inflammatory process, which also involves some proliferation of the infected cells. A variant form of the fibroma virus produces a form of inflammation without extensive cell proliferation.

Another virus which causes oral papillomatosis in rabbits (513) is apparently present in most individuals of certain rabbit colonies, where it manifests itself only by causing the formation of specific antibodies.

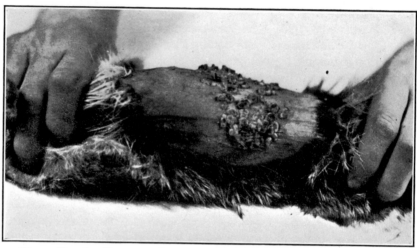

Figure 91. Papillomas produced by artificial inoculation of papilloma virus (Shope) in wild cottontail rabbit. Courtesy Dr. R. E. Shope, Rockefeller Institute, New York.

Rabbit papilloma. A very interesting virus tumor of rabbits is a papilloma (598) frequently observed in the wild cottontail rabbits (figure 91). The virus extracted from the papillomas induces an epithelial growth intermediate between benign warts and malignant carcinomas, with some tendency to full cancerous transformation (373). The tumor is easily reproduced by rubbing its cell-free extracts on scarified skin and is probably contagious among cottontails in nature, as suggested by its geographic distribution.

A remarkable feature of the rabbit papilloma virus is that its inoculation into the domestic rabbit (an animal belonging in a different genus from the wild rabbit) results in the formation of papillomas that are similar to those of wild rabbits, but from which little or no infectious virus can be isolated. No tumor-producing agent is present in extracts of these tumors, nor are physical particles resembling those of papilloma virus found in amounts similar to those in the papilloma of the wild rabbits (57). If the papillomas in domestic rabbits are protected from mechanical injury (which otherwise causes their hard, horny mass to fall off) they regularly give rise to very malignant cancers in which no infectious virus is observed (see 564).

Is the virus absent from these tumors? Not quite. Serological data indicate that the virus persists in a *masked*, noninfectious form (602). The blood of domestic rabbits that carry a papilloma (or a carcinoma derived from it) reveals the presence of antibodies that neutralize and fix complement with the virus isolated from cottontail warts. Extracts of the domestic rabbit papillomas injected into rabbits induce an immunity against the virus. This serologically specific virus "remnant" cannot be eliminated by grafting the cancers that arise from the papillomas through several animals hyperimmunized against the virus (371). Such a procedure would eliminate foreign viruses, which accidentally or experimentally may contaminate grafted tumors (557). It should be noted that antivirus antibodies in high titer do not prevent growth of grafted cancer cells, although they prevent not only infection by the virus but also the "taking" of grafted papilloma cells.

These observations seem to indicate that the virus, although masked, is a persistent component of the tumoral cells of domestic rabbits, and probably one directly concerned in determining the tumoral properties of these cells.

There is more evidence of the actual existence of virus, possibly in modified form, in domestic rabbit papillomas. It is occasionally possible to demonstrate the virus in filtrates of extracts of these papillomas by injecting the filtrates into skin rendered hyperplastic by nonspecific irritants (241). Moreover, in two cases (590; 600) serial transmission in the domestic rabbit for 18 and for 14 passages has been successful. Return of the virus to the cottontail rabbit for 1 passage gave rise immediately to a strain of the "cottontail type," nontransferrable in the domestic rabbit (590).

It is interesting to compare these findings on the papilloma virus and on the tumors it produces in its various hosts with the findings on bacteriophage in various host situations (see chapter 9). The masked papilloma virus, like the prophage in the lysogenic bacteria, is not present in infectious form. It can be detected serologically, whereas the prophage has not yet been detected in this way, possibly because of different antigenic organization in the two types of viruses. The masked papilloma virus presumably impresses certain specific properties on the cells that carry it, like the lysogenic prophages. Occasional production of active virus from the masked papilloma virus (the equivalent of prophage maturation) may be hard to detect in view of the rather insensitive tests available for detection of papilloma virus (1 infectious unit = several millions of virus particles). Irradiation of domestic rabbit papillomas with x-rays often causes an increase in the amount of infectious virus detectable in extracts made a few hours later (240), an observation that recalls the "induction" of lysogenic bacteria by radiations (454).

One of the cancers derived from domestic rabbit papilloma, the Vx2 carcinoma, retained the antigenic remnant of the virus through the first 22 transplants but "lost" it sometimes before the 46th transplant (566). In this case, the virus might have completely disappeared; or, it might have become reduced to a true "provirus," without detectable serological cross-reaction with the mature virus. The question would then arise as to how such provirus could be detected, a question we shall discuss again in a later section.

Another interesting comparison is one between the masked papilloma virus and that of phages phenotypically modified by their hosts (see page 295). The cells of domestic rabbit might modify the virus in such a way that it was not infectious for either domestic or wild rabbit, while remaining potentially infectious for some other host. Such a possibility would be difficult to test in the specific case of papilloma. The domestic rabbit papilloma does not contain any important amounts of particles similar to the virus particles; this fact indicates that the virus, if present, must be in a thoroughly modified form.

The milk factor. Mammary cancer in mice has long been a favorite material for grafting studies and for the analysis of genetic factors in cancer causation. In 1936, Bittner (79) discovered that the tendency to develop mammary carcinoma was transmitted from the mother to the young through the milk, and that a "low-incidence" strain of mice could by foster-nursing be made into a "high-incidence" strain, and vice versa. Genetic factors are involved in determining the proportion of realized cancers and the persistence of the influence or *milk factor* in the milk of successive generations.

This milk factor exhibits all the properties of a virus (23), including stimulation of specific antibodies. It is present not only in the milk but also in many tissues of the animal. In the cancers it is found in very large amounts, and can be seen in electron micrographs of cancer cells cultivated in vitro (figure 92; 527). The virus is not transmitted through the placenta, since Caesarean delivery from high-incidence mothers yields animals with low cancer incidence. To establish itself, the virus must enter very young mice, apparently before the wall of the intestine becomes impermeable to it. This is not the only reason, however; direct injection of milk factor in adult mammary tissue generally fails to transmit the cancer. The cancer only develops in adult

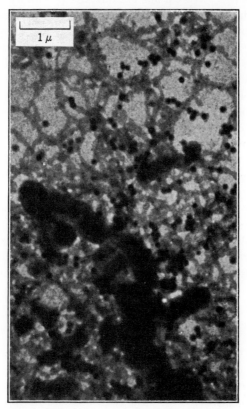

Figure 92. Electron micrograph of a portion of a cell from a tissue culture of mouse breast carcinoma. Note the abnormal, presumably viral, particles. The large, dark masses are mitochondria. From: Porter and Thompson (527). Courtesy Dr. K. R. Porter, Rockefeller Institute, New York.

females that carry the milk factor and that have given birth to one or several litters, unless artificial hormonal stimuli similar to those of pregnancy are provided (393).

Thus, the milk factor enters in early life, localizes itself in various tissues of the host, including the mammary glands, and remains there latent for most of the host's life. It produces tumors (benign at first, but becoming malignant) only in mammary gland cells that have been conditioned by hormonal influences. It is difficult, here, to decide which is the provocative and which the actuating cause of the cancer; certainly, the role of the milk factor in breast cancer is more determining than the role of foster nursing in the transplantability of certain tumors (141). We cannot exclude the possibility that different forms of the milk-factor agent may exist, some determining high incidence, some low incidence of cancers, and that one form may mutate to the other. Such a possibility could explain sudden changes to high incidence in low-incidence lines of mice that had been obtained by foster nursing (80).

A claim (644) that, from mammary cancer of mice cultivated in the yolk sac of the fertile egg, a virus directly carcinogenic to mice by injection could be recovered has not been confirmed (652). In mouse leukemia, an agent analogous to the milk factor may be involved. Cell-free extracts from leukemic cells, used to inoculate 1-day-old mice, may cause leukemia (279).

Virus tumors of plants. In plants, where most tumors (galls) are of bacterial or fungal origin, a wound tumor virus has been described (83). It causes a systemic disease, part of which consists of the formation of multiple tumors on roots and stems. The tumors develop especially at the site of wounds artificially produced or at the places where the tissues are cracked by the emergence of lateral roots or shoots. The virus is insect transmitted and has a wide host range.

THE ROLE OF VIRUSES IN TUMOR GROWTH

In all the tumors discussed above there is excellent reason for implicating viruses as causative agents. We may then ask: What is the role of the virus in transforming normal cells into tumoral cells? Does it act in the initial stage only, or throughout the development and growth of the neoplasms?

The tumor viruses reproduce with and inside the tumor cells, and the cells cannot be freed of the active virus, except for special cases of masking. The problem, thus, is one of the respective roles of the viral and of the cellular components of an integrated system, the virus-infected cell, in determining the neoplastic properties. As such, this problem and the more general problems of the roles of various cell components in cellular differentiation are still unsolved.

Stimulation of cells to increased reproduction as a result of virus infection is not infrequent. We observe it in many "destructive" virus infections, and a whole series of viruses can be arranged in order of increasing stimulatory action and decreasing necrotizing action (table 31). Tumor viruses themselves may cause necrotic reactions; for example, the Rous sarcoma virus causes an acute hemorrhagic disease in very young animals (*197*).

Table 31. From necrosis to neoplasia

From Duran-Reynals and Shrigley (*198*)

Epithelial Series	Connective Tissue Series
Foot-and-mouth disease	Canary pox
Vaccinia	Vaccinia
Fowl pox and sheep pox	Infectious myxoma
Filtrable warts (human)	Infectious fibroma
Infectious papilloma (wild rabbits)	Myxosarcomas of Rous type
Nonfiltrable papilloma (domestic rabbits)	Fibrosarcoma of chickens
Basal cell carcinoma *	Nonfiltrable fowl tumors *
Malignant epithelioma *	Mammalian sarcoma *

* Tumors without known relation to viruses.

It was pointed out by Rous (*564*) that tumoral manifestations follow intracutaneous injection of fat-soluble dyes such as Sudan III; but these manifestations regress completely with resorption of the dye, as though the stimulus had to be present all the time for continued tumoral proliferation (*222*). In virus tumors, the situation might be analogous, virus reproduction providing for the persistence of the stimulus.

There is no evidence that the neoplastic character of the cells of tumors formed in response to tumor viruses can be maintained in the absence of virus. Cells from virus tumors of fowl or rabbit are as transplantable as those of other tumors, but the virus remains harbored in them. The transplanted virus tumors of fowl grow mainly by reproduction of the implanted virus-carrying cells, rather than by neoplastic transformation of host cells, and the same is true of the metastases of the virus tumors. This, however, seems a reasonable course of events, since the virus is not necessarily liberated by the transplanted cells, which actually shelter it from host antibodies. Even when virus is liberated, the probability that it will cancerize other host cells may be as low as in the admittedly difficult induction of these tumors by injection of cell-free extracts. It is possible that the virus itself, and not only tumor cells, is sometimes responsible for the formation of metastases of fowl sarcomas, since the virus does circulate in the blood. Metastases, probably due to virus, have been obtained after fowl sarcomas had regressed as a result of x-ray treatment (515).

As for the role of the virus in determining the characteristics of a tumor, we have already mentioned its evident importance; for example, a virus from an osteochondroma of chicken causes formation of bone and cartilage from connective tissue cells if injected in other chickens (564). The host cells must be of the proper type and age. The cells that under virus action give rise to Rous sarcoma, for example, are thought to be mainly macrophages (123) or fibroblasts (430). Only rarely can a virus cause formation of a new type of tumor by infecting a different type of cell, and this may involve virus mutation and selection, as in a sarcoma produced by fowl leukomatosis virus that had been stored in glycerin (see 501).

Rous sarcoma and other fowl tumors will "take" more easily in young chickens than in older ones. Inoculation into other species, such as duck, pheasant, and guinea fowl, succeeds better in very young birds than in adults, with some differences from virus to virus. We have here the exact parallel of situations known to obtain for most viruses, which require special conditions for transmission to hosts of other species.

The neoplastic characteristics of the tumors formed in a heterologous species reflect the character of the virus, as shown by a number of observations. Injection into ducklings of filtrates of Rous sarcomas from chickens, when successful, causes relatively early formation of tumors that often regress, are poorly transplantable, and are still "chicken tumors," since extracts from them, if reintroduced in chickens, give rise to typical sarcomas with normal frequency. Transplantation of the "heterologous" tumors can be prevented by the use of antiserum against chicken tissue, an indication that the virus has actually conferred to the tumor developing in the duck some species specificity of the chicken (197a). Similarly, Fujinami sarcoma of ducks shows "duck tumor" characters (537, 538). Sometimes, the Rous sarcoma virus from chicken tumors, upon inoculation in ducks, gives rise to a different type of tumor, which develops late and is more easily transmissible from duck to duck. The virus from these late tumors has lost its typical affinity for chicken tissues, a fact that suggests a virus mutation (or host-controlled transformation) from "chicken type" to "duck type" (197a).

The situation with amphibian tumors (560) closely parallels that with virus tumors of fowl, and provides an even better illustration of the interplay of virus and host properties in determining not only the characteristics of neoplastic growths but also the characteristics of the viral agents obtained from these growths. Graft of the virus carcinoma of the kidney of Vermont frogs (429) into limbs of newts led to the formation of cartilaginous tumors in other limbs of the newts. From these cartilage tumors an agent could be obtained which, reintroduced into the Vermont frog, produced, besides the renal tumor, also bone-cartilage tumors of a type never otherwise observed in these frogs. Material from these tumors continued to produce both bone tumors and renal tumors by proper inoculations; it could also produce degenerative, histolytic changes, especially in muscles. Moreover, implantation of the bone tumors of newts into Wisconsin frogs induced renal cancers in the latter, whereas direct implantation of renal tumor from Vermont frogs to Wisconsin frogs failed to do so.

A remarkable feature of the bone tumors induced by derivatives of the frog virus is the high frequency of the formation of two tumors in exactly symmetrical bilateral locations, for example, "at the joint between the third and fourth phalanges of the fourth toe of both feet" (560). We gather the impression that the carcinogenic potentialities and the host-cell affinities of the virus are directly modified and controlled by subtle developmental properties of the host cells in which it has been produced.

The suggestion was made (560) that these transformations of the viral agent may be induced by some form of genetic recombination between the agent and some tissue-specific, cytoplasmic particles supposedly involved in the determination of the specific properties of various tissues of the host. More generally, and without introducing hypothetical entities into the picture, we may visualize the possibility of host-controlled alterations of the host-range and morphogenetic potentialities of a virus, along the same lines as the host-controlled phenotypic variations of bacteriophages (76; 446; see page 295). These alterations might well reflect subtle developmental differences of the host cells.

Be this as it may, we conclude that there are excellent grounds for attributing an essential role to the tumor viruses in the determination of the reproductive and neoplastic activities of their host cells.

VIRUSES AND SPONTANEOUS TUMORS

The evidence given in the preceding section emphasizes the role of the virus in determining the properties of a virus-induced tumor. At the same time, it indicates a very intimate fusion of cellular and viral properties. This raises the question: How far can this fusion go? May there not exist, in other tumors, viruses or viruslike agents, whose presence is responsible for the tumoral reproduction but which cannot be isolated in infectious form because their relation with their host cells is too intimate?

The large majority of neoplasms is not transmissible by cell-free extracts. Since the number of individual tumors from which viruses have been isolated is only a small fraction of those tested, and since in all probability the great majority of mammalian tumors, if tested, would yield no virus, one may be led to thinking that the virus tumors are the exception, and that viruses have nothing to do with the causation of most neoplasms.

Most pathologists incline to the opinion that the causes of tumors are multiple, and that the neoplastic transformation represents a response to any one of a number of cell disturbances. Thus, chronic irritations would favor cancerization by providing a stimulus to cell reproduction that may go beyond the needs for tissue repair. Another widely entertained hypothesis is that most spontaneous tumors arise by somatic mutations, that is, by genetic changes in some somatic cells, which transform them into neoplastic cells, just as a genetic change in a cell of the reproductive line may cause the appearance of a new hereditary trait. Another explanation of the origin of some spontaneous tumors considers their cells of origin as embryonal remnants, which late in life manifest their undiminished growth potentialities by giving rise to tumors. Tumors (*teratomas*) stemming from islets of embryonal tissues are, indeed, well known.

The question of a possible virus etiology of apparently spontaneous tumors cannot be summarily dismissed. Since the days of Borrel, the virus theory of cancer has had a growing body of proponents. It is undeniable that the virus tumors are the only neoplasms whose direct, actuating cause is understood. It is only reasonable to follow a lead that may direct us toward a unified theory of tumor etiology. Moreover, the impressive histological and biological resemblance between virus tumors and "nonvirus tumors" suggest a basic similarity of their etiological mechanisms as well. Intranuclear inclusions similar to those that characterize some virus-infected cells have been observed in tumoral cells, for example, in human gliomas (569), although they may have been due to viruses accidentally infecting the tumors (25).

Faced by the lack of transmissibility of most tumors by cell-free extracts, the proponents of the virus theory have turned to the hypothesis of latent and masked viruses as the causes of most cancers.

Whatever the ultimate outcome of this hypothesis (the case for which has ably been presented by Andrewes (25) and by Oberling (501), among others), it must be said that it has proved a fruitful working hypothesis. It has stimulated an impressive body of experimental work and has directed the thinking of pathologists toward fundamental biological problems.

The virus theory of neoplasms. As a starting point, let us consider again the rabbit papilloma of Shope (figure 93). The virus extracted

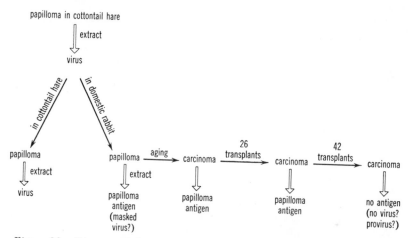

Figure 93. Diagram of the transformations of rabbit papilloma virus in various hosts.

from cottontail papillomas, if injected into domestic rabbits, causes tumors, which are papillomas at first and later become cancerized. From these tumors little or no infectious virus can be isolated. The domestic rabbit tumors contain an antigen related to the virus by its ability to stimulate production of antivirus antibody. The virus, according to Shope's terminology, is masked (602) in the domestic rabbit tumors.

Could the masking be due to a combination of virus with inhibitors (possibly antibodies)? There are cases, for example, of fowl tumors, from which active virus can only be obtained after removal of virus inhibitor by differential centrifugation (136). An inhibitor for the papilloma virus is actually formed (598) in domestic rabbit papillomas; yet, inhibitors, and especially antibodies, are certainly not the main cause of masking. Extraction methods that reveal large amounts of specific virus material in cottontail papillomas fail to extract any similar material from the domestic rabbit papillomas (57). Admittedly, the difference between domestic and cottontail rabbits might only be in the amount of virus produced. The titration methods for papilloma virus are not very sensitive (several million particles per infectious unit), and the domestic rabbit cells may not produce enough virus (241). Yet, it has been suggested that the viral material in the domestic rabbit tumors is in a *different, noninfectious form,* and we are reminded of the nonrecoverability of other viruses in the early stages of infection with most viruses (see chapter 13) and in cases of persistent latency, as for prophage in lysogenic bacteria (chapter 9). We may suppose that the virus, although present in the domestic rabbit tumors, never "matures" into infectious particles, just as in lysogenic bacteria a phage very seldom reaches maturation.

The incompleteness of the masked virus might be due to the fact that production of fully infectious virus particles requires some specific component available in the cottontail, but not in the domestic rabbit. There is some ground for such a "two-factor" hypothesis (284), at least by analogy. For example, Fujinami sarcoma virus grown in ducks is neutralized by serum against normal duck tissue, whereas the same virus grown in chickens is neutralized by serum against normal chicken tissues. Virus grown in either host is also neutralized by serum against virus-containing tissues of either host. The two antibodies are quite different: neutralization by the host-specific one requires complement; neutralization by the virus-specific one does not.[2]

The important point is that the induced papillomas of domestic rabbit and the cancers derived from them, to an observer unaware of their causation by papilloma virus, would appear indistinguishable from any spontaneous tumor. They are transplantable, nonfiltrable, and have a tendency to cancerization, just like other skin papillomas, either spontaneous or caused by chemical carcinogens. The presence of the masked virus in the tumors is detected only by testing the serum of the tumor-bearing rabbit for antibody against the virus from cottontail, but an unwarned observer would not even suspect the existence of such a virus.

---

[2] These observations (which should be confirmed by more extensive studies) can be explained independently of the two-factor hypothesis; for example, the antibody against normal tissue might remove from the virus a protective protein of cellular origin, in the absence of which the virus may become rapidly inactivated.

The suggestion that viruslike agents are present and etiologically responsible for all neoplasms requires an answer to several questions: 1. How can these agents be detected, so that the hypothesis can be tested? 2. Can the suggestion be reconciled with the known facts of carcinogenesis? 3. Where do the viruslike agents come from? 4. When and how do they enter the cells which they will make neoplastic? An attempt to answer these questions will be a useful introduction to a discussion of the origin and natural relationship of viruses.

Serological search for masked viruses in tumors. Could we test for a "viruslike something" in spontaneous tumors by serological means? There have been many failures in such attempts, but some positive results have been reported. The Brown-Pearce carcinoma of rabbits yields a nucleoprotein antigen, whose specific antibody prevents the graft of the tumor cells and their growth in vitro (372). Since, however, the Brown-Pearce tumor had stemmed many years before from an animal of unknown genetic constitution, and was transmitted by graft in rabbits of various genetic lines ever since, the immunity could be of the genetic-incompatibility type rather than a tumor-specific one.

Suppression of tumor growth by antibodies against the tumor cells or against their extracts is by no means infrequent.. The cancer literature contains a number of examples of tumors that after transplantation regress and leave the animal solidly immune to new grafts of the same tumor (see 129). Most such cases, however, can simply be interpreted as due to the heterologous character of the implanted cells, not to specific antibodies against the tumor cells as such. The serological evidence in favor of the presence of viruses in spontaneous tumors must be considered as quite inadequate.

Yet, even if the serological search for viruses in spontaneous tumors should prove fruitless, the latent-virus theory would hardly be refuted. Indeed, in the best-studied cases of virus latency, those of the prophages in lysogenic bacteria, the provirus has not been detected serologically. All available evidence suggests that most of the antigens of the mature phage are acquired only during maturation and are not present in the prophage (313).

How can we exclude the possibility that tumors are caused by proviruses, with no easily demonstrable antigens, whose maturation may either fail completely or yield "virus" with little or no infectious power? Actually, the Vx2 carcinoma, which had originated from rabbit papilloma, but does not now contain the virus-related antigen (566), may be an example of the complete evolution from a full-fledged virus (papilloma virus) to a masked virus (the antigen in domestic papillomas) to the "pure" provirus. The question is: How could such a pure, nonmaturing provirus be meaningfully distinguished from any "normal" protoplasmic constituents? We shall discuss this question in chapter 18.

The virus theory and artificial carcinogens. A reconciliation of the virus hypothesis with chemical carcinogenesis has been sought in a number of ways. Papilloma virus, injected intravenously into rabbits whose skin had previously been rubbed with tar or other carcinogens, localizes itself in the treated areas and causes a rapid formation of fast-growing cancers, definitely more malignant than the growths produced by carcinogen alone (370; 565). Tarring of the skin causes even the almost innocuous fibroma virus to give rise to less regularly regressing growths, and occasionally to generalized fibromatosis or even to true sarcomas (30). These neoplasms are transplantable and do not yield any virus.

Thus, carcinogens can provide conditions that localize and enhance virus action. Chemical carcinogens could act through viruses, if viruses were present; what has to be explained is the supposed presence of the viruses. Where could they come from, when not introduced deliberately in our experiments?

Several puzzling lines of evidence are available. McIntosh (456) produced sarcomas in chickens by injection of tar and found that some of these tumors could then be propagated by cell-free filtrates; other workers, however, could not duplicate his results (515). In more convincing experiments, it was shown that the blood of birds that carry tar-induced, nonfiltrable tumors often contains antibodies against various viruses, including Rous sarcoma virus (26). It should be pointed out that many of the fowl tumor viruses give some serological cross-reactions among themselves. Thus the carcinogens may act by providing the conditions for the neoplastic action of latent viruses.

The carcinogen might either produce a nonspecific tissue reaction, which could make the cells susceptible to the neoplastic influence of a virus (or provirus) already present within them, or it might act on the virus itself. The recently discovered ability of certain carcinogens to induce hereditary mutations in various organisms (176) has been considered as supporting the idea that tumors arise by somatic mutations, but it could equally well be used in support of the virus theory, by assuming that the carcinogens cause mutations in latent viruses. The somatic-mutation theory of cancer origin, besides lacking direct positive evidence to support it, must overcome the test of explaining the well-known precancerous reactions, in which the cells, although modified, are not yet neoplastic. When does the mutation take place? Moreover, how can the somatic-mutation theory account for virus tumors? Some ingenious suggestions, such as the requirement for many independently arisen mutant cells to form a cancer focus (223), do not overcome the above objections. The virus theory of neoplasms might account for hereditary influences on the incidence of cancer (see 425), which may actually represent quantitative genetic differences in virus susceptibility. A case could even be made for a role of somatic mutations in making a cell susceptible to carcinogenesis by a latent virus.

As far as carcinogens such as parasites are concerned, their role could even be interpreted as that of carriers of tumor viruses in masked form. A rather good model is provided by the role of the lungworm in the transmission of swine influenza virus to the hog.

A remarkable case is that of the crown gall tumor of plants (178; 607). This tumor is produced in response to infection with the bacterium *Phytomonas tumefaciens*. The tumor cells continue their neoplastic growth, both in plants and in tissue cultures, after bacteria have been eliminated in any one of a variety of ways. The bacterium apparently unleashes the neoplastic potentialities of the host cells but is not needed for their continued expression. Still, a specific agent responsible for tumoral growth seems to be present in the cells of the crown gall tumor (101). When a fragment of tumor is forced to undergo exceptionally rapid growth, it ultimately gives rise to normal plant tissue, which can reconstitute normal plant organs and become indistinguishable from original uninfected tissues. Forced rapid vegetative growth is known to remove from cells of various organisms certain cytoplasmic elements responsible for some of the properties of the organisms, such as the "killer" factor of *Paramecium aurelia* (530; see chapter 18). The abnormally rapid growth of the cells leads to dilution and removal of self-reproducing elements, whose reproduction is apparently not synchronized with cell reproduction and cannot keep up with an increased pace of the latter. Loss of latent viruses by analogous processes, for example, the loss of prophage from lysogenic bacteria repeatedly transferred in media unfavorable to phage reproduction, has been reported (135).

It seems plausible that the neoplastic character of the crown gall cells is determined by a viruslike agent of some sort, which can be eliminated from rapidly growing cells. The mechanism of the initiating role of the bacterium *Phytomonas tumefaciens* in crown gall tumors remains obscure. It might be that the bacterium brings into the plant a self-reproducing viruslike agent (possibly a bacteriophage); or it might stimulate the activity of a latent virus; or it might transform some normal cell constituent into a tumor-producing agent. More information will be needed before an answer can be given, and the ultimate answer may be quite different from any one now predictable.

Latent viruses and tumors. Chemical, genetic, and parasitic carcinogenesis, then, does not present unsurmountable objections to the theory that tumors are caused by latent viruses or viruslike agents. We must see if we can account for the postulated latent viruses themselves.

There is a whole series of transition cases between latent viruses of unknown derivation, such as pneumonia virus of mice (486) or virus III (558), and viruses that can be observed to become latent under controlled experimental conditions. Thus, the virus of lymphocytic choriomeningitis has a reservoir in the wild grey mouse (31) and can be transmitted to man and monkey by ticks; if introduced accidentally or purposefully in a colony of white mice, the virus infects in a symptomless way practically all exposed animals, being transmitted to the young, at first by infection in early age, later even in the womb (651). Active virus can be recovered from many animals of the colony, and the presence of antibody reveals a past or present infection in the others. Injection of irritating substances, such as sterile broth, into the brain of virus-carrying mice can revive the pathogenicity of the virus.

The milk factor of mammary tumor in mice provides an example of a latency lasting from the time of infection (only possible in early age) to the time of the appearance of properly susceptible cells in the breast of the multiparous females. The virus is not fully masked, since it can be demonstrated in many parts of the organism by feeding newborn mice with organ extracts; the mice later prove to be carriers of the factor (23). The latency seems to reflect only the lack of cells that can react neoplastically to the virus. A number of stimuli, such as hormones and carcinogens, can modify the breast cells in such a way that the tumors develop earlier. The virus, however, multiplies in a variety of tissues that do not show any abnormal response to its presence.

Finally, the facts of lysogenicity in bacteria, and especially of induced lysogenicity by infection of bacteria with temperate phages, provide us with a variety of conditions in which viruses become latent (= asymptomatic) and masked (= noninfectious).

Thus, virus latency and masking phenomena could provide conditions simulating the apparent spontaneous origin of tumors from which no transmissible virus can be obtained. Should we then suspect the existence of an enormous variety of latent viruses, each responsible for one specific type of tumor? This may not be necessary. The neoplastic potentialities of each tumor virus are not very restricted; the same virus strain can give rise to different manifestations in different hosts and tissues. For example, sarcomatous growth has been produced by fowl leukomatosis virus; a variety of different sarcomas are produced by Rous sarcoma virus in ducks, pheasants, and other birds; several biologically different carcinomas have arisen from rabbit papillomas. We have already described (page 332) the remarkable situation observed with the amphibian tumors provoked by the agent of the renal carcinoma of frogs (560). It is clear that virus variability, either of the genetic type or of the host-controlled type observed with bacteriophage, can well provide the necessary variety of tumor types from a relatively small number of latent viruses.

Conversely, the potential variety of latent viruses might explain why a given carcinogen produces different types of tumors in animals of different strains and races; the neoplastic potentialities of the cells would reflect, at least in part, the nature of the viruses they carry.

The real difficulty for the virus theory of tumors is the requirement for an almost ubiquitous distribution of latent tumor viruses. Where can these viruses come from? Simple transmission from tumor-bearing animals to healthy animals is out of the question, since even the experimental transmission of the known tumor viruses is difficult; the tumor-bearing animals would not represent an adequate source of viruses. Entry in early age (possibly in nursing or by vector transmission, or even in the intrauterine life through the egg) is apparently not frequent for viruses in general. We have already mentioned the failures to demonstrate milk-transmissible agents in many tumors, including some breast cancers of mice. The milk-factor tumor is apparently an exception rather than a prototype.

Some lines of research provide suggestive information. Thus, many apparently normal chickens possess antibodies against Rous sarcoma virus and other fowl tumor viruses. These antibodies develop in chicks only after hatching. Their appearance can be prevented by isolating the newly hatched chicks from adult chickens; conversely, their frequency is increased by contacts with tumor-bearing chickens. The suggestion is that most infections with tumor viruses, just as those with certain other viruses, are subclinical and nontumoral, and lead to virus latency; the tumoral transformation would be the exception.

Even if a case could be made for an almost ubiquitous distribution of tumor viruses, several problems would still remain unanswered, for example, in connection with the transplantability of tumors. If latent viruses were ubiquitous, what role would they play in the serological conditioning of graft "taking"? Why would the animals of a highly inbred line not carry the same latent viruses, and therefore be immune against tumor transplantation? Why should a spontaneous or chemically induced tumor of one of these animals (or a virus derived from it, as in fowl sarcomas) find it easier rather than harder to "take" in animals of the same breed? Moreover, agents such as Rous sarcoma virus can cause the neoplastic transformation of normal cells infected from outside; if they were ubiquitous, why would they not cause it regularly from inside? Could the true tumor viruses be mutants of ubiquitous, less active agents?

To many of the adherents of the virus theory of tumor etiology the idea of tumor viruses as latent exogenous parasites appears unsatisfactory. A role of exogenous viruses can hardly explain the specific neoplastic potentialities of different embryonal tissues transplanted into adult mice of the same breed, a situation that would require early intrauterine infection with a variety of different viruses (564). Some of the workers in the cancer field have gone a step further, and have suggested that tumors are indeed caused by viruslike agents, but that these are *new viruses*, that is, normal components of cells, which under the influence of any one of a variety of stimuli, or even by spontaneous mutation, have embarked on an abnormal career, conferring a neoplastic habit to the cells that harbor them. In extreme cases they could become transmissible from cell to cell and therefore become true viruses. Support for this viewpoint has been sought in the similarity between the chemical and physicochemical properties of some tumor viruses and of certain fractions extracted from related, nontumoral cells (138). This argument is in itself rather dangerous, in the present uncertain state of our knowledge of the structure and organization of normal protoplasm. Any number of protoplasmic components could resemble viruses in gross physicochemical properties.

Other workers have stressed more the similarity between the histological characters of virus tumors and of normal tissues, and have compared tumor viruses (of fowl) to agents supposedly responsible for cell differentiation. Similarities between these agents and the agents that cause hereditary changes in bacteria have led to their being grouped together as "transmissible mutagens" (*140*). The nontransmissible tumors would simply be produced by nontransmissible mutagens. It is clear that we are dealing here with the very nature of viruses and with their relation to the physical carriers of hereditary specificity in normal cells.

Heterogenetic theories of the origin of viruses, which postulate their frequent rise by transformation of normal cell constituents, had been proposed, for example, for viruses like herpes and choriomeningitis; these theories were later discarded when the mode of primary infection and transmission of these viruses was clarified. Virus heterogenesis, however, is bound to remain a possibility as long as our knowledge of the origin of viruses and of their taxonomic position remains obscure. With this and related problems we shall deal in chapter 18.

Origin and Nature of Viruses

In discussing the relation of viruses to tumors we have pointed out the role of some viruses in determining specific processes of cell differentiation. This poses the problem of the relation between the viruses and the normal components of cells which regulate cell properties and development, and, therefore, the problem of the natural relation and origin of viruses.

In dealing with any group of biological objects, we must inquire into their relation to each other and to other objects. The justification for this taxonomic preoccupation is inherent in the established facts of biological evolution, according to which all life on earth is related by common ancestry. In dealing with viruses as a group, however, we are immediately aware that the group possesses no obvious taxonomic unity, but is only defined on the basis of the methodology employed in virus research. None of the morphological or physiological criteria applicable to viruses carries the taxonomic weight of the criteria used to group together, for example, the phylum of arthropods, or the class of birds, or the order of rodents. Size of virus particles, obligate parasitism, and ability to penetrate some host, the criteria we used in defining viruses (see chapter 1), do not represent adequate criteria of natural relationship. There is no obvious evidence of a closer degree of relationship between any two viruses (for example, a bacteriophage and a plant virus) than between either of them and a bacterium or a protozoan or even any other animal and plant. There are, of course, close resemblances among the viruses of certain groups, such as some phages, the rod-shaped plant viruses, the mammalian pox viruses; these can be assumed to represent groups of related viruses with not too distant common ancestors. But there the morphological, serological, and physiological basis of virus classification ends, and attempts to create meaningful virus classifications beyond this point have confused rather than clarified the situation.

Nevertheless, it is important to locate the place of viruses in the biological world, that is, to understand their origin and the possible paths of their evolution. For this, we must visualize a series of possibilities suggested by the known facts about viruses and other biological objects.

Viruses as independent genetic systems. We have seen ample evidence that viruses are endowed with genetic continuity and mutability. Some viruses, moreover, may undergo a number of independent mutations, a fact which suggests a multiplicity of genetic determinants. Thus, viruses represent independent and specific genetic systems. It is, therefore, unlikely that in their host cells they simply act, directly or through the release of inhibitions, as stimuli for the production of cell elements whose specificity is intrinsic in the host cell, or, as had been suggested, as catalysts for the maturation of already specific precursors (385). No such hypothesis could explain why the various mutant forms of a virus should cause the same cell to produce just the corresponding type.

We must, therefore, consider viruses as carrying more or less complex genetic systems, separate from, and in an evolutionary sense independent of, those of the host cells which they infect from outside and in which they reproduce. As a matter of fact, most viruses may differ from their hosts genetically (and chemically, as shown by serological tests) as much as any two organisms taken at random may differ from each other.

The chemical substrate of virus activity. What do the structure and composition of virus particles tell us about their nature? Ideally, a virus particle represents the minimum amount of material needed for successful invasion of a normal host. With all reservation as to the purity of even the best virus preparations, it is accepted that all virus particles contain at least nucleic acid and protein. Moreover, the nucleic acids and protein components of viruses contain the same types of constituents (nucleotides, amino acids, etc.) as nucleic acids and protein of any other origin. These properties of viruses are unequivocal confirmation that they belong in the unique line of biological evolution and are not new forms of life, that is, new products of synthesis from inert matter. The strict parasitism of viruses itself speaks against such an origin of viruses. Furthermore, the occurrence of DNA in some viruses, of RNA in others (and in some possibly of both) may be indicative of a relation to one or another group of cell nucleoproteins. It might be suggested that the nucleoprotein content of virus particles simply reflects the incorporation into the particles of parts of cell materials that are involved in virus synthesis. Nucleoproteins or at least nucleic acids, however, are found wherever the biologist is led, by genetic or cytological evidence, to locate the material substrate of reproduction of specific biological elements. Since viruses represent systems of specificity distinct from their hosts, it is only reasonable to consider the nucleoproteins of virus particles as including the chemical materials in which virus specificity is embodied.

THE REGRESSIVE THEORY OF VIRUS ORIGIN

Biochemical evolution. The independence and complexity of viruses as genetic systems lends some support to a theory of virus origin, widely accepted today, according to which viruses represent the result of a *regressive evolution* from free-living cells.

Studies of comparative metabolism on a variety of organisms, from bacteria to man, have shown that all cells share certain basic synthetic and metabolic processes and that similar intermediate metabolites are needed by all organisms as building blocks, at least at the nonspecific, low-molecular level (amino acids, monosaccharides, aromatic bases, coenzymes). Some organisms (autotrophs) can synthesize all their required metabolites from inorganic materials; others require an external supply of some organic components either as sources of energy (heterotrophs) or as building blocks (auxotrophs) or, in most instances, for both purposes. It has been suggested (504) that the earliest self-reproducing units, the primitive life forms, came into existence in an environment rich in organic compounds, which were produced by nonenzymatic synthesis in the cooling earth utilizing the energy of ultraviolet light. Presumably, the primitive forms of life were dependent for their reproduction on the external supply of organic building blocks. They could have acquired more and more synthetic power by mutation (343), and the synthetically more endowed forms could have been selectively favored as the external supply of organic substances dwindled, thus leading to the establishment of autotrophs.

In the course of successive evolution, some of this synthetic power was often lost again and in today's world most animals and microorganisms, and many plants, are to some extent auxotrophic and heterotrophic. To this "regressive evolution" (450) has been attributed a more prominent role in biochemical evolution than it probably deserves except in the restriction of most organisms to certain ecological environments. Biochemical differentiation must have depended mostly on the appearance of new patterns of synthesis, producing new specific macromolecules (proteins, polysaccharides, nucleic acids), the chemistry and metabolism of which are still obscure.

Viruses as regressed parasites. A case has been made (*114; 271; 395*) for an origin of viruses, or at least of some viruses, by an extreme process of regressive evolution. Free-living microorganisms that require a number of preformed metabolites would become parasitic on other organisms that act as suppliers of the required substances. Parasitism, and especially intracellular parasitism, would favor further loss of synthetic abilities by providing an environment where most needed metabolites are present, thus placing little or no handicap on the synthetically more deficient mutant forms. It is argued that this process could proceed to such an extent as to cause the loss of much or most of the enzymatic machinery of the parasite, with accompanying reduction in size and transformation into a virus. A virus could ultimately be reduced to the naked genetic system (or possibly even a part of it) of a formerly free-living organism.

Appealing as this theory may be (especially to the frequent believers in an intrinsic, mystic tendency to decay in nature) there is no strong evidence to support it. Although there is some parallelism between the degree of parasitism and the nutritional requirements of facultative parasites (bacteria, fungi, and protozoa), hardly any transitional stages are known between viruses and obligately parasitic protozoa such as the malarial plasmodia, or between viruses and obligately parasitic bacteria such as the leprosy bacillus. Rickettsiae (see chapter 19) are small intracellular parasites, probably requiring a large number of specific supplies from their host cells; but their relationship to any viruses is doubtful.

In many arthropods are found a variety of intracellular symbionts, some yeastlike, some bacterialike (bacteroids, *626*), which are transmitted from mother to young by infection of the eggs and which seem to perform some functions needed by the hosts. In spite of their long association with their hosts (shown by the similarity of the symbionts in insects that have long since branched off from common ancestors, such as roaches and termites), the symbionts, whose function is unknown but probably essential to the life of the hosts, have hardly regressed at all as far as size and morphological complexity are concerned. The same is true of the algae (*Zoochlorella*) symbiotic with certain protozoa.

It is hard to see how regressive evolution through parasitism could lead to the establishment of such an intimate organizational relation between parasite and host as that found in bacteriophages and probably in many other viruses, a relation in which the virus seems to integrate itself into the synthetic and genetic machinery of the host and to determine in some cases the specificity of the whole product of synthesis.

The particles of some animal viruses, such as vaccinia, in the most purified preparations contain substances like riboflavine and biotin, known to play coenzyme roles in metabolic systems present in all cells (606). This has been taken to suggest that the virus is derived from a free-living form possessing its own metabolic machinery, and that the coenzymes represent remnants of this machinery. We cannot exclude, however, the possibility that these substances derive from the host cell and cannot be separated from the virus particles, because of the way the mature virus particle is formed. The mature virus particle, defined as the minimum piece of material needed for infectivity, may well incorporate some host components along with the essential, specific virus substance (142; 377).

For viruses whose particles contain RNA rather than DNA, the hypothesis of regressive evolution leads to the idea that the virus represents a remnant of some extrachromosomal element of the free-living ancestor. The fact that all the plant viruses thus far analyzed contain RNA favors, instead, the idea that these viruses originated by some common mechanism inherent in the plant cell—possibly by transformation of plastids.

There is, of course, no reason to believe that all groups of viruses originated by the same process; regressive evolution might account for the origin of some of the largest and most complex animal viruses. Also, we should bear in mind that the above considerations only apply insofar as the regressive evolution theory is taken to imply a relatively recent origin of viruses from free-living forms similar to those known to exist now. The possibility that in the course of evolution free-living forms have merged with cells more or less distantly related and can again emerge and become viruses, can better be discussed after we consider the possible origin of viruses from cell components.

THE RELATION OF VIRUSES TO CELL CONSTITUENTS

Viruses and cell constituents. Many workers have emphasized the similarity of viruses to some cell components and have inclined to the belief that the viruses have derived from cell constituents that have become transmissible from cell to cell—that is, infectious. Some of the supporting evidence, as far as virus research is concerned, has been discussed in chapter 17. We may recall the examples of virus latency and masking, the morphogenetic effects of some tumor viruses in stimulating cell differentiation, and the similarity between the tumors caused by viruses and those from which no virus can be extracted. The advocates of the origin of viruses from cell constituents stress the occurrence of diseases of plants, supposedly caused by viruses but transmissible only by graft, as evidence for the direct transmission from cell to cell of "infectious cell proteins." Opponents of the theory have objected, first, that several virus diseases supposedly transmissible only by graft have finally yielded bona fide viruses (52). Second, in most cases of virus latency in animals or plants some virus can be shown either to have entered the organism very early in life, or to have been transmitted through egg, sperm, or pollen.

The insect virus that causes silkworm jaundice, a polyhedral disease, can manifest itself in normal silkworms following feeding with various chemicals (hydroxylamine, acetoxime, potassium nitrite; *690a*). The claim has been made that the virus is produced by a transformation of the genes of the host into virus. It seems more reasonable to assume that the chemicals employed can induce the maturation and pathogenic action of a latent virus (provirus) transmitted from generation to generation of silkworms through the egg (*654a*).

The question, however, is deeper. If a virus can remain latent in the cells of a host for many cell generations and even through the meiotic process, it must be integrated in the normally functioning cell machinery and as such *it is* a cell component. The question should be put in a different way: Have all viruses, as we know them, entered more or less recently (from one to several thousand cell generations) the lineage of host cells in which we find them, or have they a direct genetic relation with the materials proper to some host cells? Moreover, are these two alternatives mutually exclusive? That is, can the distinction between "genetically specific components of a cell" and "exogenous specific self-reproducing elements" be legitimately made? It is clear that a meaningful approach to this problem cannot be made from the viewpoint of virology alone, but must be based on a knowledge of the genetic organization and evolution of the cell.

Viruses and chromosomal genes. As far as we are aware, all cells derive from cells. Although the cell is the only unit of reproduction observable in isolation, we trace the seat of the specificity of a cell to certain materials it contains.   Mother and daughter cells present both similarities and differences, the differences manifested in the phenomena that go under the general headings of development and differentiation.   In discussing cellular organization for our purpose, we should remember that we are looking for something that may be related to viruses.   Since viruses can exist as discrete material particles carrying more or less complex systems of hereditary determinants, it is only natural to look in the cell for something having properties of this type.

The first cellular elements to be considered are the genes, located in the nuclear chromosomes.   The genes are determinants of heredity, transmitted in an orderly manner from cell to cell at mitosis.   Their linear arrangement in the chromosome strings is proved by cyto-genetical observations on crossing over, chromosomal breaks, and rearrangements of various kinds (604).   As a rule, each gene, identified by the effects of its changes on the properties of the organism, is located at one specific position in a chromosome.   The chromosomal location of DNA and other suggestive evidence for an actual role of desoxyribonucleoproteins in the hereditary mechanism of chromosomes emphasize an important similarity between genic material and viruses such as bacteriophages and most animal viruses.   Actually, the complex recombination phenomena observed with bacteriophages (see chapter 9) and more recently with influenza viruses (120) closely resemble the behavior of gene groups such as we find in chromosomes. The multiple mutability of many other animal viruses suggests that they too are genetically complex.   These similarities between viruses and chromosomal genes may indicate a recent common origin, and the idea of viruses as "naked genes" was suggested as early as 1920 (192; 496; 683).   It would now seem more fitting to compare some viruses with naked gene complexes, chromosomes, or even groups of chromosomes or nuclei.

A rudimentary nuclear system could have derived either by regressive evolution through parasitism or by acquisition of transmissibility from cell to cell by a whole or partial nucleus.   The first possibility has been discussed above; is there any evidence for the second?   The most suggestive evidence is provided by a variety of transformation phenomena that occur in bacteria.

VIRUSES AND THE TRANSFER OF GENETIC MATERIAL IN BACTERIA

Viruses and transforming principles. Type transformation is classically observed in pneumococci (see *32*). *Diplococcus pneumoniae* occurs in a multiplicity of smooth types (SI, SII, SIII, $\cdots$) each characterized by the presence, amount, and chemical nature of a capsular polysaccharide. A stable noncapsulated (R) form can be derived from any S type by mutation. The R strain can be transformed into a hereditarily stable capsulated form, producing a specific polysaccharide, by growth in the presence of an extract of a given capsulated type. For example, an R strain derived from SII can be transformed into a strain SIII by growth with an extract of SIII cells.

The change from R to S is not the result of a selection of spontaneous bacterial mutants. It is actually induced by the extracts in an appreciable proportion of the exposed cells. The responsible agents or *transforming principles* are present in a DNA fraction of the extracts. The principles are not separable chemically from the bulk of the DNA. Presumably they represent, in part or full, the genetic determinants responsible for the production of the capsular material. The transformed organisms become, in turn, a permanent source of the corresponding transforming principles. Other characters, such as sensitivity or resistance to penicillin, can also be transferred by means of transforming principles in the DNA fraction (*350a*).

Recent developments (*210*) indicate additional similarities between transforming principles and chromosomal genes or gene complexes. The principles from different serological types (SI, SII, SIII, $\cdots$) are as a rule mutually exclusive, just like allelic forms of a certain gene. Nevertheless, interactions occur between slightly different forms of the same transforming principle, with results comparable to recombination phenomena. For example, two different principles acting together can induce into an organism a third, novel type of property, which is afterward transmissible hereditarily (or by transforming principle) without segregation into the two parental properties.

Here and in similar phenomena with *Hemophilus influenzae* (*11*), we have the closest thing to the exogenous transmission of hereditary determinants of the type usually associated with genes. Notice that the transforming principles fulfill our definition of viruses (or, in the cell, of proviruses). Yet, only a fiend for semantics would consider the capsular types in pneumococci as induced by viruses, at least as long as the word virus is used in the commonly employed sense. We are clearly at the borderline.

Bacteriophages and bacterial genes. Recent work has established even closer ties between the genetic determinants of bacteria and the viruses of the bacteriophage group. In the first place, we should recall the increasing evidence in favor of a chromosomal localization and transmission of the prophages of lysogenic bacteria (see page 205). The determinant elements of these latent viruses may find their way into the nuclear apparatus of their host and integrate themselves within it.

In the second place, recent observations implicate bacteriophages in the transmission of genetic properties from one strain of bacteria to another.

Transduction in *Salmonella*. Some bacteria of the genus *Salmonella* are lysogenic and liberate in their culture media a filtrable agent identical with the phage and which can transfer to other strains some hereditary characters of the strain from which it comes (*695*). The transferred characters include fermentative properties, antigens, and sensitivity or resistance to chemical agents. This *transduction* of properties ordinarily involves only a single character at any one time, as though single determinants of heredity were transduced from strain to strain.

We may assume that in the process of phage maturation some phage particles can receive not only their own prophage but also a portion of a chromosome. Immediately, we are led to wonder what the "own" prophage is. Could any part of the host chromosomes be a potential genetic core for a transmitting agent? Such an agent might only manifest itself as a phage if it happened to be endowed with lytic properties; otherwise, it would appear as a "pure" agent of genetic transfer. The transducing agent of *Salmonella* might indeed act on some strains as a pure gene-transferring entity, while acting as prophage carrier on the phage-sensitive cultures.

The fertility agent of *Escherichia coli*. Genetic recombination in *E. coli* K-12 has recently been shown to be a nonsymmetrical phenomenon, which requires that one or both strains possess a certain fertility factor (F^+ strains). This factor can be transmitted infectiously from F^+ to F^- strains by growth in mixed culture. The fertility factor is not filtrable; it may be extruded onto the surface of the F^+ cells, from which the F^- cells presumably can pick it up and be transformed by it into F$^+$ cells (*295; 413*). Thereafter, the fertility factor continues to be produced in the transformed cells.

Bacteriophage infection and genetic transfers. Bacteriophage research has shown that phages contain a genetic portion, which becomes infectious at maturation by acquiring a protective skin. The skin in turn mediates the introduction of the genetic portion into another host cell.

It seems justifiable to suggest that there may be a whole series of cases whose common feature is the transfer of genetic characters. The vehicles of such transfer may or may not carry lytic principles recognizable as phages. At one end we may have the transforming principles of pneumococcus and other bacteria, representing genetic determinants that can withstand artificial extraction and can enter as such into recipient cells. Transduction in *Salmonella* may require the inclusion of the genetic material to be transferred into carrier elements similar to those acquired by phages at maturation. In different instances the transferred genetic material may perform differently in the recipient cells. It may take over the nuclear controls and disrupt the cell (lysis by virulent phages), or it may introduce a latent tendency to ultimate disruption (lysogenesis for temperate phages), or it may introduce one or more properties derived from the cell in which it was formed. Lytic (incompatible) and hereditary (compatible) determinants may be included together in a single carrier. Ultimately, we may encounter cases in which the whole genome of the parent cell will be introduced into the host cell, and the carrier element will become analogous to a sperm cell.

At the other extreme, the carrier may become a purely bactericidal agent, such as a *colicine* (see page 207), which resembles phages but fails to reproduce in the host it destroys.

Not only genetically, but also biochemically, there may exist a series of agents intermediate between metabolically inert virus particles and metabolically active sperm cells. Indeed, the L forms of bacteria (including elements at the limit of microscopic visibility, copiously formed by bacteria under special circumstances; *179*) may represent such intermediate forms and may be involved in some form of transduction of genetic characters.

Thus, the phages appear to be close relatives of the genetic material of the host cells; so close indeed that it becomes hard to distinguish between a prophage and a portion of a bacterial chromosome, or between a virulent phage and an incompatible portion of genetic material. The "parasitism at the genetic level" of virulent phages (*437*) would only be one extreme in a series of possible levels of genetic integration between virus and host.

Should we consider the phages as reproductive organs of bacteria, and in a different category from all other viruses? Or do other transmissible agents defined as viruses have the same type of relationship to their host as phage? No factual evidence for a role of plant or animal viruses in the hereditary mechanisms of their host cells is available. Yet, the latency of many viruses, their deep integration in the host-cell machinery, and their directing role· on cell properties, especially clear in tumor viruses, suggest that the possibility of a relation between viruses and host-cell heredity should seriously be entertained. In an attempt to find possible relatives of these viruses, let us return to our search for viruslike elements in normal cells.

VIRUSES AND CYTOPLASMIC INHERITANCE

Outside the nucleus, the cell contains a cytoplasm, whose fine structure is largely unknown, but which contains a variety of recognizable, differentiated, discrete elements, some microscopic (centrosomes, mitochondria, plastids), others inframicroscopic (microsomes (178). Some of the cytoplasmic elements reproduce and are distributed at cell division to the daughter cells, either with some regularity, so that gross inequalities are avoided (as with the mitochondria), or with great regularity, as in the case of the centrioles, which, when present, duplicate and segregate as a part of the mitotic figure. For comparison with viruses, however, we need something more than cytological evidence of granular nature and ability to divide. Actually, a granular structure is not a necessary element of similarity to viruses, since inside the host cell the viruses may not be present in any recognizably granular form. What is needed is evidence for cytoplasmic elements endowed with individuality and intrinsic genetic continuity. Individuality means that *one* element is sufficient to determine the production of copies of itself, just as a virus or a gene. Intrinsic genetic continuity means (*a*), that the element is an indispensable source for the production of more elements like itself; and (*b*), that the specific configuration of the new elements is determined by the original element itself. The reason for making the criteria so specific is that viruses fulfill these criteria, whereas among the elements involved in the so-called cytoplasmic inheritance we find listed entities of different types, which may or may not meet our requirements.

Cytoplasmic inheritance (*126*) is defined as the transmission from generation to generation of characteristics determined by the cytoplasm rather than the nucleus. It manifests itself in sexual organisms as a difference in the result of reciprocal crosses, in which the nuclear complements are similar but the cytoplasms, mostly maternal, are different. The new phenotypes, produced by the same genes working in different cytoplasms, show some of the characters of the maternal parent. Cell differentiation, in which cells with presumably identical nuclei develop into a variety of types, has also been attributed (hypothetically) to cytoplasmic influences.

In itself, cytoplasmic inheritance does not prove that the cytoplasm contains hereditary determinants responsible for the reproduction of their own specific materials. The cytoplasm is a complex and probably highly organized mixture of organic substances, always reacting with one another, some being destroyed, others formed. The nature and rate of production of various substances may be determined mainly by the nucleus, considered as the bearer of the specific patterns for the structure of the proteins and other complex organic molecules whose production it determines. This is exemplified by the determination of enzyme and antigen specificity by chromosomal genes (*687*). The gene products will, of course, be affected by the cytoplasmic environment.

The mechanism of cytoplasmic inheritance could be a "molar" rather than a "molecular" one, depending not on specific individual determinants but on the relative amounts and distribution of interacting substances in the cytoplasm. The cytoplasm is conceivably capable of reacting in a variety of ways to chemical stimuli derived from the nucleus, according to its momentary status (*171*). Specific cytoplasmic reactions may thus appear without the intervention of specific cytoplasmic determinants of heredity.

The cytoplasm contains characteristic granules, which divide regularly at or before cell division. These include the centrioles, the mitochondria, and the plastids, and the kinetosomes of ciliate protozoa (that is, the granules from which cilia and trichocysts originate) (*451*). Such visible, regularly dividing granules are not necessarily the carriers of discrete specific determinants; they could be functionally individualized centers for the accumulation of materials of nuclear origin, whose intrinsic specificity could be gene-determined rather than cytoplasmically determined.

Sonneborn has pointed out (*617*) that the essential requirement for the recognition of a cytoplasmic element as a specific self-reproducing genetic determinant is the proof of mutability and reproduction in the mutated form, independent of environmental or genic uniformity. Only the ability to reproduce a new pattern of specificity, acquired by mutation, in the presence of any compatible genic background, represents adequate proof for the intrinsic specificity of a cytoplasmic determinant of heredity. Some such determinants are known to exist, and we shall now discuss them briefly.

Plasmagenes in relation to viruses. In plants, the plastids, cytoplasmic bodies containing chlorophyll in the green parts of the plants, are transmitted through the egg-cell protoplasm and occasionally through the pollen. They are mutable; green plastids occasionally give rise to colorless ones, and the resulting *variegation* is self-perpetuating (*551*). Nuclear genes control both the mutability and the reproduction of plastids, but not their quality. A gene may increase the rate of plastid mutation or make it impossible for a mutated plastid to reproduce, but there is no gene pair responsible for the regular production of two alternative forms of plastids. The relationship of plastids to mitochondria is generally admitted; but the proof of the genetic continuity of mitochondria would require the discovery of intrinsic mitochondrial mutability.

Some races of the protozoon *Paramecium aurelia* contain granules (0.2–0.8 μ) that give the cytochemical reactions of DNA and are identified with the *kappa* factor. This factor regulates both the secretion of a poison (*paramecin*, a substance that contains DNA and is toxic for individuals of other races) and the sensitivity of the animal to the poison (*616*). Animals with the kappa factor produce the poison and are resistant to it. In the proper genetic background (presence of a dominant gene *K* and of accessory genetic influences) an animal containing the kappa factor will produce more of it, an animal without kappa (such as can be obtained, for example, by irradiation) will not produce any: thus, kappa is self-reproducing. By proper cultural conditions, the growth rate of the animal and of kappa can be dissociated, and kappa may then be totally and irreversibly lost in some offspring. But as long as one unit of kappa remains, the factor can be restored to its normal amount of several hundred or several thousand units: thus, kappa is genetically individualized. Moreover, kappa is mutable. A mutated kappa will cause production of a different paramecin, recognizable by its toxic effects, and the animal with the mutated kappa will be specifically resistant to the corresponding paramecin. No gene difference is involved. Kappa can be introduced into suitable paramecia by contact with extract of kappa-bearing animals, and it reproduces within the new host. Thus, kappa is potentially infectious and represents another borderline case with viruses.

A similar situation exists in the case of cytoplasmic inheritance of CO_2 sensitivity in *Drosophila* (*421*). Sensitive flies are killed or injured by a short exposure to CO_2, whereas resistant flies are not affected. The agent, *sigma*, is self-reproducing, individualized, and mutable. Sigma is regularly transmitted through the egg and occasionally through the sperm, and is also transmissible by cell-free extracts of organs of CO_2-sensitive flies. Sigma has many properties of a virus. Its cycle of reproduction in flies infected by injection is similar to that of viruses. The interactions between sigma and its mutants resemble those between a temperate phage and its virulent mutants. Sigma is inactivated by doses of x-rays comparable to those required for inactivation of medium-sized viruses (*422*), whereas kappa is as sensitive to x-rays as a bacterium (*529*). This difference may not be significant, however, since kappa was irradiated intracellularly, whereas sigma was irradiated in free state. Ultrafiltration data indicate that sigma consists of particles larger than was estimated from x-ray experiments (*421*).

These examples indicate beyond doubt the existence of relatively independent hereditary determinants in the cytoplasm of certain organisms. The term *plasmagene* (*617*) is often used to designate such determinants. It has been extended to cover other cases of cytoplasmic inheritance, in which the existence of such determinants is suspected but not proved.

For example, in *Paramecium aurelia* itself, cytoplasmic inheritance is present for a variety of specific, mutually exclusive antigenic types, recognizable by the immobilization of animals of a given type by type-specific antiserum (*617*). Exposure to homologous antiserum (or other treatments) can transform the cells into another serotype, within the spectrum of antigenic potentialities of the race. Here, however (at variance with the situation for the killer factor kappa), the specificity of the alternative serotypes seems to be determined by nuclear genes. The cytoplasmic effect is due to the fact that whatever serotype happens to be present in a given clone will persist unless changes occur either in the genetic make-up (by crossing) or in the environment (for example, changes in temperature or contact with specific antisera).

In yeast, a mutation that brings about the loss of aerobic respiration and a change in colony size can occur either spontaneously or upon treatment with acriflavine (*209*). The mutant cells lack certain recognizable cytoplasmic particles analogous to mitochondria and containing the missing respiratory enzymes (cytochrome oxidase and succinic dehydrogenase). The nuclear genes are unchanged by the mutation, as proved by crosses, and have not lost their ability to support the formation of the missing enzymes. Here again, cytoplasmic inheritance is present, but the existence of specific determinants in the cytoplasm is unproved. The cytoplasmic elements may receive their specificity from the nucleus, and their role in controlling the production of more elements like themselves may be a stabilizing rather than a determining one.

What we have said can be summarized in the statement that the cytoplasm is often involved in the determination of specificity, but only in a few cases has been proved to contain discrete genetic determinants responsible for their own intrinsic specificity. Most other instances of cytoplasmic inheritance could be due to self-maintenance of alternative states of the cytoplasm through interactions among non-self-reproducing elements.

Adaptive enzymes, as analyzed in bacteria and yeasts, are instructive in this connection (487; 488; 619). The production of an adaptive enzyme is made possible by the presence of a specific gene and by the presence of the substrate or of a variety of substances (inducers) related to the substrate. The rate of formation of the enzyme is of an exponential, apparently autocatalytic type, increasing as the amount of enzyme already present increases. It is tempting to suggest that the enzyme, or a precursor of it, is self-reproducing. However, an exponential rate of synthesis is not necessarily a sign of self-reproduction. For example, all cell proteins increase exponentially in bacterial cells during the phase of exponential cell growth. This is only an expression of the overall increase in protoplasm. An adaptive enzyme, formed in growing cells, will share the growth rate of the protoplasm as a whole. In nongrowing cells the initial formation of an enzyme may release an inhibition on its further synthesis.

A true self-determination of an enzyme system seems to have been demonstrated in yeast (620; 621). Enzymatic adaptation to ferment a given sugar requires the presence of substrate and of a given gene; but, provided the substrate is present, enzyme activity persists for many generations after the gene is removed by crossing to a nonadapting form. The main interest of this observation is the suggestion it provides of a self-determination of gene-derived elements, that is, of the possible existence of "gene-initiated plasmagenes."

Returning to the well-established cases of mutable plasmagenes (kappa, sigma, plastids) it is clear that they share with viruses some essential properties, such as intrinsic mutability and dependence on specific host genes for reproduction, but not for initiation. Gene-directed mutability in viruses has not yet been demonstrated, but this may be due to inadequate study. The formal analogy goes beyond this. Both kappa in *Paramecium* and sigma in *Drosophila* can be transmitted from one organism to another by cell-free extracts. Actually, our definition of virus is fulfilled; kappa (apart from its large size, similar to that of rickettsiae) and sigma are as good "viruses" as a phage or a potato virus. The transmission of kappa or sigma by man-made extracts to properly receptive animals is, of course, an "unnatural" event. But is it more "unnatural" than the liberation of phage by a lysogenic bacterium and its chance encounter with a susceptible cell, or than the grafting of the King Edward potato, carrying the paracrinkle virus, onto a potato stock susceptible to the virus?

In guinea pig, black pigmentation of the skin is due in part to the presence of ramified cells carrying melanic pigment (melanophores). Upon transplantation of black skin into a white skin area, black pigmentation spreads to the white area, apparently by actual transformation of colorless melanophores into pigmented· ones. This transformation can be propagated indefinitely by successive grafts (78). The unknown agent is transmissible by graft, as many plant viruses are, although not yet so by cell-free extracts. There is not much sense, of course, in calling the pigment factor in guinea pig skin a virus. Because of the well-known and orthodox Mendelian inheritance of skin color in guinea pig, the nature of the pigment factor as a cell component, and its gene-derived specificity, are not easily questionable.

VIRUS ORIGIN AND THE ORIGIN OF THE CELL

It is at the point where restrictive definitions break down that we must search for meaningful tie-ups between viruses and other self-reproducing agents such as genes or plasmagenes. The matter of definition has been dismissed as immaterial by some authors concerned with cytoplasmic inheritance, but is very important for the virologist. The crucial question for the student of plasmagenes is that of *reproductive* independence; for the virologist, however, it is that of *taxonomic* independence. A virus may enter a host cell and remain in it for one cell generation or less (virulent phage), or it may enter and remain through many cell generations (prophage in lysogenic bacteria; tumor viruses; plant viruses; etc.). In sexually reproducing organisms, a recently entered virus may be transmitted through the egg (or the sperm or pollen grain), and the next generation may or may not show signs of virus presence. Thus, virus latency is a matter of duration; a long-latency virus is practically indistinguishable from a cell component. It could be called a virus or a plasmagene (or even a gene), according to the effects by which it happened to be detected, that is, an apparently "normal" manifestation or a clearly abnormal one. With lysogenic bacteria, a virus-infected cell may acquire characteristics that could also be acquired by genetic mutation, as in transduction phenomena in *Salmonella*.

Concerning virus origin, the problem is, then, 2-fold. It involves, (*a*) the relation of viruses to cell components, and (*b*) the origin of cell components.

The gene complement of a cell (its genome) is often supposed to have originated by differentiation of an original self-reproducing single element, copies of which have accidentally remained together and by mutation have assumed different forms and functions. These gene groups would have progressively developed into chromosomes, because of strong advantages that an organized mechanism for equipartition of the genetic material offers in preserving favorable gene combinations. Sexual phenomena, arising later in evolution, would bring about further complications, but in presexual organisms all genes would have originated within the single cell lineage (*monophyletic*). Several cases are actually known of genes with similar function, possibly derived from one another and situated together in the chromosome (*420*). The cytoplasm, in the simplest hypothesis, would be derived from the activity of the genes. As a result, any genetically specific cell component should be a close relative of all others within one genetic line. The transmission of such a component—gene, chromosome, or plasmagene—to another cell would represent a *merging* of a portion of a genetic line into another line, a merging that might lead to parasitism (virus formation) or to symbiosis (plasmagene).

On the other hand, the normal cell might be *polyphyletic* in origin. It is conceivable that several primitive self-reproducing molecules may have come together into a successful combination and developed into a cell; or that some such elements may have entered an already formed cell. The plastids may well be such late comers, not yet integrated into the chromosomal mechanism. The merging of genetic lines would then have occurred early in the evolution of the cell, and the fact of a gene, chromosome, or plasmagene later becoming transmissible from cell to cell might represent a reacquisition of the original independence and a repetition of the original merging process.

The "viroid" theory (12) specifically postulates such an entry of free, primordial, self-reproducing elements into cells early in evolution, the preservation on their part of primordial characteristics, and their ability to regain infectivity by mutation, thus giving rise to viruses. Mutations of viroids could also give rise to nontransmissible, abnormal plasmagenes and be responsible, for example, for the tumoral transformation of cells. The theory is somewhat more restrictive than another conceivable one, which would include, among the potentially transmissible cell constituents, the nuclear genes as well as the cytoplasmic components.

Thus, all speculation as to virus origin leads to the possible modes of merging of two genetic systems into a functioning cell. The merging is not obvious in the case of rapidly destructive viruses. Its fundamental importance has escaped some virologists, accustomed to thinking of viruses in a cell as of bacteria in a culture. Yet, even a bacterium infected with a virulent phage and doomed to early lysis is a functional, integrated cell system, whose ultimate fate—lysis and disintegration—is incidental to the primary event of genetic and biochemical integration of viral and cellular machinery.

Merging leads to a more lasting integration with viruses that are carried for several cell generations or even through the sexual process. It may become permanent, as in virus masking, for example, in the tumors that papilloma virus induces in the domestic rabbit (602), or with egg-transmitted latent viruses such as lymphocytic choriomeningitis (651). Some plasmagenes may have originated in this way. On the other hand, the facts of lysogenicity and their relation to genetic transfers in bacteria suggest possible paths of the evolution of sexual mechanisms from viruslike mechanisms (and vice versa).

Ultimately, the taxonomic position of a certain element will depend on the duration of its joint evolutionary history with other components of the same cells. The ability to regain independence may be a function not only of intrinsic mutability but also of the duration of the partnership, which may force an ever-increasing interdependence among the various cell components. There is the danger, in such an expression as the "viroid" theory, of assuming a lasting primitive quality in the "viroid" component of the system as compared with the evolving quality of the rest of the genetic materials of the cell. An exogenous element, placed within a cell lineage, would probably undergo as much evolutionary change as the other genetic elements of the cell and should not resemble its primitive ancestor any more than the other elements resemble theirs.

The basic similarity of viruses to other biological elements has thus led us to a somewhat unified viewpoint, by showing us that different theories of virus origin differ only in their interpretation of the relative duration of the companionship between cell components. Merging of genetic lines and integration at the cellular level are the common denominator of all theories. A virus could derive from any one (or several) of the genetically specific components of a cell, either by regressive evolution or by transmission of a portion of a cell to another cell (by contact between intact cells or between cells and cell extracts).

If the transmitted element proved to be rapidly destructive for the new cell system it would generally be lost, and could only maintain itself in existence through the availability of innumerable suitable hosts. Often, however, the merging could last. The meaningful question remains—and cannot be answered at present—whether such a merging is a novel and exceptional feature, leading mainly to the formation of abnormal complexes of low evolutionary value (diseased organisms) or if it is an example of a process that has played and is still playing an important role in evolution and possibly in development.

In truth, a virus may be both a regressed parasite and a cell component that has become infectious, depending simply on which phase of the evolutionary history of its genetic material we are observing. It may have been both things at different times.

The intrinsic properties of certain viruses may suggest a closer relation to one or another type of genetic determinant. Thus, bacteriophages, with their complex genetic apparatus, may be closer to systems that have already evolved into chromosomal complexity and may actually be manifestations of evolving sexual mechanisms. Plant viruses, which contain RNA, may be more closely related to plastids or, if any such exist, to other RNA-containing plasmagenes. Animal viruses containing DNA may be akin to nuclear determinants.

In conclusion, we see that, just as the study of virus structure and multiplication always leads us back to the cell as the system in which the phenomena of life take place, so does the problem of virus origin lead us back to the origin of the cell as an integrated whole. A virus is nothing but a part of the cell. We observe and recognize as viruses those parts independent enough to pass from cell to cell, and we compare them with other parts that are more tightly tied up with the whole system. It is indeed this aspect of viruses that makes them invaluable to the biologist, whom they present with the unique opportunity of observing in isolation the active determinants of biological specificity, which are truly the stuff of which all life is made.

Appendix
The Rickettsiae

A group of microorganisms, the rickettsiae, is often described together with viruses. This is because its members share some of the
properties by which viruses are characterized, namely, the small size,
the obligate intracellular parasitism, and the ability to produce abnormal manifestations in certain hosts. The main similarity between
viruses and rickettsiae is their obligate intracellular reproduction or,
at least, their inability to reproduce in any of the cell-free culture media
that have been tested. The similarity between the rickettsiae and
viruses does not go very far, however. Because of their larger size and
microscopic visibility, the rickettsiae have raised few of the methodological and operational problems involved in defining the field of
virology. They resemble bacteria much more than they resemble
viruses, and there is no definite reason to suspect that they represent
a direct evolutionary link between the two groups. At the same time,
they are an extremely interesting biological group, because their
parasitism in certain hosts and their symbiotic relation with others
throw some light on the evolution of parasitism and on the epidemiological evolution of microbial diseases (*34*).

Most efforts to classify the rickettsiae have been limited to those
recognized as causing disease in man or in other vertebrates (*518*).
This choice, however, is largely artificial, because the pathogenic
rickettsiae are only a small sample from a large group of microorganisms symbiotic with a variety of arthropods (insects or arachnids)
(*626*). Only a few of these microorganisms accidentally embark upon
a pathogenic career by being transmitted from the arthropods into some
other animals, in which they may cause disease. It is, therefore, probable that some of the rickettsiae found in diseased hosts are only distantly related among themselves and that their close relatives should

be sought among the symbiotic inhabitants of arthropods. Only in a few instances, such as for epidemic and murine (endemic) typhus, is there reason to think that the causative agents have evolved from one another since their establishment in vertebrate hosts.

The practical importance of rickettsiae is that they give rise to several important diseases, among them epidemic and endemic typhus, Rocky Mountain spotted fever, and tsutsugamushi disease (scrub typhus). The rickettsiae pathogenic for man are listed in table 32.

Table 32. Rickettsiae pathogenic for man (family Rickettsiaceae)

Slightly modified from Pinkerton (*518*)

Genus	Species	Variety	Disease
Rickettsia	*prowazeki*	*prowazeki*	Human typhus
	prowazeki	*typhi*	Murine typhus
	orientalis		Tsutsugamushi disease
Dermacentroxenus	*pediculi*		Trench fever
	rickettsi		Rocky Mountain spotted fever
	rickettsi	*conori*	Fièvre boutonneuse (variety of spotted fever)
	akari		Rickettsialpox
Coxiella	*burneti*		Q fever

Morphology, structure and composition of rickettsiae. The available information concerns mainly the pathogenic rickettsiae (*278*). The type organism, *Rickettsia prowazeki*, the etiological agent of epidemic typhus, is generally in the form of diplobacilli, $0.3 \times 0.6 \ \mu$ or somewhat longer. When in a stage of rapid growth, the bacillary forms may be in chains resembling those of streptococci. Their size makes them generally nonfiltrable, although occasionally some individuals come through bacteria-retaining filters. They are visible in the microscope and resemble in stainability the Gram-negative bacteria, possibly with a somewhat lower affinity for basic dyes. They are stained with Giemsa solution or by special methods.

Large amounts of typhus rickettsiae can be obtained either from the yolk sac of the chick embryo or from the intestine of infected lice. The yolk-sac homogenates can be purified by differential centrifugation to yield relatively pure suspensions of rickettsiae. These contain about 12% nitrogen, 1% phosphorus, and about 13% lipids, a composition resembling that of many Gram-negative bacteria (*147*). They contain DNA and possibly also RNA (*145; 608*), the RNA being relatively less abundant than in most bacteria. In the electron microscope, where the rickettsiae show all division forms common to short bacilli (*674*), there is a clearly visible cell wall surrounded by capsular material (*596*). The capsule may be the source of the soluble antigens, which play an important role in the serological diagnosis of rickettsiae. The soluble antigens consist of particles sedimentable at medium speed in the ultracentrifuge and contain protein and polysaccharides, like surface antigens of bacteria.

Other pathogenic rickettsiae fit, with minor variations, the description given above for *Rickettsia prowazeki*. *Dermacentroxenus rickettsi*, the agent of spotted fever, often consists of pointed diplococci resembling the cells of pneumococcus. Rickettsiae very seldom show any forms as large as those of most bacteria, although some of the small Gram-negative bacilli, such as *Pasteurella tularensis* and *P. pestis*, come close to rickettsiae in size.

An important fact, and one that sharply differentiates between rickettsiae and viruses, is that rickettsiae possess metabolic systems such as have never been demonstrated in any virus. Purified preparations of typhus rickettsiae oxidize glutamate, pyruvate, and succinate in vitro, and produce aspartate from glutamate (*98*). Apparently, the rickettsiae oxidize the glutamate via the tricarboxylic acid cycle, like mammalian tissue and several bacteria, and can presumably utilize the energy liberated in the oxidations. They also appear to possess a transaminating system.

Serological reactions and vaccines. The serology of pathogenic rickettsiae has been thoroughly investigated. Antiserum, either produced experimentally against rickettsiae or obtained from convalescent individuals, contains antibodies detectable by a variety of reactions (*694*). Neutralization of infectivity is tested by injection either in the yolk sac of the chick embryo or intraperitoneally in the guinea pig. The rickettsial bodies are agglutinated by antibody; the agglutination reaction, although quite sensitive and diagnostically valuable, since agglutinating antibodies appear relatively early in the course of disease, has the disadvantage of requiring large amounts of rickettsial antigen. A more convenient test is complement fixation. At least 80% of the complement-fixing antigens of *R. prowazeki* are in the form of soluble substances. These are less specific than some of the antigens present in the rickettsial bodies. For example, the soluble antigens from epidemic and endemic (murine) typhus react equally with antisera against either of the corresponding rickettsiae. Differential reactivity can be revealed by chemical treatments of the soluble antigens (149). Inside the rickettsial bodies we find both the type-specific and the group-specific antigens. The specific soluble antigens appear to play an important part in causing immunity, since their presence in a vaccine is necessary for satisfactory protection against infection.

Pathogenic rickettsiae also contain specific toxins. These, administered in sufficient dose, can kill animals in a few hours, producing some of the pathological changes observed in the course of the rickettsial infections (297). Serum neutralization tests can distinguish between the toxins of the epidemic and of the endemic typhus rickettsiae.

For vaccines, large amounts of rickettsiae are prepared by a variety of methods (154) from the yolk sac of the chick embryo, or, for the agent of Rocky Mountain spotted fever, from ground bodies of ticks. With typhus rickettsiae, the infected yolk sacs are collected at the time of maximal rickettsial growth (7–8 days after inoculation with the inocula generally used); they are homogenized in a sterile buffer, and ether is added. Freezing and thawing results in the separation of an ether phase from the aqueous phase, which is rich in antigens. The water phase is collected and used as vaccine, after addition of some preservative substance. For use as diagnostic antigens, the rickettsiae can then be washed by differential centrifugation; the washing also removes most of the group antigens.

Until the introduction of the egg vaccines, remarkable success had been obtained in typhus fever with the Weigl-type vaccines obtained by inoculating body lice rectally with rickettsial preparations and allowing the lice to feed on immune individuals. Several days later each louse contains as many as 100 million rickettsiae, as counted in microscopic preparations. The vaccine is prepared by emulsifying the intestine of the infected lice in phenolized saline solution. A Rocky Mountain spotted fever vaccine can be prepared from infected, engorged ticks homogenized in phenol or formalin solution. The crude homogenate is allowed to age for several days, after which it is diluted and clarified.

The results of vaccination with dead rickettsiae have been remarkable. During World War II, the incidence of typhus among vaccinated troops was exceedingly low. In Naples, Italy, an epidemic of typhus that developed after the Allied occupation in 1943–1944 was brought to an abrupt end by vigorous delousing measures in the population. The vaccination of troops kept the epidemics from spreading to the armies. Such a feat was achieved for the first time in the history of this dreaded disease (53; 696).

The Weil-Felix reaction. A remarkable serological reaction of rickettsiae, and one not yet fully understood, although widely utilized for diagnostic purposes, is the so-called Weil-Felix reaction (673). Sera of patients or convalescents of several rickettsial diseases have the specific property of agglutinating the cells of certain strains of the bacterium *Proteus vulgaris*. The classic strain is *Proteus* OX-19, which is agglutinated by sera from cases of endemic or epidemic typhus, less well by sera from Rocky Mountain spotted fever. The latter sera give better reaction with cells of a different strain, *Proteus* OX-2. Patients with tsutsugamushi disease have agglutinins for a different strain, *Proteus* OX-K. The agglutination involves the so-called O (somatic) antigens of the bacterium. No *Proteus* agglutinin has been found in the sera of patients with Q fever.

It is likely that the *Proteus* organisms and the rickettsiae, although not closely related, possess cross-reacting antigens because of accidental structural similarity between some of the respective antigenic determinants. Many antigenic fractions have been isolated from the rickettsial bodies, and it seems that only one of the antigens is concerned with the production of the antibodies tested in the Weil-Felix reaction.

The reproduction of rickettsiae in their vertebrate hosts. The interaction between pathogenic rickettsiae and the cells of their vertebrate hosts has been studied only to a limited extent. Titration of rickettsiae can be performed by end-point methods in the guinea pig, in eggs, or in tissue cultures. A yolk-sac suspension may contain as much as 10^9 infectious units per ml. In the chick embryo, rickettsiae grow in practically all tissues. If inoculated in fhe yolk sac, they proliferate well in the cells that line the yolk sac and many of them are liberated into the yolk. There are differences in the intracellular location of different rickettsiae. Those of the typhus group are generally intracytoplasmic; those of the Rocky Mountain fever group are mainly intranuclear. They do not seem to form characteristic inclusions exhibiting elaborate cycles of the type described for several virus diseases, for example, in psittacosis (89).

Several observations point to the fact that the reproduction of rickettsiae in the host cells takes place mainly when the cell metabolism is quite low. For example, in tissue cultures the multiplication of rickettsiae takes place mainly after the culture has been incubated for several days, when the respiratory activity of the cells has almost ceased (697). *Rickettsia prowazeki* in the chick embryo grows best at a temperature of 32° C, where the host metabolism is low. It can be made to grow at 40° C in the chick embryo by the addition of cyanide, which depresses the metabolic rate of the cells. Rickettsial multiplication is reduced by certain dyes which increase the rate of oxidations (278). Riboflavine-deficient rats are more susceptible to rickettsial infections than normal rats. All these observations suggest a greater proliferation of the parasite in conditions of metabolic deficiency of the host.

In the course of studies directed toward perfecting a chemotherapeutic approach to rickettsial diseases, the remarkable fact was observed that, whereas sulfonamides actually increase the proliferation of rickettsiae and increase the severity of the diseases, para-aminobenzoic acid, the normal metabolite whose utilization the sulfonamides inhibit, is a specific inhibitor of rickettsial reproduction (614). The mechanism of this rickettsiostatic action of para-aminobenzoic acid is unknown. This substance is a growth factor for several organisms and is probably an essential intermediary metabolite for all organisms, as a constituent of folic acid. It is possible that it plays a role in certain metabolic activities of the cells, which beyond a certain level become incompatible with rickettsial reproduction.

Among the antibiotics, penicillin is somewhat active in suppressing rickettsial growth, but the most successful agents are chloromycetin and aureomycin, which may be said to have brought the problem of the therapy of rickettsial diseases under adequate control (162).

A study of the pathology of rickettsial diseases in their vertebrate hosts yields little information about the biological properties of the agents. Most of the damage to the host depends on the invasion of the cells that surround small blood vessels and capillaries (endothelial cells and smooth muscle fibers). This explains the occurrence of hemorrhagic skin rashes, including peculiar scrotal lesions observed in typhus infection of guinea pigs and also of men. In the central nervous system perivascular nodules are observed (682).

One of the rickettsial diseases of man, Q fever, does not present these capillary lesions. Concomitantly, *Coxiella burneti*, the agent of Q fever, appears to be somewhat different from the other agents of the group, mainly because of its ability to grow extracellularly and not only as a strict intracellular parasite.

Rickettsiae and arthropods. One of the most interesting problems posed by rickettsiae is that of their relation with their arthropod hosts. It is generally agreed that, with few exceptions, rickettsiae are only accidental parasites of vertebrates and undergo most of their evolution in the body of arthropods (626).

Many insects and arachnids contain some symbionts, which resemble a variety of free-living organisms, yeasts, bacteria, or rickettsiae (626). There is no definite evidence that the symbionts that resemble bacteria ("bacteroids") have ever been cultivated outside the arthropod body; therefore, their relationship with bacteria is suggested mainly on the basis of morphological similarity. The bacteroids have very definite and specific relations with the body of their host, relations that differ from insect to insect but that indicate very precise mechanisms for the maintenance of the symbiotic relation. In most insects, the symbionts are contained in special organs, the *mycetomes*. These appear to be formed as a response to the stimulus produced by the symbionts themselves, which enter the egg at an early stage of its development.

A number of arthropods, mainly ticks and mites, carry symbionts which closely resemble in size and properties the rickettsial agents of vertebrate diseases. In general, these rickettsiae are not carried in well-formed mycetomes; they are found mainly in the cells that line the gut. From here they may reach the genital tract, infect the egg, and be transmitted from generation to generation.

The arthropod hosts do not show any abnormal symptom deriving from the presence of the symbionts. Actually, it is generally supposed that the symbionts, at least the bacteroids of the roaches, which have been investigated more than other symbionts, may perform some function useful to the host. Some roaches die if the bacteroids are eliminated by the administration of agents such as penicillin (102). Some other insects, however, may be deprived of their symbionts without damage (382).

The rickettsiae pathogenic for man present various degrees of relation with arthropod hosts, and these relations provide the basis for what seems a sensible picture of the recent evolution of these microorganisms (34; 113):

1. *Dermacentroxenus rickettsi*, the agent of Rocky Mountain spotted fever, is a natural inhabitant of the gut of many ticks, where it is transmitted from generation to generation through the egg. It is occasionally inoculated by the ticks into horses and other animals, including man. These vertebrate hosts do not play any essential part in the life cycle of the organism, except that some of them, especially wild horses, serve to transmit the rickettsiae from infected to noninfected ticks. The rickettsia is only infectious if injected by a tick recently engorged with blood. Rickettsiae from nonengorged ticks can

even be used as a vaccine without previous inactivation, with little danger of infection. This unexplained property (517) may be of importance for the survival of the rickettsiae in nature, because it may help them propagate in wild animals without causing a fatal disease.

2. *Rickettsia orientalis*, the agent of scrub typhus, is found in mites that infest wild rats. In the mite the rickettsia is transmitted from one generation to the next through the egg. The rats represent an important reservoir. Only accidentally is man infected by the bite of mites or of rat fleas.

3. In the endemic (murine) typhus, the rat has become the main reservoir of *R. prowazeki* var. *typhi* and responds to infection with an almost symptomless disease. The rat fleas transmit the disease from rat to rat and occasionally to man, but do not have any intrinsic biological relation with the rickettsiae, nor do they act as a reservoir.

4. The epidemic typhus presents a different situation. The agent, *R. prowazeki*, has a cycle restricted to man and to the human louse. The louse receives the rickettsiae from man and becomes infected. It transmits the rickettsiae by excreting them in its feces. The rickettsiae enter the human skin through scratches provoked by the louse's bites. The louse generally dies as a result of the infection. Neither man nor louse are "natural" hosts; they are both very susceptible. In the absence of a known reservoir of the usual kind, the disease is only maintained in certain areas because of its widespread occurrence. Some individuals probably act as carriers. The rickettsiae survive for a long time in dry feces of lice. These relations explain the great importance of delousing in the prevention and control of epidemics. A tremendous improvement has been brought about by the introduction of powerful insecticides such as DDT.

5. The agent of Q fever, *C. burneti*, multiplies in ticks and is excreted on cattle. In man the disease is often, but not exclusively, observed in slaughterhouse workers, who become infected by handling contaminated cattle hides.

In view of this evidence, it seems reasonable to assume that the rickettsiae represent a group of bacteria which, early in evolution, established close biological relations with arthropods, first infecting them as pathogens, then becoming symbionts. The rickettsiae may originally have resembled the symbiotic bacterioids and may have later become modified within the arthropod body. Occasionally, a rickettsia finds its way into a vertebrate host and, if endowed with pathogenic ability, may produce a disease. This is generally not important in the life history of the rickettsiae. Exceptionally, however, a rickettsia may find in the vertebrate host conditions favorable for survival, as in murine typhus in the rat. From the vertebrate it may pass into a secondary arthropod, such as the rat flea. This may create a new vertebrate-arthropod cycle and short circuit the original arthropod host, which may entirely disappear from the epidemiological picture. By shifting from one host to another, the point may be reached where the cycle consists of man plus a secondary or tertiary vector. This may be so in epidemic typhus, which has probably derived from the murine type by replacement of the rat-flea cycle with the man-louse cycle. The disease might finally become strictly human. In fact, Brill's disease, a form of epidemic typhus, appears without louse infestation and may be transmitted directly by human carriers.

As already mentioned, the typhus rickettsia kills the body louse. Thus, the relation between a rickettsia and an arthropod is not always one of symbiosis or innocuous commensalism. A rickettsialike organism, *Coxiella popillia*, is responsible for the blue disease of Japanese beetles (*199*). The organism fills the diseased cells of the larvae and is found in the larval blood. Interestingly enough, the diseased cells also contain intranuclear crystals. The formation of intranuclear crystals may be a rather general reaction to a variety of infections of insect larvae.

It is interesting to inquire whether there are any other microorganisms that may share some of the properties of rickettsiae (*518*). The closest relative is probably the bacterium *Pasteurella tularensis,* the agent of tularemia. This tiny, Gram-negative bacterium, not appreciably larger than some of the rickettsiae, is a normal inhabitant of the gut of ticks. In these animals it can be transmitted through the egg. The only important difference between *P. tularensis* and rickettsiae is that *tularensis* is cultivable in bacteriological cell-free media.

This criterion may not be very significant. If we conceive of rickettsiae as bacteria that have become intracellular parasites of arthropods, we may well expect to find that some rickettsiae are still able to grow in nonliving media. It would indeed not be surprising if several rickettsiae could soon be cultivated in cell-free media. All evidence on the metabolic relation between rickettsiae and their hosts suggests that the host acts more as a supplier of substrates than of metabolic machinery. This is at variance with the relation between viruses and host cells. Interesting in this connection is the fact that some rickettsiae have been reported to multiply, within their arthropod hosts, not only inside the cells of the intestinal tract but also at the surface of such cells, within the intestinal lumen.

Another organism that has been considered a close relative of rickettsiae is *Bartonella bacilliformis,* the agent of the South American disease, Orroya fever, and of its milder form, *verruga peruana.* The natural reservoirs of this organism have not been established. Its relation to the arthropod host, the sand-fly, has not yet been clarified.

Bibliography-Author Index

Note: Final numbers in square brackets refer to text pages.

1. Ackermann, W. W. (1951) Concerning the relation of the Krebs cycle to virus propagation. *J. Biol. Chem.* **189:** 421–428 [229]
2. Ackermann, W. W. (1951) The role of *l*-methionine in virus propagation. *J. Exp. Med.* **93:** 337–343 [146, 230]
3. Ackermann, W. W., and Francis, T., Jr. (1950) Some biochemical aspects of herpes infection. *Proc. Soc. Exp. Biol. Med.* **74:** 123–126 [238]
4. Ackermann, W. W., and Kurtz, H. (1952) The relation of herpes virus to host cell mitochondria. *J. Exp. Med.* **96:** 151–157 [237]
5. Adams, M. H. (1948) Surface inactivation of bacterial viruses and of proteins. *J. Gen. Physiol.* **31:** 417–431 [143]
6. Adams, M. H. (1949) The stability of bacterial viruses in solutions of salts. *J. Gen. Physiol.* **32:** 579–594 [138, 141, 142]
7. Adams, M. H. (1949) The calcium requirement of coliphage T5. *J. Bact.* **62:** 505–516 [168]
8. Adams, M. H. (1951) The hybridization of coliphage T5 and *Salmonella* phage PB. *J. Immunol.* **67:** 313–320 [293]
9. Adams, M. H. (1952) Classification of bacterial viruses: Characteristics of the T5 species and of the T2, C16 species. *J. Bact.* **64:** 387–396 [17, 18, 19]
10. Adams, M. H., and Lark, G. (1950) Mutation to heat resistance in coliphage T5. *J. Immunol.* **64:** 335–347 [293]
11. Alexander, H., and Leidy, G. (1951) Determination of inherited traits of *H. influenzae* by desoxyribonucleic acid fractions isolated from type-specific cells. *J. Exp. Med.* **93:** 345–359 [126, 351]
12. Altenburg, E. (1946) The "viroid" theory in relation to plasma-genes, viruses, cancer and plastids. *Am. Naturalist* **80:** 559–567 [361]
13. American Public Health Association. (1948) *Diagnostic procedures for virus and rickettsial diseases.* New York [133]
13a. Anderson, E. S., and Felix, A. (1953) Degraded Vi strains and variation in Vi-phage II of *Salmonella typhi. J. Gen. Microbiol.* **8:** 408–420 [207]
13b. Anderson, E. S., and Felix, A. (1953) The Vi-type determining phages carried by *Salmonella typhi. J. Gen. Microbiol.* **9:** 65–88 [207]
14. Anderson, K. (1942) Dual virus infections of single cells. *Am. J. Path.* **18:** 577–583 [238, 284]
15. Anderson, S. G. (1947) The mechanism of the union between influenza virus and susceptible cells. *Austral. J. Sci.* **10:** 83 [258]
16. Anderson, S. G., Burnet, F. M., Fazekas de St. Groth, S., McCrea, J. F., and Stone, J. D. (1948) Mucins and mucoids in relation to influenza virus action. *Austral. J. Exp. Biol. Med. Sci.* **26:** 403–411 [258]

17. Anderson, T. F. (1946) Morphological and chemical relations in viruses and bacteriophages. *Cold Spring Harbor Symp. Quant. Biol.* **11**: 1–13 [166]

18. Anderson, T. F. (1948) The growth of T2 virus on ultraviolet-killed host cells. *J. Bact.* **56**: 403–410 [179]

19. Anderson, T. F. (1949) The reaction of bacterial viruses with their host cells. *Bot. Rev.* **15**: 464–505 [159]

20. Anderson, T. F. (1950) Destruction of bacterial viruses by osmotic shock. *J. Appl. Phys.* **21**: 70 [65]

21. Anderson, T. F., and Doermann, A. H. (1952) Sonic reactivation of anti-serum-neutralized bacteriophage T3. *J. Bact.* **63**: 291–292 [123]

22. Anderson, T. F., and Stanley, W. M. (1941) A study by means of the electron microscope of the reaction between tobacco mosaic virus and its antiserum. *J. Biol. Chem.* **139**: 339–344 [67]

23. Andervont, H. B. (1945) The milk influence in the genesis of mammary tumors. In: *A Symposium on Mammary Tumors in Mice.* A.A.A.S., Washington [328, 340]

24. Andrewes, C. H. (1929) Virus III in tissue cultures. II, III. *Br. J. Exp. Path.* **10**: 273–280 [227, 229, 281]

25. Andrewes, C. H. (1934) Viruses in relation to the aetiology of tumours. *Lancet* (2) **227**: 63–69; 117–123 [334, 335]

26. Andrewes, C. H. (1936) Evidence for the presence of virus in a nonfilterable tar sarcoma of the fowl. *J. Path. Bact.* **43**: 23–33 [338]

27. Andrewes, C. H. (1942) Interference by one virus with the growth of another in tissue culture. *Br. J. Exp. Path.* **23**: 214–220 [267, 283]

28. Andrewes, C. H. (1952) The place of viruses in nature. *Proc. Roy. Soc.* (London) B, **139**: 313–326 [272]

29. Andrewes, C. H., and Elford, W. J. (1933) Observations on antiphage sera. I. The "percentage law." *Br. J. Exp. Path.* **14**: 367–376 [122]

30. Andrewes, C. H., Ahlstrom, C. G., Foulds, L., and Gye, W. E. (1937) Reaction of tarred rabbits to the infectious fibroma virus (Shope). *Lancet* (2) **233**: 893–895 [338]

31. Armstrong, C., Wallace, J. J., and Ross, L. (1940) Lymphocytic choriomeningitis. Gray mice, *Mus musculus*, a reservoir for the infection. *U. S. Pub. Health Rep.* **55**: 1222–1229 [38, 309, 340]

32. Avery, O. T., MacLeod, C. M., and McCarty, M. (1944). Studies on the chemical nature of the substance inducing transformation of pneumococcal types. Induction of transformation by a desoxyribonucleic acid fraction isolated from pneumomoccus type III. *J. Exp. Med.* **79**: 137–158 [100, 351]

33. Backus, R. C., and Williams, R. C. (1950) The use of spraying methods and volatile suspending media in the preparation of specimens for electron microscopy. *J. Appl. Phys.* **21**: 11–15 [211]

34. Baker, A. C. (1943) The typical epidemic series. *Am. J. Trop Med.* **23**: 559–567 [364, 370]

35. Bald, J. G. (1937) The use of numbers of infections for comparing the concentration of plant virus suspensions. IV. *Austral. J. Exp. Biol. Med. Sci.* **15**: 211–220 [54]

36. Banfield, W. G., Bunting, H., Strauss, M. J., and Melnick, J. L. (1951) Electron micrographs of thin sections of molluscum contagiosum. *Proc. Soc. Exp. Biol. Med.* **77**: 843–847 [234]

37. Bang, F. B. (1948) Studies on Newcastle disease virus. III. *J. Exp. Med.* **88**: 251–266 [82]

37a. Bang, F. B., and Gye, G. O. (1952) Comparative susceptibility of cultured cell strains to the virus of Eastern equine encephalomyelitis. *Bull. Johns Hopkins Hosp.* **91**: 427–461 [227]

38. Barnard, J. E. (1932) Discussion on the microscopy of the filterable viruses. *J. Roy. Microsc. Soc.* **52**: 233–235 [60]

39. Barnard, J. E. (1935) Microscopical evidence of the existence of saprophytic viruses. *Br. J. Exp. Path.* **16**: 129–133 [4]

40. Barton-Wright, E., and McBain, A. (1932) Studies in the physiology of the virus diseases of the potato: a comparison of the carbohydrate metabolism of normal with that of leaf-roll potatoes. *Trans. Roy. Soc. Edinburgh* **57**: 309–349 [218]

41. Bauer, D. J. (1953) Metabolic aspects of virus multiplication. In: *The Nature of Virus Multiplication*, Cambridge University Press [84, 108, 109]

42. Baumgartner, G. (1935) Infektionversuche mit isolierten oxychromatischen Einschlüssen des Herpes. *Schweiz. med. Wochenschr.* **16**: 759–760 [237]

43. Bawden, F. C. (1950) *Plant Viruses and Virus Diseases*, 3rd Ed. Waltham, Mass., Chronica Botanica [3, 6, 16, 17, 93, 94, 121, 137, 141, 215, 216, 218, 315]

44. Bawden, F. C., and Kassanis, B. (1945) The suppression of one plant virus by another. *Ann. Appl. Biol.* **32**: 52–57 [278]

45. Bawden, F. C., and Kassanis, B. (1949) Some effects of host nutrition on the multiplication of viruses. *Ann. Appl. Biol.* **37**: 215–228 [219]

46. Bawden, F. C., and Kassanis, B. (1951) Serologically related strains of potato virus Y that are not mutually antagonistic in plants. *Ann. Appl. Biol.* **38**: 402–410 [278]

47. Bawden, F. C., and Kleczkowski, A. (1945) Protein precipitation and virus inactivation by extracts of strawberry plants. *J. Pomol.* **21**: 2–7 [87]

48. Bawden, F. C., and Nixon, H. L. (1953) Quoted by Bawden and Pirie in: *The Nature of Virus Multiplication*, Cambridge University Press [213]

49. Bawden, F. C., and Pirie, N. W. (1950) Some factors affecting the activation of virus preparations made from tobacco leaves infected with a tobacco necrosis virus. *J. Gen. Microbiol.* **4**: 464–481 [110, 128, 215]

50. Bawden, F. C., and Pirie, N. W. (1950) The varieties of macromolecules in extracts from virus-infected plants. In: Delbrück, *Viruses 1950*, Pasadena, Cal. Inst. Technol. Bookstore [86]

51. Bawden, F. C., and Roberts, F. M. (1948) Photosynthesis and predisposition of plants to infection with certain viruses. *Ann. Appl. Biol.* **35**: 418–428 [219]

52. Bawden, F. C., Kassanis, B., and Nixon, H. L. (1950) The mechanical transmission and some properties of potato paracrinkle virus. *J. Gen. Microbiol.* **4**: 210–219 [34, 349]

53. Bayne-Jones, S. (1948)   Epidemic typhus in the Mediterranean area during World War II. In: *The Rickettsial Diseases of Man*. A.A.A.S., Washington   [368]

54. Beale, H. P. (1937)   Relation of Stanley's crystalline tobacco-virus protein to intracellular crystalline deposits. *Contrib. Boyce Thompson Inst.* 8: 413–431   [215]

54a. Beale, H. P. (1947)   The interference phenomenon between the ribgrass and tobacco-mosaic viruses in bean. *Phytopath.* 37: 847   [277]

55. Beale, H. P., and Jones, C. R. (1951)   Virus diseases of tobacco mosaic and potato yellow dwarf not controlled by certain antibiotics. *Contrib. Boyce Thompson Inst.* 16: 395–407   [219]

56. Beard, J. W. (1948)   Purified animal viruses. *J. Immunol.* 58: 49–108   [105, 106]

57. Beard, J. W., Bryan, W. R., and Wyckoff, R. W. G. (1939)   The isolation of the rabbit papilloma virus protein. *J. Infectious Diseases* 65: 43–52   [327, 336]

58. Beijerinck, M. W. (1899)   Über ein Contagium vivum fluidum als Ursache der Fleckenkrankheit der Tabaksblätter. *Zentr. Bakt., Parasit., II*, 5: 27–33   [6]

59. Bennett, C. W. (1935)   Studies on properties of the curly top virus. *J. Agr. Res.* 50: 211–241   [33]

60. Bennett, C. W. (1937)   Correlation between movement of the curly top virus and translocation of food in tobacco and sugar beet. *J. Agr. Res.* 54: 479–502   [217]

61. Bennett, C. W. (1940)   Acquisition and transmission of viruses by dodder (*Cuscuta subinclusa*). *Phytopath.* 30: 2   [34]

61a. Bennett, C. W. (1940)   The relation of viruses to plant tissues. *Bot. Rev.* 6: 427–473   [216]

62. Bennett, C. W. (1944)   Latent virus of dodder and its effect on sugar beet and other plants. *Phytopath.* 34: 77–91   [37]

63. Bennett, C. W., and Wallace, H. E. (1938)   Relation of the curly top virus to the vector *Eutettix tenellus*. *J. Agr. Res.* 56: 31–51   [317]

64. Benzer, S. (1952)   Resistance to ultraviolet light as an index to the reproduction of bacteriophage. *J. Bact.* 63: 59–72   [156, 195, 196]

65. Benzer, S., et al. (1950)   A syllabus of procedures, facts, and interpretations in phage. In: Delbrück, *Viruses 1950*, Pasadena, Cal. Inst. Technol. Bookstore   [7]

66. Bergold, G. (1947)   Die Isolierung des Polyeder-Virus und die Natur der Polyeder. *Z. Naturforsch.* 2b: 122–143   [83, 110]

67. Bergold, G. (1948)   Über die Kapselvirus-Krankheit. *Z. Naturforsch.* 3b: 338–342   [83]

68. Bergold, G. H. (1950)   The multiplication of insect viruses as organisms. *Canad. J. Res., E*, 28: 5–11   [83]

68a. Bergold, G. H. (1953)   Insect viruses. *Adv. Virus Research* 1: 91–139   [19, 83, 110, 237]

69. Bernal, J. D., and Fankuchen, I. (1941)   X-ray and crystallographic studies of plant virus preparations. *J. Gen. Physiol.* 25: 111–165   [93, 94, 95]

70. Bernal, J. D., Fankuchen, I., and Riley, D. P. (1938)   Structure of the crystals of tomato bushy stunt virus preparations. *Nature* 142: 1075   [91]

71. Bernkopf, H. (1950) Study of infectivity and hemagglutination of influenza virus in deembryonated eggs. *J. Immunol.* **65:** 571–583 [265]

72. Bernkopf, H., and Kligler, I. J. (1940) Characteristics of a fixed rabies virus cultivated on developing chick embryos. *Proc. Soc. Exp. Biol. Med.* **45:** 332–335 [245, 246]

73. Berry, G. P., and Dedrick, H. M. (1936) A method for changing the virus of rabbit fibroma (Shope) into that of infectious myxomatosis (Sanarelli). *J. Bact.* **31:** 50 [302]

74. Bertani, G. (1951) Studies on lysogenesis. I. *J. Bact.* **62:** 293–300 [202]

75. Bertani, G. (1953) Infection bactériophagique secondaire des bactéries lysogènes. *Ann. Inst. Pasteur* **84:** 273–280 [203, 277]

76. Bertani, G., and Weigle, J. J. (1952) Host-controlled variation in bacterial viruses. *J. Bact.* **65:** 113–121 [197, 198, 295, 333]

77. Beveridge, W. I. B., and Burnet, F. M. (1946) The cultivation of viruses and rickettsiae in the chick embryo. *Med. Res. Council Spec. Rep.* No. 256 [42, 239, 241, 247, 249]

78. Billingham, R. E., and Medawar, P. B. (1948) Pigment spread and cell heredity in guinea-pig's skin. *Heredity* **2:** 29–47 [359]

78a. Bird, F. T. (1949) Tumours associated with a virus infection in an insect. *Nature* **163:** 777–778 [325]

79. Bittner, J. J. (1936) Some possible effects of nursing on the mammary gland tumor incidence in mice. *Science* **84:** 162 [328]

80. Bittner, J. J. (1941) Changes in the incidence of mammary carcinoma in mice of the A stock. *Cancer Res.* **1:** 113–114 [330]

81. Black, L. M. (1941) Specific transmission of varieties of potato yellow dwarf virus by related insects. *Am. Potato J.* **18:** 231–233 [315]

82. Black, L. M. (1941) Further evidence for multiplication of the aster-yellow virus in the aster leafhopper. *Phytopath.* **31:** 120–125 [317]

83. Black, L. M. (1945) A virus tumor disease of plants. *Am. J. Bot.* **32:** 408–415 [7, 29, 216, 317, 330]

84. Black, L. M. (1950) A plant virus that multiplies in its insect vector. *Nature* **166:** 852–853 [317]

85. Black, L. M., and Brakke, M. K. (1952) Multiplication of wound-tumor virus in an insect vector. *Phytopath.* **42:** 269–273 [318]

86. Black, L. M., Morgan, C., and Wyckoff, R. W. G. (1950) Visualization of tobacco mosaic virus within infected cells. *Proc. Soc. Exp. Biol. Med.* **73:** 119–122 [213]

87. Blanc, G. (1948) Dengue. In: Levaditi and Lépine, *Les ultravirus des maladies humaines*, 2nd Ed., Paris, Maloine [311]

88. Blanc, G., and Caminopetros, J. (1929) Durée de conservation du virus de la dengue chez les Stegomyas. L'influence de la saison froide sur le pouvoir infectant. *C. r. acad. sci.* **188:** 1273–1275 [312]

89. Bland, J. O. W., and Canti, R. G. (1935) The growth and development of psittacosis virus in tissue cultures. *J. Path. Bact.* **40:** 231–241 [58, 232, 233, 247, 368]

90. Bland, J. O. W., and Robinow, C. F. (1939) The inclusion bodies of vaccinia and their relationship to the elementary bodies studied in cultures of the rabbit's cornea. *J. Path. Bact.* **48:** 381–403 [233]

91. Bodian, D. (1952) A reconsideration of the pathogenesis of poliomyelitis. *Am. J. Hyg.* **55**: 414–438   [308]

92. Bodian, D., and Howe, H. A. (1941) The rate of progression of poliomyelitis virus in nerves. *Bull. Johns Hopkins Hosp.* **69**: 79–85   [308]

93. Bodian, D., and Howe, H. A. (1947) The significance of lesions in peripheral ganglia in chimpanzee and in human poliomyelitis. *J. Exp. Med.* **85**: 231–242   [308]

94. Born, H. J., Lang, A., and Schramm, G. (1943) Markierung von Tabakmosaikvirus mit Radiophosphor. *Arch. ges. Virusforsch.* **2**: 461–479   [210]

95. Borrel, A. (1903) Epithélioses infectieuses et épithéliomas. *Ann. Inst. Pasteur* **17**: 81–84   [324]

96. Borrel, A. (1904) Sur les inclusions de l'épithélioma contagieux des oiseaux. *C. r. soc. biol.* **57**: 642–643   [232]

97. Borrel, A. (1907) Le problème du cancer. *Bull. Inst. Pasteur* **5**: 497–512, 545–562, 593–608, 641–662   [324]

98. Bovarnich, M. R., and Miller, J. C. (1950) Oxidation and transamination of glutamate by typhus rickettsiae. *J. Biol. Chem.* **184**: 661–676   [366]

98a. Bowen, G. (1953) Kinetic studies on the mechanism of photoreactivation of bacteriophage T2 inactivated by ultraviolet light. *Ann. Inst. Pasteur* **84**: 218–221   [195]

99. Boyd, J. S. K. (1950) The symbiotic bacteriophages of *Salmonella typhimurium*. *J. Path. Bact.* **62**: 501–517   [206, 208]

100. Boyd, J. S. K. (1951) Mutation in a bacterial virus. *Nature* **168**: 994–995   [203, 293]

100a. Brakke, M. K. (1951) Density gradient centrifugation: A new separation technique. *J. Am. Chem. Soc.* **73**: 1847   [89]

100b. Brakke, M. K., Black, L. M., and Wyckoff, R. W. G. (1951) The sedimentation rate of potato yellow-dwarf virus. *Am. J. Bot.* **38**: 332–342   [92]

100c. Brakke, M. K., Vatter, A. E., and Black, L. M. Personal communication.   [318]

101. Braun, A. C. (1952) The crown-gall disease. *Ann. N. Y. Acad. Sci.* **54**: 1153–1160   [167, 339]

101a. Briody, B. A., and Stannard, C. (1951) Studies on vaccinia virus. I. The development of hemagglutinating and infective particles in the chorioallantois of the chick embryo. *J. Immunol.* **67**: 403–411   [269]

102. Brues, C. T., and Dunn, R. C. (1945) The effect of penicillin and certain sulfa drugs on the intracellular bacteroids of the cockroach. *Science* **101**: 336–337   [370]

103. Bryan, W. R., and Beard, J. W. (1939) Estimation of purified papilloma virus protein by infectivity measurements. *J. Infectious Diseases* **65**: 306–321   [45]

104. Bryan, W. R., and Beard, J. W. (1940) Host influence in the characterization of response to the papilloma protein and to vaccinia virus. *J. Infectious Diseases* **67**: 5–24   [53, 54]

105. Bryan, W. R., and Beard, J. W. (1941) Studies on the purification and properties of the rabbit-papilloma-virus protein. *J. Nat. Cancer Inst.* **1**: 607–673   [120]

106. Buist, J. B. (1887) *Vaccinia and Variola: A Study of Their Life History,* London, Churchill [6, 58]

107. Burmester, B. R. (1952) Studies on fowl lymphomatosis. *Ann. N. Y. Acad. Sci.* **54:** 992–1003 [239, 325]

108. Burnet, F. M. (1929) A method for the study of bacteriophage multiplication in broth. *Br. J. Exp. Path.* **10:** 109–115 [162]

109. Burnet, F. M. (1930) Bacteriophage activity and antigenic structure of bacteria. *J. Path. Bact.* **33:** 647–664 [168]

110. Burnet, F. M. (1933) The serological classification of Coli-dysentery phages. *J. Path. Bact.* **36:** 307–318 [122]

111. Burnet, F. M. (1933) A specific soluble substance from bacteriophages. *Br. J. Exp. Path.* **14:** 100–108 [111]

112. Burnet, F. M. (1940) The production of antibodies. *Monographs from Walter and Eliza Hall Institute,* I [132]

113. Burnet, F. M. (1942) The rickettsial diseases in Australia. *Med. J. Australia* **2:** 129–134 [370]

114. Burnet, F. M. (1945) *Virus as Organism,* Cambridge, Harvard University Press [4, 5, 37, 271, 290, 302, 310, 319, 347]

115. Burnet, F. M. (1948) The initiation of cellular infection by influenza and related viruses. *Lancet* (1) **254:** 7–11 [253, 254, 256]

116. Burnet, F. M. (1951) Some biological implications of studies on influenza viruses. *Bull. Johns Hopkins Hosp.* **88:** 119–180 [253]

117. Burnet, F. M., and Boake, W. C. (1946) The relationship between the virus of infectious ectromelia of mice and vaccinia virus. *J. Immunol.* **53:** 1–13 [301]

118. Burnet, F. M., and Bull, D. R. (1943) Changes in influenza virus associated with adaptation to passage in chick embryos. *Austral. J. Exp. Biol. Med. Sci.* **21:** 55–69 [253, 300]

118a. Burnet, F. M., and Edney, M. (1951) Recombinant viruses obtained from double infections with the influenza A viruses MEL and Neuro-WS. *Austral. J. Exp. Biol. Med. Sci.* **39:** 353–362 [267, 268]

119. Burnet, F. M., and Lind, P. E. (1950) Haemolysis by Newcastle disease virus. II. *Austral. J. Exp. Biol. Med. Sci.* **28:** 129–150 [254]

120. Burnet, F. M., and Lind, P. E. (1951) A genetic approach to variation in influenza viruses. I–IV. *J. Gen. Microbiol.* **5:** 46–82 [267, 302, 350]

120a. Burnet, F. M., and McKie, M. (1929) Observations on a permanently lysogenic strain of B. enteritidis Gaertner. *Austral. J. Exp. Biol. Med. Sci.* **6:** 277–284 [30]

120b. Burnet, F. M., Fraser, K. B., and Lind, P. E. (1953) Genetic interaction between influenza viruses. *Nature* **171:** 163–165 [268]

121. Burnet, F. M., Keogh, E. V., and Lush, D. (1937) The immunological reactions of the filterable viruses. *Austral. J. Exp. Biol. Med. Sci.* **15:** 231–368 [7, 119, 122, 128, 131]

121a. Burnet, F. M., and others. (1953) Virus and rickettsial classification and nomenclature. *Ann. N. Y. Acad. Sci.* **56:** 381–622 [16]

122. Cairns, H. J. F., Fazekas de St. Groth, S., and Edney, M. (1952) Quantitative aspects of influenza virus multiplication. I–IV. *J. Immunol.* **69:** 155–181 [261, 263, 286]

382   Bibliography

123. Carrel, A. (1925) Comparaison des macrophages normaux et des macrophages transformés en cellules malignes. *C. r. soc. biol.* **92:** 584–587 [332]

124. Carrel, A. (1926) Some conditions of the reproduction *in vitro* of the Rous virus. *J. Exp. Med.* **43:** 647–668 [226, 227]

124a. Carter, W. (1928) Transmission of the virus of curly-top of sugar beets through different solutions. *Phytopath.* **18:** 675–679 [317]

125. Casals, J., Olitsky, P. K., and Anslow, R. O. (1951) A specific complement-fixation test for infection with poliomyelitis virus. *J. Exp. Med.* **94:** 123–137 [134]

126. Caspari, E. (1948) Cytoplasmic inheritance. *Adv. Genetics* **2:** 1–66 [355]

127. Caspersson, T. (1939) Über die Rolle der Desoxyribosenucleinsäure bei der Zellteilung. *Chromosoma* **1:** 147–156 [238]

128. Chargaff, E. (1950) Chemical specificity of nucleic acids and mechanism of their enzymatic degradation. *Experientia* **6:** 201–240 [97]

129. Cheever, F. S., and Janeway, C. A. (1941) Immunity induced against the Brown-Pearce carcinoma. *Cancer Res.* **1:** 23–27 [337]

130. Chester, K. S. (1936) Serological tests with Stanley's crystalline tobacco-mosaic protein. *Phytopath.* **26:** 715–734 [88]

131. Chu, C. M., Dawson, I. M., and Elford, W. J. (1949) Filamentous forms associated with newly isolated influenza virus. *Lancet* (1) **256:** 602–603 [82]

132. Chu, L. W., and Morgan, H. P. (1950) Studies of the hemolysis of red blood cells by mumps virus. *J. Exp. Med.* **91:** 393–402 [254]

133. Clark, F., and Nagler, F. P. O. (1943) Haem-agglutination by viruses. The range of susceptible cells with special reference to agglutination by vaccinia virus. *Austral. J. Exp. Biol. Med. Sci.* **21:** 103–106 [251]

134. Clark, P. F. (1949) The influence of nutrition on experimental virus infection. *Bact. Rev.* **13:** 122–127 [31, 223]

135. Clarke, N. A. (1952) Studies on the host-virus relationship in a lysogenic strain of *Bacillus megaterium.* II. *J. Bact.* **63:** 187–192 [205, 339]

136. Claude, A. (1937) Preparation of an active agent from inactive tumor extracts. *Science* **85:** 294–295 [335]

137. Claude, A. (1938) Concentration and purification of chicken tumor I agent. *Science* **87:** 467–468 [107]

138. Claude, A. (1938) A fraction from normal chick embryo similar to the tumor-producing fraction of chicken tumor I. *Proc. Soc. Exp. Biol. Med.* **39:** 398–403 [342]

139. Claude, A. (1939) Chemical composition of the tumor-producing fraction of chicken tumor I. *Science* **90:** 213–214 [324]

140. Claude, A., and Murphy, J. B. (1933) Transmissible tumors of the fowl. *Physiol. Rev.* **13:** 246–275 [325, 343]

141. Cloudman, A. M. (1941) The effect of an extra-chromosomal influence upon transplanted spontaneous tumors in mice. *Science* **93:** 380–381 [322, 330, 348]

142. Cohen, S. S. (1944) Cytoplasmic particles of chorio-allantoic membrane and their relations to purified preparations of influenza virus. *Proc. Soc. Exp. Biol. Med.* **57:** 358–360 [107]

143. Cohen, S. S. (1947) The synthesis of bacterial viruses in infected cells. *Cold Spring Harbor Symp. Quant. Biol.* **12:** 35–49 [175, 178]

144. Cohen, S. S. (1949) Growth requirements of bacterial viruses. *Bact. Rev.* **13:** 1–24 [176, 177, 178, 179]

145. Cohen, S. S. (1950) Studies on commercial typhus vaccines. IV. *J. Immunol.* **65:** 475–483 [366]

146. Cohen, S. S., and Arbogast, R. (1950) Chemical studies in host-virus interaction. VI. *J. Exp. Med.* **91:** 607–618 [88, 103]

147. Cohen, S. S., and Chargaff, E. (1944) Studies on the composition of Rickettsia prowazeki. *J. Biol. Chem.* **154:** 691–704 [366]

148. Cohen, S. S., and Stanley, W. M. (1942) The molecular size and shape of the nucleic acid of tobacco mosaic virus. *J. Biol. Chem.* **144:** 589–598 [100]

149. Cohen, S. S., Chambers, L. A., and Clawson, J. R. (1950) Studies on commercial typhus vaccines. III. *J. Immunol.* **65:** 465–473 [367]

150. *Cold Spring Harbor Symp. Quant. Biol.* **12** (1947) [99]

150a. Commoner, B., and Dietz, P. M. (1952) Changes in non-protein nitrogen metabolism during tobacco mosaic virus biosynthesis. *J. Gen. Physiol.* **35:** 847–856 [210, 218]

151. Commoner, B., and Mercer, F. (1951) Inhibition of the biosynthesis of tobacco mosaic virus by thiouracil. *Nature* **168:** 113–114 [146, 210]

152. Commoner, B., Mercer, F. L., Merrill, P., and Zimmer, A. J. (1950) Microanalytic determination of the rate of tobacco mosaic virus synthesis in tobacco leaf tissue. *Arch. Biochem.* **27:** 271–286 [210, 211, 212]

153. Cosslett, V. E. (1951) *Practical Electron Microscopy,* New York, Academic Press [60]

154. Cox, H. R. (1948) The preparation and standardization of rickettsial vaccines. In: *The Rickettsial Diseases of Man.* A.A.A.S., Washington [367]

155. Craigie, J. (1932) The nature of the vaccinia flocculation reaction, and observations on the elementary bodies of vaccinia. *Br. J. Exp. Path.* **13:** 259–268 [89]

156. Craigie, J. (1946) The significance and applications of bacteriophage in bacteriological and virus research. *Bact. Rev.* **10:** 73–88 [167]

157. Craigie, J., and Felix, A. (1947) Typing of typhoid bacilli with Vi-bacteriophages. *Lancet* (1) **252:** 823–826 [167, 206]

157a. Craigie, J., and Yen, C. H. (1938) The demonstration of types of *B. typhosus* by means of preparations of Type II Vi phage. I, II. *Canad. Publ. Health J.* **29:** 448–463 and 484–496 [167, 206]

158. Crawford, G. N. C., and Sanders, F. K. (1952) The multiplication of vaccinia virus in tissue cultures of adult rabbit skin. *Quart. J. Microscop. Sci.* **93:** 119–132 [269, 270]

159. Crouse, H. V., Coriell, L. L., Blank, H., and McNair Scott, T. F. (1950) Cytochemical studies on the intranuclear inclusion of herpes simplex. *J. Immunol.* **65:** 119–128 [237]

160. Curnen, E. C., and Horsfall, F. L. (1946) Studies on pneumonia virus of mice (PVM). III. *J. Exp. Med.* **83:** 105–132 [87]

161. Curtis, M. R., Dunning, W. F., and Bullock, F. D. (1933) Genetic factors in relation to the etiology of malignant tumors. *Am. J. Cancer* **17:** 894–923 [323]

384   Bibliography

162. Cutting, W. C. (1949) Actions of antibiotics in vivo. *Ann. Rev. Microbiol.* **3:** 137–158   [223, 369]

162a. Davenport, F. M. (1952) Toxicity of NDV for mouse lung. *J. Immunol.* **69:** 461–470   [223, 224]

163. Davenport, F. M., and Francis, T., Jr. (1951) A comparison of the growth curves of adapted and unadapted lines of influenza virus. *J. Exp. Med.* **93:** 129–137   [221]

164. DeBurgh, D., Yu, P. C., Howe, C., and Bovarnick, M. (1948) Preparation from human red cells of a substance inhibiting virus hemagglutination. *J. Exp. Med.* **87:** 1–9   [258]

164a. DeCarlo, M. R., Sarles, W. B., and Knight, S. G. (1953) Lysogenicity of *Bacillus megatherium.* *J. Bact.* **65:** 53–55   [206]

165. Delbrück, M. (1940) Adsorption of bacteriophages under various physiological conditions of the host. *J. Gen. Physiol.* **23:** 631–642   [166]

166. Delbrück, M. (1940) The growth of bacteriophage and lysis of the host. *J. Gen. Physiol.* **23:** 643–660   [168]

167. Delbrück, M. (1945) Effect of specific antisera on the growth of bacterial viruses. *J. Bact.* **50:** 137–150   [125, 164]

168. Delbrück, M. (1945) Interference between bacterial viruses. III. *J. Bact.* **50:** 151–170   [187, 188, 273]

169. Delbrück, M. (1946) Bacterial viruses or bacteriophages. *Biol. Rev.* **21:** 30–40   [122, 159]

170. Delbrück, M. (1948) Biochemical mutants of bacterial viruses. *J. Bact.* **56:** 1–16   [146, 166, 167, 293]

171. Delbrück, M. (1949) Discussion of paper by Beale and Sonneborn. In: *Unités biologiques douées de continuité génétique.* Centre Nat. Rech. Scientifique, Paris   [355]

172. Delbrück, M. *Viruses 1950,* Pasadena, Cal. Inst. Technol. Bookstore   [1]

173. Delbrück, M., and Bailey, W. T., Jr. (1946) Induced mutations in bacterial viruses. *Cold Spring Harbor Symp. Quant. Biol.* **11:** 33–37   [189, 274]

174. Delbrück, M., and Luria, S. E. (1942) Interference between bacterial viruses. I. *Arch. Biochem.* **1:** 111–141   [159, 273]

175. DeMars, R. I., Luria, S. E., Fisher, H., and Levinthal, C. (1953) The production of incomplete bacteriophage particles by the action of proflavine, and the properties of the incomplete particles. *Ann. Inst. Pasteur* **84:** 113–128   [84, 111, 120, 126, 127, 171, 172, 173, 199]

176. Demerec, M. (1949) Chemical mutagens. *Proc. VIII Intern. Congr. Genetics,* Stockholm, 201–209   [338]

177. Demerec, M., and Fano, U. (1945) Bacteriophage-resistant mutants in *Escherichia coli. Genetics* **30:** 119–136   [22, 186]

178. DeRobertis, E. E. D. P., Nowinsky, W. W., and Saez, F. A. (1948) *General Cytology,* Philadelphia, Saunders   [339, 354]

178a. DeRopp, R. S. (1951) The crown-gall problem. *Bot. Rev.* **17:** 629–670   [216]

179. Dienes, L., and Weinberger, H. J. (1951) The L forms of bacteria. *Bact. Rev.* **15:** 245–288   [4, 353]

180. Dodd, K., Johnston, L. M., and Buddingh, G. J. (1938) Herpetic stomatitis. *J. Pediatr.* **12:** 95–102   [38]

181. Doermann, A. H. (1948) Lysis and lysis inhibition with *Escherichia coli* bacteriophage. *J. Bact.* **55**: 257–276 [184, 292]

182. Doermann, A. H. (1952) The intracellular growth of bacteriophages. I. *J. Gen. Physiol.* **35**: 645–656 [170, 171]

183. Doermann, A. H., and Dissosway, C. F.-R. (1949) Intracellular growth and genetics of bacteriophage. *Carnegie Inst. Wash. Yearbook* **48**: 170–176 [190]

184. Doermann, A. H., and Hill, M. B. (1953) Genetic structure of bacteriophage T4 as described by recombination studies of factors influencing plaque morphology. *Genetics* **38**: 79–90 [190]

185. Doerr, R. (1939) Die qualitative Virusnachweis. Anreichungsverfahren. In: Doerr and Hallauer, 2 (Ref. 187) [35]

186. Doerr, R. (1939) Die quantitative Bestimmung der Infektiosität. In: Doerr and Hallauer, 2 (Ref. 187) [42]

187. Doerr, R., and Hallauer, C. (1938–1939) *Handbuch der Virusforschung*, Wien, Springer [1]

188. den Dooren de Jong, L. E. (1931) Über Bac. megatherium und den darin anwesenden Bakteriophagen. *Zentr. Bakt., Parasit., I, Orig.* **120**: 1–15 [201]

189. Doty, P., and Steiner, R. F. (1950) Light scattering and spectrophotometry of colloidal solutions. *J. Chem. Physics* **18**: 1211–1220 [80]

190. Douglas, S. R., Smith, W., and Price, L. R. W. (1929) Generalized vaccinia in rabbits with special reference to lesions in the internal organs. *J. Path. Bact.* **39**: 99–120 [300]

191. DuBuy, H. G., and Woods, M. W. (1943) Evidence for the evolution of phytopathogenic viruses from mitochondria and their derivatives. II. *Phytopath.* **33**: 766–777 [213, 214]

192. Duggar, B. M., and Armstrong, J. K. (1923) Indications respecting the nature of the infective particles in the mosaic disease of tobacco. *Ann. Missouri Botan. Garden* **10**: 191–212 [350]

193. Dulbecco, R. (1950) Experiments on photoreactivation of bacteriophages inactivated with ultraviolet radiation. *J. Bact.* **59**: 329–347 [155, 194]

194. Dulbecco, R. (1952) A critical test of the recombination theory of multiplicity reactivation. *J. Bact.* **63**: 199–207 [195]

195. Dulbecco, R. (1952) Mutual exclusion between related phages. *J. Bact.* **63**: 209–217 [189, 274, 275]

196. Dulbecco, R. (1952) Production of plaques in monolayer tissue cultures by single particles of an animal virus. *Proc. Nat. Acad. Sci.* **38**: 747–752 [42, 48, 226]

197. Duran-Reynals, F. (1940) A hemorrhagic disease occurring in chicks inoculated with the Rous and Fujinami viruses. *Yale J. Biol. Med.* **13**: 77–98 [331]

197a. Duran-Reynals, F. (1942) The reciprocal infection of ducks and chickens with tumor-inducing viruses. *Cancer Research* **2**: 343–369 [332]

198. Duran-Reynals, F., and Shrigley, E. W. (1945) Virus infection as an etiologic agent of cancer. *Res. Conf. on Cancer, A.A.A.S.*, Washington [31, 331]

199. Dutky, S. R., and Gooden, E. L. (1952) *Coxiella popillia*, n. sp., a rickettsia causing blue disease of Japanese beetle larvae. *J. Bact.* **63**: 743–750 [372]

386   Bibliography

199a. Eaton, M. D. (1952) Observations on growth of virus and the energy-yielding activities of the host cell. *Arch. ges. Virusforsch.* **5**: 53–72 [146]

200. Eaton, M. D., Magasanik, B., and Perry, M. E. (1951) Inhibition of influenza and mumps viruses in tissue culture by basic amino acids. *Proc. Soc. Exp. Biol. Med.* **77**: 505–508   [230]

201. Eddy, B. E., and Wyckoff, R. W. G. (1950) Influenza virus in sectioned tissues. *Proc. Soc. Exp. Biol. Med.* **75**: 290–293   [267]

202. Ehrlich, H. L., and Watson, D. W. (1949) Lysogenesis of *Bacillus megatherium. J. Bact.* **58**: 627–632   [205]

203. Eklund, C. M. (1946) Human encephalitis of the Western equine type in Minnesota in 1941: Clinical and epidemiological study of serologically positive cases. *Am. J. Hyg.* **43**: 171–193   [314]

204. Elford, W. J. (1938) The sizes of virus and bacteriophages and methods for their determination. In: Doerr and Hallauer, 1 (Ref. 187)   [71, 72, 78]

204a. Ellermann, V., and Bang, O. (1908) Experimentelle Leukämie bei Huhnern. *Zentr. Bakt., Parasit., I, Orig.* **46**: 595–609   [324]

205. Ellis, E. L., and Delbrück, M. (1939) The growth of bacteriophage. *J. Gen. Physiol.* **22**: 365–384   [41, 48, 49, 159, 162]

206. Ellis, E. L., and Spizizen, J. (1941) The rate of bacteriophage inactivation by filtrates of *Escherichia coli* cultures. *J. Gen. Physiol.* **24**: 437–445 [168]

207. Enders, J. F., and Pearson, H. E. (1941) Resistance of chicks to infection with influenza A virus. *Proc. Soc. Exp. Biol. Med.* **48**: 143–146   [227]

208. Enders, J. F., Cohen, S., and Kano, L. W. (1945) Immunity in mumps. II. *J. Exp. Med.* **81**: 119–135   [134]

209. Ephrussi, B., and Hottinguer, H. (1951) On an unstable cell state in yeast. *Cold Spring Harbor Symp. Quant. Biol.* **16**: 75–85   [357]

210. Ephrussi-Taylor, H. (1951) Genetic aspects of transformations of pneumococci. *Cold Spring Harbor Symp. Quant. Biol.* **16**: 445–456   [115, 351]

210a. Epstein, H. T. (1953) Identification of radiosensitive volume with nucleic acid volume. *Nature* **171**: 384–395   [152]

211. Esau, K. (1938) Some anatomical aspects of plant virus disease problems. *Bot. Rev.* **4**: 579; **14**: 413–449   [214]

212. Fazekas de St. Groth, S., and Donnelley, M. (1950) Studies in experimental immunology of influenza. IV. *Austral. J. Exp. Biol. Med. Sci.* **28**: 61–75   [132]

213. Feemster, R. F., and Wells, W. F. (1933) Experimental and statistical evidence of the particulate nature of the bacteriophage. *J. Exp. Med.* **58**: 385–391   [52]

213a. Felix, A., and Anderson, E. S. (1951) Bacteriophages, virulence and agglutination tests with a strain of *Salmonella typhi* of low virulence. *J. Hyg.* **49**: 349–364   [206]

213b. Felix, A., and Callow, B. R. (1951) Paratyphoid-B Vi-phage typing. *Lancet* (2) **261**: 10–14   [207]

214. Feller, A. E., Enders, J. F., and Weller, T. H. (1940) The prolonged

coexistence of vaccinia virus in high titer and living cells in roller tube cultures of chick embryonic tissues. *J. Exp. Med.* **72**: 367–388 [228]

215. Fenner, F. (1949) Mouse pox (infectious ectromelia of mice): A review. *J. Immunol.* **63**: 341–373 [64, 220]

215a. Fenner, F., Day, M. F., and Woodroofe, G. M. (1952) The mechanism of the transmission of myxomatosis in the European rabbit (*Oryctolagus cuniculus*) by the mosquito *Aedes aegypti*. *Austral. J. Exp. Biol. Med. Sci.* **30**: 139–152 [320]

216. Findlay, G. M. (1930) Warts. In: *A System of Bacteriology in Relation to Medicine*, Medical Research Council, Great Britain, **7**: 252–258 [325]

217. Findlay, G. M. (1938) Inclusion bodies and their relationships to viruses. In: Doerr and Hallauer, 1 (Ref. 187) [6, 230]

218. Findlay, G. M. (1939) Variation in viruses. In: Doerr and Hallauer, 2 (Ref. 187) [290, 298]

219. Findlay, G. M., and Howard, E. M. (1950) Virus exaltation. *Br. J. Exp. Path.* **31**: 45–50 [284]

220. Findlay, G. M., and Ludford, R. J. (1926) The ultra-microscopic viruses. *Br. J. Exp. Path.* **7**: 223–255 [230]

221. Findlay, G. M., and MacCallum, F. O. (1937) An interference phenomenon in relation to yellow fever and other viruses. *J. Path. Bact.* **44**: 405–424 [283]

222. Fischer, B. (1906) Die experimentelle Erzeugung atypischer Epitelwucherungen und die Entstehung bösartiger Geschwülste. *Munch. med. Wochenschr.* **53**: 2041–2047 [331]

223. Fisher, J. C., and Hollomon, J. H. (1950) A mechanism for the origin of cancer foci. *Science* **112**: 424 [239]

224. Flewett, T. H. (1953) Growth of viruses of the influenza group as revealed by electron microscopy of infected cells. In: *The Nature of Virus Multiplication*, Cambridge University Press [267]

225. Flewett, T. H., and Challice, C. E. (1951) The intracellular growth of fowl-plague virus. A phase-contrast and electron microscopical study of infected tissue cultures. *J. Gen. Microbiol.* **5**: 279–286 [234]

226. Florman, A. L., and Enders, J. F. (1942) The effect of homologous antiserum and complement on the multiplication of vaccinia virus in rollertube cultures of blood-mononuclear cells. *J. Immunol.* **43**: 159–174 [229]

227. Foster, R. A. C. (1948) The action of proflavine on bacteriophage growth. *J. Bact.* **56**: 795–809 [170, 293]

228. Foulds, L. (1934) Filtrable tumors of fowls. *Imperial Cancer Res. Fund, 11th Rept., Suppl.* [324]

229. Foulds, L. (1937) Observations on non-filterable fowl tumours. The production of neutralizing sera against filtrates of Rous sarcoma I by non-infective extracts of a sarcoma induced by 1:2:5:6– dibenzanthracene. *Am. J. Cancer* **31**: 404–413 [324]

230. Francis, T., Jr. (1947) Dissociation of hemagglutinating and antibody-measuring capacities of influenza virus. *J. Exp. Med.* **85**: 1–7 [257, 258]

231. Francis, T., Jr. (1950) The significance of multiple immunological types of influenza virus. *Cincinnati J. Med.* **31**: 97–101 [301]

232. Francis, T., Jr., and Kurtz, H. B. (1950) The relation of herpes virus to the cell nucleus. *Yale J. Biol. Med.* **22:** 579–587 [237]

233. Francis, T., Jr., and Salk, J. E. (1942) A simplified procedure for the concentration and purification of influenza virus. *Science* **96:** 499–500 [89]

234. Fraser, D. (1951) Bursting bacteria by release of gas pressure. *Nature* **167:** 33–34 [170]

235. Fredericq, P. (1950) Rapports entre colicines et bactériophages. *Bull. acad. roy. méd. Belgique* **15:** 491–510 [207]

236. Freeman, V. J. (1951) Studies on the virulence of bacteriophage-infected strains of *Corynebacterium diphtheriae*. *J. Bact.* **61:** 675–688 [206]

237. French, R. C., Graham, A. F., Lesley, S. M., and Van Rooyen, C. E. (1952) The contribution of phosphorus from T2r+ bacteriophage to progeny. *J. Bact.* **64:** 597–607 [176, 186]

238. French, R. C., Lesley, S. M., Graham, A. F., and Van Rooyen, C. E. (1951) Studies on the relationship between virus and host cell. III. *Canad. J. Med. Sci.* **29:** 144–148 [186, 189, 274]

239. Friedewald, W. F., and Anderson, R. S. (1941) Influence of extraneous protein and virus concentration on the inactivation of the rabbit papilloma virus by X-rays. *J. Exp. Med.* **74:** 463–487 [148]

240. Friedewald, W. F., and Anderson, R. S. (1943) The effect of Roentgen rays on cell-virus associations. Findings with virus-induced rabbit papillomas and fibromas. *J. Exp. Med.* **78:** 285–303 [156, 328]

241. Friedewald, W. F., and Kidd, J. G. (1944) The recoverability of virus from papillomas produced therewith in domestic rabbits. *J. Exp. Med.* **79:** 591–605 [327, 336]

242. Friedewald, W. F., and Pickels, E. G. (1944) Centrifugation and ultra-filtration studies on allantoic fluid preparations of influenza virus. *J. Exp. Med.* **79:** 301–317 [253, 264]

243. Friedrich-Freksa, H., Melchers, G., and Schramm, G. (1946) Biologischer, chemischer und serologischer Vergleich zweier parallelmutanten phytopathogener Viren mit ihren Ausgangsformen. *Biol. Zentr.* **65:** 187–222 [102, 297]

244. Fujinami, A., and Inamoto, K. (1914) Über Geschwülste bei japanischen Haushühnern, insbesondere über einen transplantablen Tumor. *Z. Krebsforsch.* **14:** 94. Quoted by Oberling (Ref. 501) [324]

245. Fukushi, T. (1940) Further studies on the dwarf disease of rice plant. *J. Fac. Agr. Hokkaido Imp. Univ.* **45:** 85–152 [317]

246. Fulton, F. (1949) Growth cycle of influenza virus. *Nature* **164:** 189 [267]

247. Gaddum, J. H. (1933) Methods of biological assay depending on a quantal response. *Med. Res. Counc. Spec. Rep.* No. 183 [53]

248. Gard, S. (1943) Purification of poliomyelitis viruses. Experiments on murine and human strains. *Acta Medica Scand., Suppl.* 143 [45, 53, 82, 221]

249. Gard, S., and Von Magnus, P. (1948) Studies on interference in experimental influenza. II. *Ark. Kemi, Miner. Geol.* **24B:** 1–4 [265]

250. Garen, A., and Puck, T. T. (1951) The first two steps of the invasion of host cells by bacterial viruses. II. *J. Exp. Med.* **94:** 177–189 [165, 167, 260, 303]

250a. Gerstel, D. U. (1943) Inheritance in *Nicotiana tabacum*. XVII. *Genetics* **28**: 533–536 [304]

250b. Gerstel, D. U. (1948) Transfer of the mosaic-resistance factor between H chromosomes of *Nicotiana glutinosa* and *N. tabacum*. *J. Agr. Res.* **76**: 219–223 [304]

250c. Giddings, N. J. (1950) Some interrelationships of virus strains in sugar-beet curly top. *Phytopath.* **40**: 377–388 [278]

251. Gilpatrick, J. D., and Weintraub, M. (1952) An unusual type of protection with the carnation mosaic virus. *Science* **115**: 701–702 [276, 278]

252. Ginsberg, H. S., and Horsfall, F. L., Jr. (1949) Concurrent infection with influenza virus and mumps virus or pneumonia virus of mice (PVM) as bearing on the inhibition of virus multiplication by bacterial polysaccharides. *J. Exp. Med.* **89**: 37–52 [259]

253. Ginsberg, H. S., and Horsfall, F. L., Jr. (1949) A resistant variant of mumps virus. Multiplication of the variant in the presence of inhibitory quantities of Friedländer bacillus polysaccharide. *J. Exp. Med.* **90**: 393–407 [269]

254. Ginsberg, H. S., and Horsfall, F. L., Jr. (1951) Characteristics of the multiplication cycle of pneumonia virus of mice (PVM). *J. Exp. Med.* **93**: 151–160 [222, 269]

255. Ginsberg, H. S., and Horsfall, F. L., Jr. (1951) Therapy of infection with pneumonia virus of mice (PVM). Effect of polysaccharide on the multiplication cycles of the virus and on the course of the viral pneumonia. *J. Exp. Med.* **93**: 161–171 [222]

256. Ginsberg, H. S., Goebel, W. F., and Horsfall, F. L., Jr. (1948) The inhibitory effect of polysaccharide on mumps virus multiplication. *J. Exp. Med.* **87**: 383–410 [259]

256a. Glasstone, S. K., Laidler, K. L., and Eyring, H. (1941) *The Theory of Rate Processes*. New York, McGraw-Hill [139]

257. Gledhill, A. W., and Andrewes, C. H. (1951) A hepatitis virus of mice. *Br. J. Exp. Path.* **32**: 559–568 [146]

257a. Goebel, W. F., and Jesaitis, M. A. (1953) Chemical and antiviral properties of the somatic antigens of phase II "Sh. sonnei" and of a phage resistant variant, II/3, 4, 7. *Ann. Inst. Pasteur* **84**: 66–72 [168]

258. Goodner, K. (1941) Collodion fixation; a new immunological reaction. *Science* **94**: 241–242 [119]

259. Goodpasture, E. W. (1933) Borreliotoses: fowl pox, molluscum contagiosum, variola-vaccinia. *Science* **77**: 119–121 [18]

260. Goodpasture, E. W., and Anderson, K. (1940) Immunity to fowl-pox studied by means of skin grafts on chorioallantois of chick embryo. *Arch. Path.* **30**: 212–225 [246]

261. Goodpasture, E. W., and Anderson, K. (1942) Virus infection of human fetal membranes grafted to the chorioallantois of chick embryos. *Am. J. Path.* **18**: 563–575 [246]

262. Goodpasture, E. W., and Woodruff, C. E. (1931) A comparison of the inclusion bodies of fowl-pox and molluscum contagiosum. *Am. J. Path.* **7**: 1–8 [231]

390 Bibliography

263. Gough, G. A. C., and Burnet, F. M. (1934) The chemical nature of the phage-inactivating agent in bacterial extracts. *J. Path. Bact.* **38**: 301–311 [168]

264. Gowen, J. W. (1941) Mutation in *Drosophila*, bacteria and viruses. *Cold Spring Harbor Symp. Quant. Biol.* **9**: 187–193 [297]

265. Gowen, J. W. (1948) Inheritance of immunity in animals. *Ann. Rev. Microbiol.* **2**: 215–254 [7, 305]

266. Graham, A. F., and McClelland, L. (1950) The uptake of radioactive phosphorus by influenza virus A (PR8 strain). *Canad. J. Res., E,* **28**: 121–134 [249]

267. Granoff, A., Liu, O. C., and Henle, W. (1950) A small hemagglutinating component in preparations of Newcastle disease virus. *Proc. Soc. Exp. Biol. Med.* **75**: 684–691 [264]

268. Gratia, A. (1934) La centrifugation des bactériophages. *C. r. soc. biol.* **117**: 1228–1230 [78]

269. Gratia, A. (1936) Des relations numériques entre bactéries lysogènes et particules de bactériophage. *Ann. Inst. Pasteur* **57**: 652–694 [41]

270. Gratia, A. (1937) Le phénomène du halo et la synergie des bactériophages. *C. r. soc. biol.* **126**: 418–421 [199]

271. Green, R. G. (1935) On the nature of filterable viruses. *Science* **82**: 443–445 [4, 347]

272. Green, R. G., and Stulberg, C. S. (1946) Cell-blockade in canine distemper. *Proc. Soc. Exp. Biol. Med.* **61**: 117–121 [288]

273. Green, R. H., and Woolley, D. W. (1947) Inhibition by certain polysaccharides of hemagglutination and of multiplication of influenza virus. *J. Exp. Med.* **86**: 55–64 [259]

274. Green, R. H., Anderson, T. F., and Smadel, J. E. (1942) Morphological structure of the virus of vaccinia. *J. Exp. Med.* **75**: 651–656 [59, 61]

275. Greene, H. S. N. (1941) Heterologous transplantation of mammalian tumors. II. *J. Exp. Med.* **73**: 475–486 [322]

276. Greenstein, J. P. (1947) *Biochemistry of Cancer,* New York, Academic Press [323]

277. Gregg, N. M. (1941) Congenital cataract following German measles in the mother. *Trans. Ophthalm. Soc. Australia* **3**: 35–46 [246]

278. Greiff, D. (1948) Biology of the rickettsiae. In: *The Rickettsial Diseases of Man,* A.A.A.S., Washington [365, 369]

279. Gross, L. (1951) "Spontaneous" leukemia developing in C3H mice following inoculation, in infancy, with AK-leukemic extracts, or AK embryos. *Proc. Soc. Exp. Biol. Med.* **76**: 27–32 [330]

280. Gulland, J. M. (1947) The structures of nucleic acids. *Cold Spring Harbor Symp. Quant. Biol.* **12**: 95–103 [97]

281. Guérin, M. C. (1905) Contrôle de la valeur des vaccins Jenneriens par la numération des éléments virulents. *Ann. Inst. Pasteur* **19**: 317–320 [42]

281a. Gupta, B. M., and Price, W. C. (1952) Mechanism of inhibition of plant virus infection by fungal growth products. *Phytopath.* **42**: 45–51 [137]

282. Gye, G. O. (1933) On improved technic for the massive tissue culture. *Am. J. Cancer* **17**: 752–756 [225]

283. Gye, G. O., and Bang, F. B. (1939) Experimental studies on the cul-

tural behavior and the infectivity of lymphopatia venerea virus maintained in tissue culture. *Bull. Johns Hopkins Hosp.* **65**: 393–417   [229]

284. Gye, W. E. (1925) The aetiology of malignant new growths. *Lancet* (2) **209**: 109–117   [336]

285. Gye, W. E. (1936) Tumors transmissible by viruses. *II Intern. Cancer Congr.* **1**: 48–58   [324]

286. Hagemann, P. K. H. (1937) Fluoreszenzmikroskopische Untersuchungen über Virus und andere Mikroben. *Zentr. Bakt., Parasit., I, Orig.* **140**: 184–187   [60]

287. Hallauer, C. (1938) Die Züchtung der Virusarten ausserhalb ihrer Wirte. In: Doerr and Hallauer, 1 (Ref. 187)   [224, 280]

288. Hallauer, C. (1939) Die erworbene Immunität gegen Virusinfektionen. In: Doerr and Hallauer, 2 (Ref. 187)   [229]

289. Hamburger, V., and Habel, K. (1947) Teratogenetic and lethal effects of influenza A and mumps viruses on early chick embryos. *Proc. Soc. Exp. Biol. Med.* **66**: 608–617   [246, 266]

290. Hanig, M., and Bernkopf, H. (1950) The sedimentable components of influenza virus propagated in deembryonated eggs. *J. Immunol.* **65**: 585–590   [265, 266]

291. Hardy, P. H., Jr., and Horsfall, F. L., Jr. (1948) Reactions between influenza virus and a component of allantoic fluid. *J. Exp. Med.* **88**: 463–484   [259]

292. Hargett, M. V., Burruss, H. W., and Donovan, A. (1943) Aqueous-base yellow fever vaccine. *U. S. Publ. Health Rep.* **58**: 505–512   [248]

293. Haurowitz, F. (1949) Biological problems and immunochemistry. *Quart. Rev. Biol.* **24**: 93–101   [100]

294. Haurowitz, F. (1950) *Chemistry and Biology of Proteins,* New York, Academic Press   [98]

295. Hayes, W. (1953) Observations on a transmissible agent determining sexual differentiation in *Bacterium coli.* *J. Gen. Microbiol.* **8**: 72–88   [353]

296. Heinmets, F. (1948) Studies with the electron microscope on the interaction of red cells and influenza virus. *J. Bact.* **55**: 823–831   [250, 253]

297. Henderson, R. G., and Topping, N. H. (1945) Epidemic typhus fever: Neutralization of the toxic substance. *Nat. Inst. Health Bull.* **183**: 41–56   [367]

298. Henle, G., and Henle, W. (1946) Studies on the toxicity of influenza viruses. I, II. *J. Exp. Med.* **84**: 623–660   [31, 223, 266, 271]

299. Henle, W. (1949) Studies on host-virus interactions in the chick embryo-influenza virus system. I, II. *J. Exp. Med.* **90**: 1–22   [261, 263]

300. Henle, W. (1950) Interference phenomena between animal viruses: A review. *J. Immunol.* **64**: 203–236   [280, 284, 285, 286, 287]

301. Henle, W., and Henle, G. (1947) The effect of ultraviolet irradiation on various properties of influenza viruses. *J. Exp. Med.* **85**: 347–364   [137, 155]

302. Henle, W., and Henle, G. (1949) Studies on host-virus interactions in the chick embryo-influenza virus system. III. *J. Exp. Med.* **90**: 23–37   [131, 264]

303. Henle, W., and Liu, O. C. (1951) Studies on host-virus interactions in the chick embryo-influenza virus system. VI. *J. Exp. Med.* **94**: 305–322 [156, 268]

304. Henle, W., and Rosenberg, E. B. (1949) One-step growth curves of various strains of influenza A and B viruses and their inhibition by inactivated virus of the homologous type. *J. Exp. Med.* **89**: 279–285   [261]

305. Henle, W., Henle, G., and Rosenberg, E. B. (1947) The demonstration of one-step growth curves of influenza viruses through the blocking effect of irradiated virus on further infection. *J. Exp. Med.* **86**: 423–437   [261, 262]

306. d'Hérelle, F. (1917) Sur un microbe invisible antagoniste des bacilles dysentériques. *C. r. acad. sci.* **165**: 373–375   [7]

307. d'Hérelle, F. (1921) Le bactériophage; son rôle dans l'immunité. Paris, Masson   [48]

307a. Herriott, R. M. (1951) Nucleic acid synthesis in mustard gas-treated *E. coli* B. *J. Gen. Physiol.* **34**: 761–764   [182]

308. Herriott, R. M. (1951) Nucleic-acid-free T2 virus "ghosts" with specific biological action. *J. Bact.* **61**: 752–754   [143, 174, 199]

309. Hershey, A. D. (1946) Mutations of bacteriophage with respect to type of plaque. *Genetics* **31**: 620–640   [184, 274, 292, 293]

310. Hershey, A. D. (1946) Spontaneous mutations in bacterial viruses. *Cold Spring Harbor Symp. Quant. Biol.* **11**: 67–76   [7, 189, 294]

311. Hershey, A. D., and Bronfenbrenner, J. (1947) Effects of complement on the specific neutralization of bacteriophage. *Fed. Proc.* **6**: 428   [126]

312. Hershey, A. D., and Chase, M. (1951) Genetic recombination and heterozygosis in bacteriophages. *Cold Spring Harbor Symp. Quant. Biol.* **16**: 471–479   [193]

313. Hershey, A. D., and Chase, M. (1952) Independent function of viral protein and nucleic acid in growth of bacteriophage. *J. Gen. Physiol.* **36**: 39–56   [65, 84, 104, 173, 174, 176, 337]

314. Hershey, A. D., and Rotman, R. (1948) Linkage among genes controlling inhibition of lysis in a bacterial virus. *Proc. Nat. Acad. Sci.* **34**: 89–96 [189, 190, 267, 274, 292]

315. Hershey, A. D., and Rotman, R. (1949) Genetic recombination between host-range and plaque-type mutants of bacteriophage in single bacterial cells. *Genetics* **34**: 44–71   [189, 190]

315a. Hershey, A. D., Dixon, J., and Chase, M. (1953) Nucleic acid economy in bacteria infected with bacteriophage T2. I. *J. Gen. Physiol.* **36**: 777–789   [174, 177]

316. Hershey, A. D., Kalmanson, G., and Bronfenbrenner, J. (1943) Quantitative methods in the study of the phage-antiphage reaction. *J. Immunol.* **46**: 267–279   [41]

317. Hershey, A. D., Kalmanson, G., and Bronfenbrenner, J. (1943) Quantitative relationships in the phage-antiphage reaction: unity and homogeneity of the reactants. *J. Immunol.* **46**: 281–299   [125]

318. Hershey, A. D., Kimura, F., and Bronfenbrenner, J. (1947) Uniformity of size of bacteriophage particles. *Proc. Soc. Exp. Biol. Med.* **64**: 7–12 [79]

319. Hershey, A. D., Kamen, M. D., Kennedy, J. W., and Gest, H. (1951) The mortality of bacteriophage containing assimilated radioactive phosphorus. *J. Gen. Physiol.* **34**: 305–319 [105, 154]

320. Herzberg, K. (1927) Eine Methode zur Zählung von Herpes—und Vakzinekeimen. *Zentr. Bakt., Parasit., I, Orig.* **105**: 57–86 [42]

321. Herzberg, K. (1936) Der Vorgang der Vakzinevirusvermehrung in der Zelle. *Zentr. Bakt., Parasit., I, Orig.* **136**: 257–260 [233, 247]

322. Himmelweit, F. (1938) Observations on living vaccinia and ectromelia viruses by high power microscopy. *Br. J. Exp. Path.* **19**: 108–123 [233, 247]

323. Hirst, G. K. (1941) The agglutination of red cells by allantoic fluid of chick embryos infected with influenza virus. *Science* **94**: 22–23 [250]

324. Hirst, G. K. (1942) Adsorption of influenza hemagglutinins and virus by red blood cells. *J. Exp. Med.* **76**: 195–209 [250, 253]

325. Hirst, G. K. (1943) Adsorption of influenza virus on cells of the respiratory tract. *J. Exp. Med.* **78**: 99–109 [254]

326. Hirst, G. K. (1947) Studies on the mechanism of adaptation of influenza virus to mice. *J. Exp. Med.* **86**: 357–366 [270, 301]

327. Hirst, G. K. (1948) The nature of the virus receptors of red cells. II. *J. Exp. Med.* **87**: 315–328 [142, 256]

328. Hirst, G. K. (1949) The nature of the virus receptors of red cells. IV. *J. Exp. Med.* **89**: 233–243 [257]

329. Hirst, G. K. (1949) Laboratory diagnostic procedures for influenza. In: Horsfall, *Diagnosis of Viral and Rickettsial Infections*, New York, Columbia University Press [245, 249]

330. Hirst, G. K. (1950) Receptor destruction by viruses of the mumps-NDV-influenza group. *J. Exp. Med.* **91**: 161–175 [110, 254]

331. Hirst, G. K. (1950) The relationship of the receptors of a new strain of virus to those of the mumps-NDV-influenza group. *J. Exp. Med.* **91**: 177–184 [254]

332. Hirst, G. K. (1950) Hemagglutination as applied to the study of virus infection. In: Delbrück, *Viruses 1950*, Pasadena, Cal. Inst. Technol. Bookstore [254, 259]

333. Holmes, F. O. (1929) Local lesions in tobacco mosaic. *Bot. Gaz.* **87**: 39–55 [22, 46]

334. Holmes, F. O. (1930) Local and systemic increase of tobacco mosaic virus. *Am. J. Bot.* **17**: 789–805 [209]

335. Holmes, F. O. (1931) Local lesions of mosaic in *Nicotiana tabacum* L. *Contrib. Boyce Thompson Inst.* **3**: 163–172 [24, 216]

336. Holmes, F. O. (1932) Movement of mosaic virus from primary lesions in *Nicotiana tabacum* L. *Contrib. Boyce Thompson Inst.* **4**: 297–322 [216]

337. Holmes, F. O. (1934) Inheritance of ability to localize tobacco-mosaic virus. *Phytopath.* **24**: 984–1002 [22, 304]

338. Holmes, F. O. (1934) A masked strain of tobacco-mosaic virus. *Phytopath.* **24**: 845–873 [31]

339. Holmes, F. O. (1937) Inheritance of resistance to tobacco-mosaic disease in the pepper. *Phytopath.* **27**: 637–642 [22, 304]

339a. Holmes, F. O. (1938) Inheritance of resistance to tobacco-mosaic disease in tobacco. *Phytopath.* 28: 553–561   [304]

340. Holmes, F. O. (1946) A comparison of the experimental host ranges of tobacco-etch and tobacco mosaic viruses. *Phytopath.* 36: 643–659   [217]

341. Holmes, F. O. (1948) Order Virales: The filterable viruses. In: *Bergey's Manual of Determinative Bacteriology*, 6th Ed., Baltimore, Williams and Wilkins   [17]

341a. Holmes, F. O. (1951) Indications of a new-world origin of tobacco-mosaic virus. *Phytopath.* 41: 341–349   [319]

342. Holt, R. L., and Kintner, J. H. (1931) Location of dengue virus in the body of mosquitoes. *Am. J. Trop. Med.* 11: 103–111   [311]

343. Horowitz, N. H. (1945) On the evolution of biochemical syntheses. *Proc. Nat. Acad. Sci.* 31: 153–157   [346]

344. Horsfall, F. L., Jr. (1940) A low temperature storage cabinet for the preservation of viruses. *J. Bact.* 40: 559–568   [55]

345. Horsfall, F. L., Jr. (1949) *Diagnosis of Viral and Rickettsial Infections*, New York, Columbia University Press   [133]

346. Horsfall, F. L., Jr. (1950) Approaches to the control of viral diseases. *Bact. Rev.* 14: 219–224   [146]

347. Horsfall, F. L., Jr., and Ginsberg, H. S. (1951) The dependence of the pathological lesion upon the multiplication of pneumonia virus of mice (PVM). Kinetic relation between the degree of viral multiplication and the extent of pneumonia. *J. Exp. Med.* 93: 139–150   [222]

348. Horsfall, F. L., Jr., and Hahn, R. G. (1940) A latent virus in normal mice capable of producing pneumonia in its natural host. *J. Exp. Med.* 71: 391–408   [37]

349. Horsfall, F. L., Jr., Hardy, P. H., Jr., and Davenport, F. M. (1948) The significance of combinations between viruses and host cells. *Bull. N. Y. Acad. Sci.* 24: 470–475   [260]

350. Hoskins, M. (1935) A protective action of neurotropic against viscerotropic yellow fever virus in *Macacus rhesus*. *Am. J. Trop. Med.* 15: 675–680   [283]

350a. Hotchkiss, R. D. (1951) Transfer of penicillin resistance in pneumococci by the desoxyribonucleate derived from resistant cultures. *Cold Spring Harbor Symp. Quant. Biol.* 16: 457–461   [351]

350b. Houston, B. R., Esau, K., and Hewitt, W. B. (1947) The mode of vector feeding and the tissues involved in the transmission of Pierce's disease virus in grape and alfalfa. *Phytopath.* 37: 247–253   [317]

351. Howe, H. A. (1952) Poliomyelitis. In: Rivers, *Viral and Rickettsial Diseases of Man*, 2nd Ed., Philadelphia, Lippincott   [310]

352. Howe, H. A., and Bodian, D. (1942) Neural mechanisms in poliomyelitis. Commonwealth Fund, New York   [308]

353. Hoyle, L. (1948) The growth cycle of influenza virus A. A study of the relations between virus soluble antigen and host cell in fertile eggs inoculated with influenza virus. *Br. J. Exp. Path.* 29: 390–399   [261, 263]

354. Hoyle, L. (1950) The multiplication of influenza viruses in the fertile egg. *J. Hyg.* 48: 277–297   [266]

355. Hoyle, L., and Fairbrother, R. W. (1937) Antigenic structure of influenza viruses; the preparation of elementary body suspensions and the nature of the complement-fixing antigen. *J. Hyg.* 37: 512–520   [130, 131]

355a. Hughues, F. M. (1952) Development of the inclusion bodies of a granulosis virus. *J. Bact.* **64**: 375–380   [84]

356. Hurlbut, H. S. (1950) The recovery of poliomyelitis virus after parenteral introduction into cockroaches and houseflies. *J. Infectious Diseases* **86**: 103–104   [309]

356a. Hutton, E. M., and Wark, D. C. (1952) A relationship between immunity and localized reaction to virus X in the potato (*Solanum tuberosum*). *Austral. J. Sci. Res. B*, **5**: 237–243   [24]

357. Hydén, H. (1947) The nucleoproteins in virus reproduction. *Cold Spring Harbor Symp. Quant. Biol.* **12**: 104–114   [60, 238]

358. Isaacs, A., and Edney, M. (1950) Interference between inactive and active viruses in the chick embryo. I. *Austral. J. Exp. Biol. Med. Sci.* **28**: 219–230   [284]

359. Iwanowski, D. (1903) Über die Mosaikkrankheit der Tabakspflanze. *Z. Pflanzenkr.* **13**: 1–41   [214]

359a. Jacob, F. (1952) Développement spontané et induit des bactériophages chez des *Pseudomonas pyocyanea* polylysogènes. *Ann. Inst. Pasteur* **83**: 671–692   [202]

360. Jacob, F., Siminovitch, L., and Wollman, E. (1951) Induction de la production d'une colicine par le rayonnement ultraviolet. *C. r. acad. sci.* **233**: 1500–1502   [207]

361. Jenner, E. (1798) An inquiry into the causes and effects of the variolae vaccinae, a disease discovered in some of the western counties of England, particularly Gloucestershire, and known by the name of the cow pox. London   [6]

361a. Jensen, J. H. (1933) Isolation of yellow-mosaic viruses from plants infected with tobacco mosaic. *Phytopath.* **23**: 964–974   [7]

362. Jensen, J. H. (1937) Studies on representative strains of tobacco mosaic virus. *Phytopath.* **27**: 69–84   [296]

363. Johnson, F. (1941) Transmission of plant viruses by dodder. *Phytopath.* **31**: 649–656   [34]

364. Kalmanson, G., and Bronfenbrenner, S. (1939) Studies on the purification of bacteriophage. *J. Gen. Physiol.* **23**: 203–228   [103]

365. Kalmanson, G. M., and Bronfenbrenner, J. (1942) Evidence of serological heterogeneity of polyvalent "pure line" bacteriophage. *J. Immunol.* **45**: 13–19   [123]

366. Kalmanson, G. M., and Bronfenbrenner, J. (1943) Restoration of activity of neutralized biologic agents by removal of the antibody with papain. *J. Immunol.* **47**: 387–407   [123, 125]

367. Kassanis, B. (1939) Intranuclear inclusions in virus-infected plants. *Ann. Appl. Biol.* **26**: 705–709   [215]

368. Kausche, G. A. (1940) Über eine das Virusprotein inaktivierende Substanz in Samen von *Nicotiana tabacum* Samsun. *Biol. Zentr.* **60**: 423–438   [218]

369. Keogh, E. V. (1938) Ectodermal lesions produced by the virus of Rous sarcoma. *Br. J. Exp. Path.* **19**: 1–9   [246]

370. Kidd, J. G., and Rous, P. (1938) The carcinogenic effect of a papilloma virus on the tarred skin of rabbits. II. *J. Exp. Med.* **68**: 529–562   [338]

371. Kidd, J. G. (1942) The enduring partnership of a neoplastic virus and carcinoma cells. *J. Exp. Med.* **75**: 7–20   [327]

372. Kidd, J. G. (1946) Suppression of growth of Brown-Pearce tumor cells by a specific antibody. *J. Exp. Med.* **83**: 227–250 [337]

373. Kidd, J. G., and Rous, P. (1940) Cancers deriving from the virus papillomas of wild rabbits under natural conditions. *J. Exp. Med.* **71**: 469–494 [326]

374. Kirber, H. P., Kirber, M. W., and Henle, W. (1950) Transplantation of cornea to chorioallantoic membrane, with observations on virus inoculation. *Proc. Soc. Exp. Biol. Med.* **73**: 481–485 [246]

375. Kleczkowski, A. (1950) Interpreting relationships between the concentrations of plant virus and numbers of local lesions. *J. Gen. Microbiol.* **4**: 53–69 [54]

376. Kligler, I. J., and Olenick, E. (1943) Inactivation of phage by aldehydes and aldoses and subsequent reactivation. *J. Immunol.* **47**: 325–333 [144]

377. Knight, C. A. (1946) Precipitin reactions of highly purified influenza viruses and related materials. *J. Exp. Med.* **83**: 281–294 [107, 260, 348]

378. Knight, C. A. (1947) The nucleic acid and carbohydrate of influenza virus. *J. Exp. Med.* **85**: 99–116 [107]

379. Knight, C. A. (1947) Amino acid composition of highly purified viral particles of influenza A and B. *J. Exp. Med.* **86**: 125–129 [108]

380. Knight, C. A. (1947) The nature of some of the chemical differences among strains of tobacco mosaic virus. *J. Biol. Chem.* **171**: 297–308 [102, 297]

381. Knight, C. A. (1949) Constituents of viruses. *Ann. Rev. Microbiol.* **3**: 121–136 [103]

382. Koch, A. (1936) Symbiosestudien. II. Experimentelle Untersuchungen an *Oryzaephilus surinamensis* L. (Cucujidae, Coleopt.). *Z Morphol. Ökol. Tiere* **32**: 137–180 [370]

383. Koprowski, H. (1950) Immunological reactions in viral diseases. *Ann. Rev. Microbiol.* **4**: 261–282 [111, 179]

383a. Kozloff, L. M. (1953) Desoxyribonuclease inhibitor and bacteriophage infection. *Fed. Proc.* **12**: 234 [179]

384. Kozloff, L., Putnam, F. W., and Evans, E. A., Jr. (1950) Precursors of bacteriophage nitrogen and carbon. In: *Viruses 1950*, Pasadena, Cal. Inst. Technol. Bookstore [176]

385. Krueger, A. P. (1937) The mechanism of bacteriophage production. *Science* **86**: 379–380 [178, 345]

386. Kunkel, L. O. (1934) Studies on acquired immunity with tobacco and aucuba mosaics. *Phytopath.* **24**: 437–466 [277]

387. Kunkel, L. O. (1936) Immunological studies on the three peach diseases, yellows, rosette, and little peach. *Phytopath.* **26**: 201–219 [278]

388. Kunkel, L. O. (1936) Heat treatments for the cure of yellows and other virus diseases of peach. *Phytopath.* **26**: 809–830 [31]

389. Kunkel, L. O. (1937) Effect of heat on ability of *Cicadula sexnotata* (Fall.) to transmit aster yellows. *Am. J. Bot.* **24**: 312–327 [138, 317]

390. Kunkel, L. O. (1941) Heat cure of aster yellows in periwinkles. *Am. J. Bot.* **28**: 761–769 [138, 145, 317]

391. Kunkel, L. O. (1943) New hosts as a key to progress in plant virus disease research. In: *Virus Diseases,* Ithaca, Cornell University Press [34, 36]

392. Labaw, L. W. (1951) The origin of phosphorus in *Escherichia coli* bacteriophages. *J. Bact.* **62:** 169–173 [176]

393. Lacassagne, A. (1936). Hormonal pathogenesis of adenocarcinoma of the breast. *Am. J. Cancer* **27:** 217–228 [329]

394. Lahelle, O., and Horsfall, F. L., Jr. (1949) Multiplication of influenza virus in dead chick embryos. *Proc. Soc. Exp. Biol. Med.* **70:** 547–551 [245]

395. Laidlaw, P. P. (1938) *Virus Diseases and Viruses,* Cambridge, Cambridge University Press [4, 347]

396. Laidlaw, P. P., and Elford, W. J. (1936) A new group of filterable organisms. *Proc. Roy. Soc.* (London) *B,* **120:** 292–303 [4]

397. Landsteiner, K. (1945) *The Specificity of Serological Reactions,* Cambridge, Harvard University Press [117]

398. Lanni, F., and Beard, J. W. (1948) Inhibition by egg-white of hemagglutination by swine influenza virus. *Proc. Soc. Exp. Biol. Med.* **68:** 312–313 [257]

399. Lanni, F., and Lanni, Y. T. (1952) A quantitative theory of influenza virus hemagglutination-inhibition. *J. Bact.* **64:** 865–882 [258]

399a. Lanni, F., and Lanni, Y. T. (1953) Antigenic structure of bacteriophage T2. *Fed. Proc.* **12:** 450–451 [126, 127]

400. Lanni, F., Sharp, D. C., Eckert, E. A., Dillon, E. S., Beard, D., and Beard, J. W. (1949) The egg white inhibitor of influenza virus hemagglutination. I. *J. Biol. Chem.* **179:** 1275–1287 [258]

401. Lanni, Y. T. (1953) Infection by bacteriophage T5 and the intracellular formation of phage antigen and active phage. *Bact. Proc.* 39 [174]

402. Latarjet, R., and Wahl, R. (1945) Précisions sur l'inactivation des bactériophages par les rayons ultraviolets. *Ann. Inst. Pasteur* **71:** 336–339 [154]

403. Lauffer, M. A. (1943) The sedimentation rate of the infectious principle of tobacco mosaic virus. *J. Biol. Chem.* **151:** 627–634 [93]

404. Lauffer, M. A., and Price, W. C. (1945) Infection by viruses. *Arch. Biochem.* **8:** 449–468 [50, 51, 54]

405. Lauffer, M. A., Price, W. C., and Petre, A. W. (1949) The nature of viruses. *Adv. Enzymol.* **9:** 171–240 [7, 79, 82, 93, 96, 140, 141, 144]

406. Law, L. W. (1942) Foster nursing and the growth of transplantable leukemias in mice. *Cancer Res.* **2:** 108–115 [322]

407. Lea, D. E. (1946) *Actions of Radiations on Living Cells,* Cambridge University Press [150, 151, 152]

408. Lea, D., Smith, K. M., Holmes, B., and Markham, R. (1944) Direct and indirect actions of radiations on viruses and enzymes. *Parasitology* **36:** 110–118 [148]

409. Lederberg, E. M., and Lederberg, J. (1953) Genetic studies of lysogenicity in *Escherichia coli. Genetics* **38:** 51–64 [205, 303]

410. Lederberg, J. (1949) Aberrant heterozygotes in *Escherichia coli. Proc. Nat. Acad. Sci.* **35:** 178–184 [303]

411. Lederberg, J., and Lederberg, E. M. (1952) Replica plating and indirect selection of bacterial mutants. *J. Bact.* **63:** 399–406 [303]

412. Lederberg, J., and Tatum, E. L. (1946) Novel genotypes in mixed cul-

tures of biochemical mutants of bacteria. *Cold Spring Harbor Symp. Quant. Biol.* **11**: 113–114   [205]

413. Lederberg, J., Cavalli, L. L., and Lederberg, E. M. (1952) Sex compatibility in *Escherichia coli. Genetics* **37**: 720–730   [353]

414. Levaditi, C., Lépine, P., and Verge, J. (1943) *Les ultravirus des maladies animales*, Paris, Maloine   [29]

415. Levine, P., and Frisch, A. W. (1934) On specific inhibition of bacteriophage action by bacterial extracts. *J. Exp. Med.* **59**: 213–228   [168]

416. Levinson, S. O., Milzer, A., Shaughnessy, H. J., Neal, J. L., and Oppenheimer, F. (1944) Production of potent inactivated vaccines with ultraviolet irradiation. II. *J. Am. Med. Assoc.* **125**: 531–532   [154]

416a. Levinthal, C. (1953) Recombination in phage: its relationship to heterozygosis and growth. *Genetics* (in press)   [194]

417. Levinthal, C., and Fisher, H. (1952) The structural development of a bacterial virus. *Biochem. Biophys. Acta* **9**: 419–429   [172, 175]

418. Levinthal, W. (1935) Recent observations on psittacosis. *Lancet* (1) **228**: 1207–1210   [232, 247]

419. Lewis, D. J., Hughes, T. P., and Mahaffy, A. F. (1942) Experimental transmission of yellow fever by three common species of mosquitoes from the Anglo-Egyptian Sudan. *Ann. Trop. Med. Parasit.* **36**: 34–37   [311]

420. Lewis, E. B. (1951) Pseudoallelism and gene evolution. *Cold Spring Harbor Symp. Quant. Biol.* **16**: 159–174   [360]

421. L'Héritier, P. (1951) The CO_2 sensitivity problem in *Drosophila. Cold Spring Harbor Symp. Quant. Biol.* **16**: 99–112   [357]

422. L'Héritier, P., and Plus, N. (1950) Inactivation par les rayons X du virus responsable de la sensibilité au CO_2 chez la *Drosophile. C. r. acad. sci.* **231**: 192–194   [357]

423. Li, C. P., and Rivers, T. M. (1930) Cultivation of vaccine virus. *J. Exp. Med.* **52**: 465–470   [225]

424. Lieb, M. (1953) The establishment of lysogenicity in *Escherichia coli. J. Bact.* **65**: 642–651   [203]

425. Little, C. C. (1947) The genetics of cancer in mice. *Biol. Rev.* **22**: 315–343   [322, 339]

426. Liu, O. C., and Henle, W. (1951) Studies on host-virus interactions in the chick embryo-influenza virus system. IV. *J. Exp. Med.* **94**: 269–289 [263, 267, 287]

427. Liu, O. C., and Henle, W. (1951) Studies on host-virus interactions in the chick embryo-influenza virus system. V. *J. Exp. Med.* **94**: 291–304 [261]

428. Loeffler, F., and Frosch, P. (1898) Berichte der Kommission zur Erforschung der Maul- und Klauenseuche bei dem Institut für Infektionskrankheiten in Berlin. *Zentr. Bakt., Parasit., I, Orig.* **23**: 371–391   [6]

429. Lucké, B. (1938) Carcinoma in the leopard frog: its probable causation by a virus. *J. Exp. Med.* **68**: 457–468   [325, 333]

430. Ludford, R. J. (1937) The production of tumours by cultures of normal cells treated with filtrates of filterable fowl tumours. *Am. J. Cancer* **31**: 414–429   [332]

431. Luria, S. (1940) Méthodes statistiques appliquées à l'étude du mode d'action des ultravirus. *Ann. Inst. Pasteur* **64**: 415–436   [48, 52]

432. Luria, S. E. (1944) Dissociation of the growth of bacterial viruses and of their host by means of temperatures above optimum. *Proc. Indiana Acad. Sci.* **53**: 28–29   [138]

433. Luria, S. E. (1944) A growth-delaying effect of ultraviolet radiation on bacterial viruses. *Proc. Nat. Acad. Sci.* **30**: 393–397   [137, 153]

434. Luria, S. E. (1945) Mutation of bacterial viruses affecting their host range. *Genetics* **30**: 84–99   [183, 184, 293]

435. Luria, S. E. (1946) Spontaneous bacterial mutations to resistance to anti-bacterial agents. *Cold Spring Harbor Symp. Quant. Biol.* **11**: 130–137 [187, 303]

436. Luria, S. E. (1947) Reactivation of irradiated bacteriophage by transfer of self-reproducing units. *Proc. Nat. Acad. Sci.* **33**: 253–264   [156, 268]

437. Luria, S. E. (1950) Bacteriophage: An essay on virus reproduction. *Science* **111**: 507–511   [182, 353]

438. Luria, S. E. (1951) The frequency distribution of spontaneous bacteriophage mutants as evidence for the exponential rate of phage reproduction. *Cold Spring Harbor Symp. Quant. Biol.* **16**: 463–470   [185, 292]

439. Luria, S. E. (1953) An analysis of bacteriophage multiplication. In: *The Nature of Virus Multiplication*, Cambridge University Press   [84]

440. Luria, S. E., and Anderson, T. F. (1942) The identification and characterization of bacteriophages with the electron microscope. *Proc. Nat. Acad. Sci.* **28**: 127–130   [67]

441. Luria, S. E., and Delbrück, M. (1942) Interference between inactivated bacterial virus and active virus of the same strain and of a different strain. *Arch. Biochem.* **1**: 207–218   [165, 168, 194]

442. Luria, S. E., and Delbrück, M. (1943) Mutations in bacteria from virus sensitivity to virus resistance. *Genetics* **28**: 491–511   [186, 303]

443. Luria, S. E., and Dulbecco, R. (1949) Genetic recombination leading to production of active bacteriophage from ultraviolet inactivated bacteriophage particles. *Genetics* **34**: 93–125   [195]

444. Luria, S. E., and Exner, F. M. (1941) The inactivation of bacteriophages by X-rays. Influence of the medium. *Proc. Nat. Acad. Sci.* **27**: 370–375 [148, 150]

445. Luria, S. E., and Human, M. L. (1950) Chromatin staining of bacteria during bacteriophage infection. *J. Bact.* **59**: 551–560   [169, 180]

446. Luria, S. E., and Human, M. L. (1952) A nonhereditary, host-induced variation of bacterial viruses. *J. Bact.* **64**: 557–569   [197, 207, 295, 333]

447. Luria, S. E., and Latarjet, R. (1947) Ultraviolet irradiation of bacteriophage during intracellular growth. *J. Bact.* **53**: 149–163   [195, 196]

448. Luria, S. E., Delbrück, M., and Anderson, T. F. (1943) Electron microscope studies of bacterial viruses. *J. Bact.* **46**: 57–77   [67, 69, 159]

449. Luria, S. E., Williams, R. C., and Backus, R. C. (1951) Electron micrographic counts of bacteriophage particles. *J. Bact.* **61**: 179–188   [53, 54, 68]

450. Lwoff, A. (1943) *L'évolution physiologique. Étude des pertes de fonctions chez les microorganismes,* Paris, Hermann   [346]

400 Bibliography

451. Lwoff, A. (1950) *Problems of Morphogenesis in Ciliates,* New York, Wiley [355]

452. Lwoff, A. (1953) The nature of phage production. In: *The Nature of Virus Multiplication,* Cambridge University Press [201]

453. Lwoff, A., and Guttman, A. (1950) Recherches sur un *Bacillus megatherium* lysogène. *Ann. Inst. Pasteur* **78:** 711–738 [30, 201]

454. Lwoff, A., Siminovitch, L., and Kjeldgaard, N. (1950) Induction de la production de bactériophages chez une bactérie lysogène. *Ann. Inst. Pasteur* **79:** 815–859 [156, 201, 328]

455. MacCallum, F. O. (1936) The necessity of living cells for the cultivation of psittacosis virus. *Br. J. Exp. Path.* **17:** 472–481 [228]

456. McIntosh, J. (1933) On the nature of the tumors induced in fowls by injections of tar. *Br. J. Exp. Path.* **14:** 422–434 [338]

457. McKinney, H. H. (1926) Virus mixtures that may not be detected in young tobacco plants. *Phytopath.* **16:** 893 [7, 297]

458. McKinney, H. H. (1929) Mosaic diseases in the Canary Islands, West Africa, and Gilbraltar. *J. Agr. Res.* **39:** 557–578 [276]

459. McKinney, H. H. (1935) The inhibiting influence of a virus on one of its mutants. *Science* **82:** 463–464 [278]

460. McKinney, H. H. (1941) Virus-antagonism tests and their limitations for establishing relationship between mutants, and nonrelationship between distinct viruses. *Am. J. Bot.* **28:** 770–778 [278]

461. McLean, I. W., Jr., Beard, D., Taylor, A. R., Sharp, D. G., Beard, J. N., Feller, A. E., and Dingle, J. H. (1944) Influence of temperature of incubation on the increase of influenzal virus B (Lee strain) in the chorio-allantoic fluid of chick embryos. *J. Immunol.* **48:** 305–316 [248]

462. McWhorter, F. P., and Price, W. C. (1949) Evidence that two different plant viruses can multiply simultaneously in the same cell. *Science* **109:** 116–117 [215, 279]

463. Maaløe, O., and Stent, G. S. (1952) Radioactive phosphorus tracer studies on the reproduction of T4 bacteriophage. I. *Acta Path. Microb. Scand.* **30:** 149–157 [176]

464. Maaløe, O., and Symonds, N. (1953) Radioactive sulfur tracer studies on the reproduction of T4 bacteriophage. *J. Bact.* **65:** 177–182 [172, 175]

465. Maaløe, O. C., and Watson, J. D. (1951) The transfer of radioactive phosphorus from parental to progeny phage. *Proc. Nat. Acad. Sci.* **37:** 507–513 [176]

466. Magrassi, F. (1935) Studii sull'infezione e sull'immunità da virus erpetico. II. *Z. Hyg. Infectionskrh.* **117:** 501–528 [280]

467. Magrassi, F. (1935) Studii sull'infezione e sull'immunità da virus erpetico. III. *Z. Hyg. Infectionskrh.* **117:** 573–620 [282]

468. Maitland, H. B., and Laing, A. W. (1930) Experiments on the cultivation of vaccinia virus. *Br. J. Exp. Path.* **11:** 119–126 [229]

469. Maitland, H. B., and Maitland, M. C. (1928) Cultivation of vaccinia virus without tissue culture. *Lancet* (2) **215:** 596–597 [225]

470. Maramorosch, K. (1952) Direct evidence for the multiplication of aster-yellows virus in its insect vector. *Phytopath.* **42:** 59–64 [318]

471. Markham, R. (1953) Nucleic acids in virus multiplication. In: *The Nature of Virus Multiplication,* Cambridge University Press [97, 100, 101, 110]

472. Markham, R., and Smith, J. D. (1950) Chromatographic studies on nucleic acids. *Biochem. J.* **46:** 513–517 [100, 101]

473. Markham, R., and Smith, K. M. (1949) Studies on the virus of turnip yellow mosaic. *Parasitology* **39:** 330–342 [91, 101, 110, 128, 215]

474. Markham, R., Smith, K. M., and Lea, D. (1942) The sizes of viruses and the methods employed in their estimation. *Parasitology* **34:** 315–352 [72]

475. Markham, R., Smith, K. M., and Wyckoff, R. W. G. (1948) Molecular arrangement in tobacco necrosis virus crystals. *Nature* **161:** 760–761 [91, 92]

476. Mason, J. H., Coles, J. D. W. A., and Alexander, R. A. (1940) Cultivation of bluetongue virus in fertile eggs produced on a vitamin deficient diet. *Nature* **145:** 1022 [223]

477. Matthews, R. E. F. (1953) Chemotherapy and plant viruses. *J. Gen. Microbiol.* **8:** 277–288 [146, 210]

478. Melnick, J. L. (1947) Poliomyelitis virus in urban sewage in epidemic and in non-epidemic times. *Am. J. Hyg.* **45:** 240–253 [309]

479. Meneghini, M., and Delwiche, C. C. (1951) The multiplication of tobacco mosaic virus in the host tobacco plant. *J. Biol. Chem.* **189:** 177–186 [210, 214]

480. Merrill, M. H. (1936) The mass factor in immunological studies upon viruses. *J. Immunol.* **30:** 169–184 [118]

481. Merrill, M. H., and TenBroeck, C. (1935) The transmission of equine encephalomyelitis virus by *Aedes aegypti. J. Exp. Med.* **62:** 687–695 [311, 312]

482. Merrill, M. H., Lacaillade, C. W., and TenBroeck, C. (1934) Mosquito transmission of equine encephalomyelitis. *Science* **80:** 251–252 [312]

483. Meyer, K. F. (1942) The ecology of psittacosis and ornithosis. *Medicine* **21:** 175–206 [302]

484. Miller, E. M., and Goebel, W. F. (1949) Studies on bacteriophage. I. *J. Exp. Med.* **90:** 255–265 [168, 284]

485. Miller, G. L., and Lauffer, M. A., and Stanley, W. M. (1944) Electrophoretic studies on PR8 influenza virus. *J. Exp. Med.* **80:** 549–559 [80]

486. Mills, K. C., and Dochez, A. R. (1944) Specific agglutination of murine erythrocytes by a pneumonia virus in mice. *Proc. Soc. Exp. Biol. Med.* **57:** 140–143 [37, 340]

486a. Mommaerts, E. B., Eckert, E. A., Beard, D., Sharp, D. G., and Beard, J. W. (1952) Dephosphorylation of adenosine triphosphate by concentrates of the virus of avian erythromyeloblastic leucosis. *Proc. Soc. Exp. Biol. Med.* **79:** 450–455 [108]

487. Monod, J. (1941) The phenomenon of enzymatic adaptation. *Growth* **11:** 223–289 [358]

488. Monod, J., and Cohn, M. (1952) La biosynthèse induite des enzymes (adaptation enzymatique). *Adv. Enzymol.* **13:** 67–119 [358]

489. Monod, J., and Wollman, E. (1947) L'inhibition de la croissance et de

402 Bibliography

l'adaptation enzymatique chez les bactéries infectées par le bactériophage. *Ann. Inst. Pasteur* **73**: 937–957   [179]

489a. Moore, A. E. (1952) Viruses with oncolytic properties and their adaptation to tumors. *Ann. N. Y. Acad. Sci.* **54**: 945–952   [306]

490. Morgan, C., and Wyckoff, R. W. G. (1950) The electron microscopy of fowl pox virus within the chorioallantoic membrane. *J. Immunol.* **65**: 285–295   [234]

491. Morgan, I. M. (1941) Influence of age on susceptibility and on immune response of mice to Eastern equine encephalomyelitis virus. *J. Exp. Med.* **74**: 115–132   [306]

492. Morgan, I. M. (1947) The role of antibody in experimental poliomyelitis. III. *Am. J. Hyg.* **45**: 390–400   [282, 314]

493. Morgan, I. M. (1949) Mechanism of immunity in poliomyelitis and its bearing on differentiation of types. *Am. J. Med.* **6**: 556–562   [133]

494. Mosley, V. M., and Wyckoff, R. W. G. (1946) Electron micrography of the virus of influenza. *Nature* **157**: 263   [82]

495. Muckenfuss, R. S., and Rivers, T. M. (1930) Survival of vaccine virus separated from living host cells by collodion membranes. *J. Exp. Med.* **51**: 149–159   [227]

496. Muller, H. J. (1922) Variation due to change in the individual gene. *Am. Naturalist* **56**: 32–50   [350]

496a. Muller, R. H., and Rose, H. M. (1952) Purification of influenza virus (PR8 strain) by a cation exchange resin. *Proc. Soc. Exp. Biol. Med.* **80**: 27–29   [89]

497. Murphy, J. B. (1913) Transplantability of tissues to the embryo of foreign species. *J. Exp. Med.* **17**: 482–493   [322]

498. Murray, R. G. E., Gillen, D. H., and Heagy, F. G. (1950) Cytological changes in *Escherichia coli* produced by infection with phage T2. *J. Bact.* **59**: 603–615   [180]

498a. Nolla, J. A. B. (1938) Inheritance in *Nicotiana*. III. *J. Hered.* **29**: 42–48   [304]

499. Northrop, J. H. (1939) *Crystalline Enzymes*, New York, Columbia University Press   [99, 103]

500. Novick, A., and Szilard, L. (1951) Virus strains of identical phenotype but different genotype. *Science* **113**: 34–35   [295]

501. Oberling, C. (1952) *The Riddle of Cancer*, 2nd Ed., New Haven, Yale University Press   [332, 335]

502. Oberling, C., Guérin, M., and Guérin, P. (1935) A propos de la transformation sarcomateuse des fibroadenomes mammaires transplantables du rat blanc. *Bull. assoc. franç. étude cancer* **24**: 232   [323]

503. Ocfemia, G. O. (1934) An insect vector of the Fiji disease of sugar cane. *Am. J. Bot.* **22**: 113–120   [216]

504. Oparin, A. I. (1938) *The Origin of Life*, New York, Macmillan   [346]

505. Orlando, A., and Silberschmidt, K. (1946) Quoted by Bawden (Ref. 43)   [34]

506. Oster, G., and McLaren, A. D. (1950) The ultraviolet light and photosensitized inactivation of tobacco mosaic virus. *J. Gen. Physiol.* **33**: 215–228   [153]

507. Oster, G., and Stanley, W. M. (1946) An electronmicroscope study of the contents of hair cells from leaves diseased with tobacco mosaic virus. *Br. J. Exp. Path.* **27**: 261–265 [93]

508. Pang, K. H., and Zia, S. H. (1940) Studies of virus of encephalitis (St. Louis type) grown on agar tissue medium. *Chinese Med. J.,* Suppl. **3**:446–457 [225]

508a. Pardee, A. B., and Williams, I. (1953) Enzymatic activity and bacteriophage infection. III. *Ann. Inst. Pasteur* **84**: 147–156 [179]

508b. Parker, R. C. (1950) *Methods of Tissue Cultures,* 2nd Ed., New York, Hoeber [225]

509. Parker, R. F. (1938) Statistical studies of the nature of the infectious unit of vaccine virus. *J. Exp. Med.* **67**: 725–738 [51, 53]

510. Parker, R. F. (1940) Studies on the infectious unit of myxoma. *J. Exp. Med.* **71**: 439–444 [53]

511. Parker, R. F., and Rivers, T. M. (1936) Immunological and chemical investigations of vaccine virus. IV. *J. Exp. Med.* **64**: 439–452 [44]

512. Parker, R. F., Bronson, L. H., and Green, R. H. (1941) Further studies on the infectious unit of vaccinia. *J. Exp. Med.* **74**: 263–281 [53]

513. Parsons, R. J., and Kidd, J. G. (1943) Oral papillomatosis of rabbits: a virus disease. *J. Exp. Med.* **77**: 233–250 [326]

514. Paschen, E. (1917) Technik zur Darstellung der Elementarkörperchen (Paschensche Körperchen) in der Variolapustel. *Deutsch. med. Wochenschr.* **43**: 1036 [6, 58]

515. Peacock, P. R. (1935) Studies of fowl tumours induced by carcinogenic agents. II. *Am. J. Cancer* **25**: 49–65 [332, 338]

516. Perdrau, J. R., and Todd, C. (1933) The photodynamic action of methylene blue on certain viruses. *Proc. Roy. Soc.* (London) *B,* **112**: 288–298 [154]

517. Pinkerton, H. (1942) The pathogenic rickettsiae with particular reference to their nature, biologic properties, and classification. *Bact. Rev.* **6**: 37–78 [371]

518. Pinkerton, H. (1948) The classification of rickettsiae and rickettsial diseases. In: *The Rickettsial Diseases of Man,* A.A.A.S., Washington [364, 365, 372]

519. Pirie, A. (1937) The metabolism of the filter-passing organism "C" from sewage. *Br. J. Exp. Path.* **18**: 96–102 [4]

520. Pirie, N. W. (1940) The criteria of purity used in the study of large molecules of biological origin. *Biol. Rev.* **15**: 377–404 [85]

521. Pirie, N. W. (1945) Physical and chemical properties of tomato bushy stunt virus and the strains of tobacco mosaic virus. *Adv. Enzymol.* **5**: 1–29 [56]

522. Pirie, N. W. (1950) A biochemical approach to viruses. *Nature* **166**: 495–496 [86]

523. Plotz, H., and Ephrussi, B. (1933) La culture de la peste aviaire en présence de cellules vivantes non proliférantes. *C. r. soc. biol.* **113**: 711–712 [227]

524. Poisson, S. D. (1837) Recherches sur la probabilité des jugements en matière criminelle et en matière civile, précédées des règles générales du calcul des probabilités. Paris [49]

525. Polson, A., and Shepard, C. C. (1949) On the diffusion rates of bacterio-phages. *Biochem. Biophys. Acta* **3**: 137–145   [79]
526. Polson, A., and Wyckoff, R. W. G. (1948) The amino acid content of bacteriophage. *Science* **108**: 501   [104]
527. Porter, K. R., and Thompson, A. P. (1948) A particulate body associated with epithelial cells cultured from mammary carcinomas of mice of a milk-factor strain. *J. Exp. Med.* **88**: 15–24   [328, 329]
528. Porter, K. R., Claude, A., and Fullam, E. F. (1945) A study of tissue culture cells by electron microscopy. Methods and preliminary observations. *J. Exp. Med.* **81**: 233–246   [234]
529. Preer, J. R. (1948) A study of some properties of the cytoplasmic factor "kappa" in *Paramecium aurelia*, variety 2. *Genetics* **33**: 349–404   [357]
530. Preer, J. R. (1946) Some properties of a genetic cytoplasmic factor in *Paramecium*. *Proc. Nat. Acad. Sci.* **32**: 247–253   [339]
531. Price, W. C. (1934) Isolation and study of some yellow strains of cucumber mosaic. *Phytopath.* **24**: 743–761   [297]
532. Price, W. C. (1938) Studies on the virus of tobacco necrosis. *Am. J. Bot.* **25**: 603–612   [308]
533. Price, W. C. (1940) Acquired immunity from plant virus diseases. *Quart. Rev. Biol.* **15**: 338–361   [276, 278]
533a. Price, W. C. (1943) Severity of curly top in tobacco affected by site of inoculation. *Phytopath.* **33**: 586–601   [279]
534. Price, W. H. (1947) Bacteriophage formation without bacterial growth. I. *J. Gen. Physiol.* **31**: 119–126   [179]
535. Puck, T. T., Garen, A., and Cline, J. (1951) The mechanism of virus attachment to host cells. I. *J. Exp. Med.* **93**: 65–88   [165, 166, 260]
536. Purdy, H. A. (1929) Immunologic reactions with tobacco mosaic virus. *J. Exp. Med.* **49**: 919–935   [127]
537. Purdy, W. J. (1933) The hetero-transfer of two filterable tumours: an investigation by means of resistance induced by embryo tissue. *Br. J. Exp. Path.* **14**: 9–17   [332]
538. Purdy, W. J. (1933) The hetero-transfer of two filterable tumours: an investigation by means of immune sera. *Br. J. Exp. Path.* **14**: 260–267   [332]
539. Putnam, F. W. (1950) Molecular kinetics and electrophoretic properties of bacteriophages. *Science* **111**: 481–488   [79, 80]
540. Rafelson, M. E., Jr., Winzler, R. J., and Pearson, H. E. (1949) The effect of Theiler's GD VII virus on P^{32} uptake by minced one-day-old mouse brain. *J. Biol. Chem.* **181**: 583–593   [238]
541. Raff, N., and Cohen, S. S. (1950) The effect of virus infection on the utilization of tryptophan by *Escherichia coli*. *J. Bact.* **60**: 69–80   [179]
542. Raffel, S., and Schulz, E. W. (1940) Immunological reactions in poliomyelitis. *J. Immunol.* **39**: 265–286   [49, 134]
543. Rake, G. (1948) Chlamydozoaceae *Moshkovsky*. In: *Bergey's Manual of Determinative Bacteriology*, 6th Ed., Baltimore, Williams and Wilkins   [298]
544. Rake, G., and Jones, H. P. (1944) Studies on lymphogranuloma venereum. I, II. *J. Exp. Med.* **75**: 323–338; **79**: 463–486   [223, 247]
545. Rakieten, M. L., and Rakieten, T. L. (1937) Relationship between staphy-

lococci and bacilli belonging to the subtilis group as shown by bacteriophage absorption. *J. Bact.* **34**: 285–300 [167]

545a. Ratcliffe, F. N., Myers, K., Fennessy, B. V., and Calaby, J. H. (1952) Myxomatosis in Australia. *Nature* **170**: 7–11 [320]

546. Reed, L. J., and Muench, H. (1938) A simple method of estimating fifty per cent endpoints. *Am. J. Hyg.* **27**: 493–497 [43, 44]

547. Reed, W., and Carroll, J. (1902) The etiology of yellow fever; a supplementary note. *Am. Med.* **3**: 301–305 [7]

548. Reed, W., Carroll, J., Agramonte, A., and Lazear, J. W. (1911) Yellow fever: a compilation of various publications. *U. S. 61st Congress, Docum.* No. 822, Washington [310]

549. Reeves, W. C. (1945) Observations on the natural history of western equine encephalomyelitis. *Proc. XLIX Meeting U. S. Livestock Sanitary Assoc.* 150–158 [312]

550. Remlinger, P. (1939) Quoted by Doerr in: Doerr and Hallauer (Ref. 187) [223]

551. Rhoades, M. M. (1946) Plastid mutations. *Cold Spring Harbor Symp. Quant. Biol.* **11**: 202–207 [356]

552. Richards, O. W. (1946) Biological phase microscopy. *Cold Spring Harbor Symp. Quant. Biol.* **11**: 208–214 [60]

553. Rickard, E. R., and Francis, T., Jr. (1938) The demonstration of lesions and virus in the lungs of mice receiving large intraperitoneal inoculations of epidemic influenza virus. *J. Exp. Med.* **67**: 953–972 [281]

554. Rivers, T. M. (1936) Immunity in virus diseases with particular reference to poliomyelitis. *Am. J. Publ. Health* **26**: 136–142 [132]

555. Rivers, T. M. (1937) Viruses and Koch's postulates. *J. Bact.* **33**: 1–12 [32]

556. Rivers, T. M. (1942) Immunity in virus infections. *Science* **95**: 107–112 [132, 280]

557. Rivers, T. M., and Pearce, L. (1925) Growth and persistence of filterable viruses in a transplantable rabbit neoplasm. *J. Exp. Med.* **42**: 523–537 [327]

558. Rivers, T. M., and Tillett, W. S. (1924) Further observations on the phenomena enountered in attempting to transmit varicella to rabbits. *J. Exp. Med.* **39**: 777–802 [36, 340]

559. Rivers, T. M., Haagen, E., and Muckenfuss, R. S. (1929) A study of vaccinal immunity in tissue cultures. *J. Exp. Med.* **50**: 673–685 [281]

560. Rose, S. M., and Rose, F. C. (1952) Tumor agent transformations in amphibia. *Cancer Res.* **12**: 1–12 [325, 332, 333, 341]

561. Ross, A. F., and Stanley, W. M. (1938) The partial reactivation of formalized tobacco mosaic virus protein. *J. Gen. Physiol.* **22**: 165–191 [144]

561a. Ross, A. F., Rochow, W. F., and Siegel, B. M. (1952) High concentrations of virus X in plants doubly infected with potato viruses X and Y. *Phytopath.* **42**: 473 [279]

562. Rous, P. (1911) Transmission of a malignant new growth by means of a cell-free filtrate. *J. Am. Med. Assoc.* **56**: 198 [7, 324]

563. Rous, P. (1943) The nearer causes of cancer. *J. Am. Med. Assoc.* **122**: 573–581 [323, 325]

564. Rous, P. (1946) Concerning the cancer problem. *Am. Scientist* **34**: 329–
    358   [327, 331, 332, 342]
565. Rous, P., and Kidd, J. G. (1938) The carcinogenic effect of a papilloma
    virus on the tarred skin of rabbits. *J. Exp. Med.* **67**: 399–428   [338]
566. Rous, P., Kidd, J. G., and Smith, W. E. (1952) Experiments on the cause
    of the rabbit carcinomas derived from virus-induced papillomas. *J. Exp.
    Med.* **96**: 159–174   [328, 337]
567. Rous, P., McMaster, P. D., and Hudack, S. S. (1935) The fixation and
    protection of viruses by the cells of susceptible animals. *J. Exp. Med.*
    61: 657–688   [228]
568. Ruska, H., and Kausche, G. A. (1943) Über Form, Grosserverteilung und
    Struktur einiger Virus-Elementarkörper. *Zentr. Bakt., Parasit., I, Orig.*
    150: 311–318   [64]
569. Russell, D. S. (1932) The occurrence and distribution of intranuclear
    "inclusion bodies" in gliomas. *J. Path. Bact.* **35**: 625–634   [334]
570. Sabin, A. B. (1935) The mechanism of immunity to filterable viruses.
    Br. J. Exp. Path. **16**: 70–84   [128]
571. Sabin, A. B. (1941) The filterable microorganisms of the pleuropneu-
    monia group. *Bact. Rev.* **5**: 1–66   [4]
572. Sabin, A. B. (1952) Nature of inherited resistance to viruses affecting the
    nervous system. *Proc. Nat. Acad. Sci.* **38**: 540–546   [30, 305]
573. Sabin, A. B., and Ward, R. (1941) The natural history of human polio-
    myelitis. I. *J. Exp. Med.* **73**: 771–793   [308]
574. Salaman, R. N., and LePelley, R. H. (1930) Para-crinkle: a potato dis-
    ease of the virus group. *Proc. Roy. Soc. (London) B,* **106**: 140–175
    [34]
575. Salk, J. E. (1944) A simplified procedure for titrating hemagglutinating
    capacity of influenza-virus and the corresponding antibody. *J. Immunol.*
    49: 87–98   [250, 252]
576. Sanarelli, G. (1898) Das myxomatogene Virus. Beitrag zum Studium
    der Krankheitserreger ausserhalb des Sichtbaren. *Zentr. Bakt., Parasit.,
    I, Orig.* **23**: 865–873   [326]
576a. Sanders, F. K. (1953) Multiplication cycles in neurotropic viruses. In:
    The Nature of Virus Multiplication, Cambridge University Press   [269]
577. Sanders, M. (1939) Cultivation of the viruses. A critical review. *Arch.
    Path.* **28**: 541–586   [224]
577a. Scherer, W. F., and Syverton, J. T. (1952) Studies on the propagation in
    vitro of poliomyelitis viruses. III. *J. Exp. Med.* **96**: 389–400   [227]
577b. Scherer, W. F., Syverton, J. T., and Gey, G. O. (1953) Studies on the
    propagation in vitro of poliomyelitis viruses. IV. Viral multiplication in a
    stable strain of human malignant epithelial cells (Strain Hela) derived
    from an epidermoid carcinoma of the cervix. *J. Exp. Med.* **97**: 695–710
    [228]
578. Schlesinger, M. (1932) Über die Bindung des Bakteriophagen an homo-
    loge Bakterien. I, II. *Z. Hyg. Infectionskrh.* **114**: 130–160   [164]
579. Schlesinger, R. W. (1948) Viral diseases of the central nervous system.
    Scope and limitations of specific diagnostic methods. *Pediatrics* **1**: 625–
    633   [305]

580. Schlesinger, R. W. (1949) The mechanism of active cerebral immunity to equine encephalomyelitis virus. II. *J. Exp. Med.* **89**: 507–527 [282]

581. Schlesinger, R. W. (1949) Local immune response and viral growth rate as factors in immunity to equine encephalomyelitis virus. *Fed. Proc.* **8**: 622–624 [131, 282]

582. Schlesinger, R. W. (1950) Incomplete growth cycle of influenza virus in mouse brain. *Proc. Soc. Exp. Biol. Med.* **74**: 541–548 [31, 223, 246, 265]

583. Schlesinger, R. W. (1950) Interference between animal-pathogenic viruses. In: *Viruses 1950*, Pasadena, Cal. Inst. Technol. Bookstore [280, 283]

584. Schlesinger, R. W. (1951) Studies on interference between influenza and equine encephalomyelitis viruses. *Arch. ges. Virusforsch.* **4**: 501–517 [284]

585. Schlesinger, R. W., Olitski, P. K., and Morgan, I. M. (1944) Induced resistance of the central nervous system to experimental infection with equine encephalomyelitis virus. III. *J. Exp. Med.* **80**: 197–211 [283]

586. Schnitzer, R. J., Buck, M., and Steiger, N. (1951) Chemotherapeutic effect of 2-hydroxy-1,4-naphthoquinonimine on infections of mice with Col SK virus. *Proc. Soc. Exp. Biol. Med.* **77**: 182–187 [223]

587. Schramm, G. (1947) Über die Spaltung des Tabakmosaik-Virus und die Wiedervereinigung der Spaltstucke zu hohermolekularen Proteines. I. Die Spaltungreaktion. *Z. Naturforsch.* **2b**: 112–121 [96, 101, 142]

588. Schramm, G., and Müller, H. (1940) Zur Chemie des Tabakmosaikvirus. Über die Einwirkung von Keten und Phenylisocyanat auf das Virusprotein. *Z. physiol. Chem.* **266**: 43–55 [144]

589. Seiffert, G. (1937) Über das Vorkommen filtrabler Mikro-organismen in der Natur und ihre Züchtbarkeit. *Zentr. Bakt., Parasit., I, Orig.* **139**: 337–342 [4]

590. Selbie, F. R., Robinson, R. H. M., and Shope, R. E. (1948) Shope papilloma virus: reversion of adaptation to domestic rabbit by passage through cottontail. *Br. J. Cancer* **2**: 375–380 [327]

591. Sharp, D. G., Eckert, E. A., Beard, D., and Beard, J. W. (1952) Morphology of the virus of avian erythromyeloblastic leucosis and a comparison with the agent of Newcastle disease. *J. Bact.* **63**: 151–161 [82]

592. Sharp, D. G., Hook, A. E., Taylor, A. R., Beard, D., and Beard, J. W. (1946) Sedimentation characters and pH stability of the T2 bacteriophage of *Escherichia coli*. *J. Biol. Chem.* **165**: 259–270 [79]

593. Sharp, D. J., Taylor, A. R., McLean, I. W., Jr., Beard, D., and Beard, J. W. (1944) Density and size of influenza virus A (PR8 strain) in solution. *Science* **100**: 151–153 [76]

594. Sharpless, G. R., Davies, M. C., and Cox, H. R. (1950) Antagonistic action of certain neurotropic viruses toward a lymphoid tumor in chickens with resulting immunity. *Proc. Soc. Exp. Biol. Med.* **73**: 270–275 [306]

595. Sheffield, F. M. L. (1939) Micrurgical studies on virus-infected plants. *Proc. Roy. Soc.* (London) B, **126**: 529–538 [214]

596. Shepard, C. G., and Wyckoff, R. W. G. (1946) The nature of the soluble antigen from typhus rickettsiae. *U. S. Publ. Health Rep.* **61**: 761–767 [366]

408   Bibliography

597. Shope, R. E. (1932) A filtrable virus causing a tumor-like condition in rabbits and its relationship to virus myxomatosum. *J. Exp. Med.* **56:** 803–822 [325]

598. Shope, R. E. (1933) Infectious papillomatosis of rabbits. *J. Exp. Med.* **58:** 607–624 [326, 335]

599. Shope, R. E. (1935) Experiments on the epidemiology of pseudorabies. I. *J. Exp. Med.* **62:** 85–99 [309]

600. Shope, R. E. (1937) Immunization of rabbits to infectious papillomatosis. *J. Exp. Med.* **65:** 219–231 [327]

601. Shope, R. E. (1943) Swine influenza. In: *Virus Diseases,* Ithaca, Cornell University Press [7, 314]

602. Shope, R. E. (1950) "Masking," transformation, and interepidemic survival of animal viruses. In: *Viruses 1950,* Pasadena, Cal. Inst. Technol. Bookstore [30, 299, 327, 335, 361]

602a. Shope, R. E. (1953) An antiviral substance from *Penicillium funiculosum.* I, II, III. *J. Exp. Med.* **97:** 601–650 [223]

603. Sigel, M. M., Girardi, A. J., and Allen, E. G. (1951) Studies on the psittacosis-lymphogranuloma group. I. *J. Exp. Med.* **94:** 401–413 [269]

603a. Siminovitch, L., and Rapkine, S. (1951) Modifications biochimiques au cours du développement des bactériophages chez une bactérie lysogène. *C. r. acad. sci.* **232:** 1603–1605 [182]

604. Sinnott, E. W., Dunn, L. C., and Dobzhansky, T. (1950) *Principles of Genetics,* 4th Ed., New York, McGraw-Hill [350]

605. Smadel, J. E. (1952) Serologic reactions in viral and rickettsial infections. In: Rivers, *Viral and Rickettsial Infections of Man,* 2nd Ed., Philadelphia, Lippincott [133]

606. Smadel, J. E., and Hoagland, C. L. (1942) Elementary bodies of vaccinia. *Bact. Rev.* **6:** 79–110 [53, 54, 110, 120, 130, 348]

607. Smith, E. F. (1916) Studies on the crowngall of plants: Its relation to human cancer. *J. Cancer Res.* **1:** 231–310 [339]

608. Smith, J. D., and Stocker, M. G. P. (1951) The nucleic acids of *Rickettsia burneti. Br. J. Exp. Path.* **32:** 433–441 [366]

609. Smith, K. M. (1941) Some notes on the relationship of plant viruses with vector and non-vector insects. *Parasitology* **33:** 110–116 [317]

610. Smith, K. M. (1950) *An Introduction to the Study of Viruses,* New York, Pitman [1]

611. Smith, K. M., and Wyckoff, R. W. G. (1951) Electron microscopy of insect viruses. *Research* **4:** 148–155 [83, 110]

612. Smith, M. G., Blattner, R. J., and Heys, F. M. (1946) St. Louis encephalitis. *J. Exp. Med.* **84:** 1–6 [312]

612a. Smith, M. H. D. (1952) The Berry-Dedrick transformation of fibroma into myxoma in the rabbit. *Ann. N. Y. Acad. Sci.* **54:** 1141–1152 [302]

613. Smith, W., Westwood, M. A., Westwood, J. C. N., and Belyavin, G. (1951) Spontaneous mutation of influenza virus A during routine egg passage. *Br. J. Exp. Path.* **32:** 422–432 [301]

614. Snyder, J. C., Yeomans, A., Clements, D. H., Murray, E. S., Zarafonetis, C. J. D., and Tierney, A. (1947) Further observations on the treatment of

typhus fever with para-aminobenzoic acid. *Ann. Int. Med.* **27**: 1–27 [369]

615. Solomon, A. K. (1950) Cancer: Biophysics. In: Glasser, *New Medical Physics.*, Chicago, Year Book Publishers [323]

616. Sonneborn, T. M. (1949) Beyond the gene. *Am. Scientist* **37**: 33–59 [356]

617. Sonneborn, T. M. (1950) The cytoplasm in heredity. *Heredity* **4**: 11–36 [355, 357]

618. Soper, F. L. (1938) Situation de la fièvre jaune au Brésil. *Bull. Off. Int. Emat. Hyg. Publ.* **30**: 1205–1208 [313]

618a. Spencer, E. L., and Price, W. C. (1943) Accuracy of the local lesion method for measuring virus activity. I. *Am. J. Bot.* **30**: 280–290 [47]

619. Spiegelman, S. (1946) Nuclear and cytoplasmic factors controlling enzymatic adaptation. *Cold Spring Harbor Symp. Quant. Biol.* **11**: 256–277 [358]

620. Spiegelman, S., and DeLorenzo, W. F. (1952) Substrate stabilization of enzyme-forming capacity during the segregation of a heterozygote. *Proc. Nat. Acad. Sci.* **38**: 583–592 [358]

621. Spiegelman, S., Lindegren, C. C., and Lindegren, G. (1945) Maintenance and increase of a genetic character by a substrate-cytoplasmic interaction in the absence of the specific gene. *Proc. Nat. Acad. Sci.* **31**: 95–102 [358]

621a. Stanley, W. M. (1934) Chemical studies on the virus of tobacco mosaic. I. *Phytopath.* **24**: 1055–1085 [137]

622. Stanley, W. M. (1935) Isolation of a crystalline protein possessing the properties of tobacco-mosaic virus. *Science* **81**: 644–645 [92, 93]

623. Stanley, W. M. (1937) Chemical studies on the virus of tobacco mosaic. *J. Biol. Chem.* **121**: 205–217 [209]

624. Stanley, W. M. (1943) Chemical structure and the mutation of viruses. In: *Virus Diseases*, Ithaca, Cornell University Press [103, 137, 144]

625. Steere, R. L. (1952) Virus increment curves obtained from counts of particles in clarified plant juice. *Am. J. Bot.* **39**: 211–220 [211, 212]

625a. Steere, R. L., and Williams, R. C. (1953) Identification of crystalline inclusion bodies extracted intact from plant cells infected with tobacco mosaic virus. *Am. J. Bot.* **40**: 81–84 [96]

626. Steinhaus, E. A. (1946) *Insect Microbiology,* Ithaca, Comstock [347, 364, 370]

627. Steinhaus, E. A. (1949) Nomenclature and classification of insect viruses. *Bact. Rev.* **13**: 203–223 [83]

627a. Stent, G., and Maaløe, O. (1953) Radioactive phosphorus tracer studies on the reproduction of T4 bacteriophage. II. *Biochem. Biophys. Acta* **10**: 55–69 [176]

628. Stent, G. S., and Wollman, E. L. (1950) Studies on activation of T4 bacteriophage by cofactor. II. *Biochem. Biophys. Acta* **6**: 307–316 [167]

629. Stephenson, F. J., Schultz, E. S., and Clark, C. F. (1939) Inheritance of immunity from virus X (latent mosaic) in the potato. *Phytopath.* **29**: 362–365 [24]

630. Stone, J. D. (1947) Prevention of virus infection with enzyme of *V. cholerae.* I. *Austral. J. Exp. Biol. Med. Sci.* **26**: 49–64 [257]

631. Stone, J. D., and Ada, G. L. (1950) Electrophoretic studies of virus-red cell interaction. *Br. J. Exp. Path.* **31**: 275–284 [254]

632. Storey, H. H. (1933) Investigations of the mechanism of the transmission of plant viruses by insect vectors. I. *Proc. Roy. Soc.* (London) *B,* **113**: 463–485 [33, 304, 315, 318]

633. Strauss, M. J., Shaw, E. W., Bunting, H., and Melnick, J. L. (1949) "Crystalline" virus-like particles from skin papillomas characterized by intranuclear inclusion bodies. *Proc. Soc. Exp. Biol. Med.* **72**: 46–50 [105, 237]

633a. Stuart-Harris, C. H. (1939) A neurotropic strain of human influenza virus. *Lancet* (1) **236**: 497–499 [266]

634. Sugg, J. Y. (1949) An influenza virus pneumonia of mice that is non-transferable by serial passage. *J. Bact.* **57**: 399–403 [271]

635. Sugg, J. Y., and Magill, T. P. (1948) The serial passage of mixtures of different strains of influenza virus in embryonated eggs and in mice. *J. Bact.* **56**: 201–206 [284, 288]

636. Svedmyr, A. (1948) Studies on a factor in normal allantoic fluid inhibiting influenza virus haemagglutination. Occurrence, physicochemical properties, and mode of action. *Br. J. Exp. Path.* **29**: 295–308 [257, 258]

637. Syverton, J. T., and Berry, G. P. (1936) Coexistent infections of individual cells by more than one filterable virus. *J. Bact.* **32**: 356–357 [238]

638. Syverton, J. T., and Berry, G. P. (1941) Hereditary transmission of the Western type of equine encephalomyelitis virus in the wood tick, *Dermacentor andersoni* Stiles. *J. Exp. Med.* **73**: 507–530 [311]

639. Syverton, J. T., and Berry, G. B. (1947) Multiple virus infection of single host cells. *J. Exp. Med.* **86**: 145–152 [284]

640. Takahashi, W. N. (1941) Changes in nitrogen and virus content of detached tobacco leaves in darkness. *Phytopath.* **31**: 1117–1122 [210]

641. Takahashi, W. N., and Rawlins, T. E. (1933) Rod-shaped particles in tobacco mosaic virus demonstrated by stream double refraction. *Science* **77**: 26–27 [94]

641a. Tall, M. G., Price, W. C., and Wertman, K. (1949) Differentiation of tobacco and tomato ringspot viruses by cross immunization and complement fixation. *Phytopath.* **39**: 288–299 [127]

642. Tamm, I., and Horsfall, F. L., Jr. (1950) Characterization and separation of an inhibitor of viral hemagglutination present in urine. *Proc. Soc. Exp. Biol. Med.* **74**: 108–114 [257]

643. Tang, F. F., and Wei, H. (1937) Morphological studies on vaccinia virus cultivated in the developing egg. *J. Path. Bact.* **45**: 317–323 [233]

644. Taylor, A. (1943) The successful production of a mammalian tumor with a virus-like principle. *Science* **97**: 123 [330]

645. Taylor, A. R. (1946) Chemical analysis of the T2 bacteriophage and its host, *Escherichia coli* (strain B). *J. Biol. Chem.* **165**: 271–284 [103]

646. Theiler, M. (1937) Spontaneous encephalomyelitis of mice, a new virus disease. *J. Exp. Med.* **65**: 705–719 [37]

647. Theiler, M., and Smith, H. H. (1937) The effect of prolonged cultivation in vitro upon the pathogenicity of yellow fever virus. *J. Exp. Med.* **65**: 767–786 [300]

648. Thompson, R. L., Price, M. L., Minton, S. A., Jr., Elion, G. B., and Hitchings, G. H. (1950) Effects of purine derivatives and analogues on multiplication of the vaccinia virus. *J. Immunol.* **65:** 529–534 [230]

648a. Thompson, R. L., Price, M., Minton, S. A., Jr., Falco, E. A., and Hitchings, G. H. (1951) Protection of mice against the vaccinia virus by the administration of phenoxythiouracils. *J. Immunol.* **67:** 483–491 [223]

648b. Thung, T. H. (1931) Quoted by Price (Ref. 533) [276]

649. Trager, W. (1935) Cultivation of the virus of grasserie in silkworm tissue cultures. *J. Exp. Med.* **61:** 501–513 [237]

650. Trager, W. (1938) Multiplication of the virus of equine encephalomyelitis in surviving mosquito tissues. *Am. J. Trop. Med.* **18:** 387–393 [312]

651. Traub, E. (1939) Epidemiology of lymphocytic choriomeningitis in a mouse stock observed for four years. *J. Exp. Med.* **69:** 801–817 [38, 309, 340, 361]

652. Twombly, G. H., and Meisel, D. (1946) The growth of mammalian tumors in fertile eggs. Is a filterable cancer virus produced? *Cancer Res.* **6:** 82–91 [330]

653. Twort, F. W. (1915) An investigation on the nature of ultramicroscopic viruses. *Lancet* (2), **189:** 1241–1243 [7]

654. Uppal, B. M. (1934) The movement of tobacco mosaic virus in leaves of *Nicotiana sylvestris. Indian J. Agr. Sci.* **4:** 865–873 [216]

654a. Vago, C. (1951) Phénomènes de "latentia" dans une maladie à ultravirus des insectes. *Rev. can. biol.* **10:** 299–308 [320, 349]

654b. Valleau, W. D. (1946) Breeding tobacco varieties resistant to mosaic. *Phytopath.* **36:** 412 [304]

654c. Valleau, W. D. (1952) The evolution of susceptibility to tobacco mosaic in *Nicotiana* and the origin of tobacco mosaic virus. *Phytopath.* **42:** 40–42 [319]

655. Van Rooyen, C. E., and Rhodes, A. J. (1948) *Virus Diseases of Man,* 2nd Ed., New York, Nelson [29, 58, 224, 241]

656. Vilches, A., and Hirst, G. K. (1947) Interference between neurotropic and other unrelated viruses. *J. Immunol.* **57:** 125–140 [266, 284]

657. Visconti, N., and Delbrück, M. (1953) The mechanism of genetic recombination in phage. *Genetics* **38:** 5–33 [190, 193]

658. Volkerts, M., and Horsfall, F. L., Jr. (1947) Studies on a lung tissue component which combines with pneumonia virus of mice (PVM). *J. Exp. Med.* **86:** 393–407 [260]

659. Von Magnus, P. (1951) Propagation of the PR8 strain of influenza A virus in chick embryo. I. *Acta Path. Microb. Scand.* **28:** 250–277 [261, 288]

660. Von Magnus, P. (1951) Propagation of the PR8 strain of influenza A virus in chick embryo. II. *Acta Path. Microb. Scand.* **28:** 278–293 [265]

661. Wahl, R., and Blum-Emerique, L. (1949) Purification et concentration du bactériophage. II. *Ann. Inst. Pasteur* **76:** 103–121 [103]

662. Wallace, J. M. (1944) Acquired immunity from curly top in tobacco and tomato. *J. Agr. Res.* **69:** 187–214 [7, 279]

663. Wallace, J. M. (1950) Immunological properties of plant viruses. In: *Viruses 1950,* Pasadena, Cal. Inst. Technol. Bookstore [279]

664. Warren, J., Weil, M. L., Russ, S. B., and Jeffries, H. (1949) Purification of

certain viruses by use of protamine sulfate. *Proc. Soc. Exp. Biol. Med.* **72:** 662–664 [88, 105]

665. Watson, J. D. (1950) The properties of X-ray inactivated bacteriophage. I. *J. Bact.* **60:** 697–718 [135, 149, 168, 194]

666. Watson, J. D. (1952) The properties of X-ray inactivated bacteriophage. II. *J. Bact.* **63:** 473–485 [149]

666a. Watson, J. D., and Crick, F. H. C. (1953) Genetical implications of the structure of deoxyribonucleic acid. *Nature* **171:** 964–996 [100]

667. Watson, M. A., and Roberts, F. M. (1940) Evidence against the hypothesis that certain plant viruses are transmitted mechanically by aphides. *Ann. Applied Biol.* **27:** 227–233 [315]

667a. Weed, L. L., and Cohen, S. S. (1951) The utilization of host pyrimidines in the synthesis of bacterial viruses. *J. Biol. Chem.* **192:** 693–700 [176]

668. Weidel, W. (1951) Über die Zellmembran von *Escherichia coli* B. *Z. Naturforsch.* **6b:** 251–259 [168]

669. Weigle, J. J., and Delbrück, M. (1951) Mutual exclusion between an infecting phage and a carried phage. *J. Bact.* **62:** 301–318 [189, 202, 274]

670. Weil, M. L., Beard, D., Sharp, D. C., and Beard, J. W. (1948) Purification, *p*H stability and culture of the mumps virus. *J. Immunol.* **60:** 561–582 [245, 248]

671. Weiss, E. (1949) The extracellular development of agents of the psittacosis-lymphogranuloma group (Chlamydozoaceae). *J. Infectious Diseases* **84:** 125–149 [232]

672. Weller, T. H., Robbins, F. C., and Enders, J. F. (1949) Cultivation of poliomyelitis virus in cultures of human foreskin and embryonic tissues. *Proc. Soc. Exp. Biol. Med.* **72:** 153–155 [227]

673. Wertman, K. (1948) The Weil-Felix reaction. In: *The Rickettsial Diseases of Man*, A.A.A.S., Washington [368]

674. Weyer, F., Friedrich-Freksa, H., and Bergold, G. (1944) Die Beziehungen der Rickettsien zu Bakterien und Viren. *Naturwiss.* **32:** 361–365 [366]

675. Wildman, S. G., Cheo, C. C., and Bonner, J. (1949) The proteins of green leaves. III. *J. Biol. Chem.* **180:** 985–1001 [209, 210]

676. Wilkins, M. H. F., Stockes, A. R., Seeds, W. E., and Oster, G. (1950) Tobacco mosaic virus crystals and tri-dimensional microscopic vision. *Nature* **166:** 127–139 [96]

676a. Williams, R. C. (1952) High-resolution electron microscopy of the particles of tobacco mosaic virus. *Biochem. Biophys. Acta* **8:** 227–244 [95]

677. Williams, R. C., and Backus, R. C. (1949) Macromolecular weights determined by direct particle counting. I. *J. Am. Chem. Soc.* **71:** 4052–4057 [67]

678. Williams, R. C., and Steere, R. L. (1951) Electron microscopic observations on the unit of length of the particles of tobacco mosaic virus. *J. Am. Chem. Soc.* **73:** 2057–2061 [94]

679. Williams, R. C., and Wyckoff, R. W. G. (1946) Applications of metallic shadow-casting to microscopy. *J. Appl. Phys.* **17:** 23–33 [61]

680. Williams, R. C., Backus, R. C., and Steere, R. L. (1951) Macromolecular

weights determined by direct particle counting. II. *J. Am. Chem. Soc.* 72: 2062–2066 [68]

681. Whitman, L. (1937) The multiplication of the virus of yellow fever in *Aedes aegypti*. *J. Exp. Med.* 66: 133–143 [311]

682. Wolbach, S. B. (1948) The pathology of the rickettsial diseases of man. In: *The Rickettsial Diseases of Man*, A.A.A.S., Washington [369]

683. Wollman, E. (1927) Recherches sur la bactériophagie (Phénomène de Twort-d'Hérelle). *Ann. Inst. Pasteur* 41: 883–918 [350]

684. Wollman, E., and Lacassagne, A. (1940) Évaluation des dimensions des bactériophages au moyen des rayons X. *Ann. Inst. Pasteur* 64: 5–39 [152]

685. Woodruff, A. M., and Goodpasture, E. W. (1931) Susceptibility of chorio-allantoic membrane of chick embryo to infection with fowl-pox virus. *Am. J. Path.* 7: 209–222 [239]

686. Woods, M. W., and DuBuy, H. G. (1943) Evidence for the evolution of phytopathogenetic viruses from mitochondria and their derivatives. I. *Phytopath.* 33: 637–655 [213]

687. Wright, S. (1941) The physiology of the gene. *Physiol. Rev.* 21: 487–527 [355]

687a. Wyatt, G. R. (1952) Specificity in the composition of nucleic acids. *Expt. Cell Res.*, Suppl. 2: 201–215 [97]

687b. Wyatt, G. R., and Cohen, S. S. (1952) A new pyrimidine-base from bacteriophage nucleic acids. *Nature* 170: 1072–1073 [105, 174, 180]

688. Wyckoff, R. W. G. (1949) *Electron Microscopy*, New York, Interscience [60, 91, 92, 93]

689. Wyckoff, R. W. G. (1951) The virus of vaccinia in chick embryo membrane. *Proc. Nat. Acad. Sci.* 37: 565–569 [234]

690. Wynd, F. L. (1943) Metabolic phenomena associated with virus infection in plants. *Bot. Rev.* 9: 395–465 [218]

690a. Yamafuji, K. (1952) Mechanism of artificial virus formation in silkworm tissues. *Enzymologia* 15: 223–231 [320, 349]

690b. Yarwood, C. E. (1952) Latent period and generation time for two plant viruses. *Ann. J. Bot.* 39: 613–618 [212]

691. Youden, W. J. (1937) Use of incomplete block replications in estimating tobacco-mosaic virus. *Contrib. Boyce Thompson Inst.* 9: 41–48 [47]

692. Youden, W. J., and Beale, H. P. (1934) A statistical study of the local lesion method for estimating tobacco mosaic virus. *Contrib. Boyce Thompson Inst.* 6: 437–454 [47]

693. Youden, W. J., Beale, H. P., and Guthrie, J. D. (1935) Relation of virus concentration to the numbers of lesions produced. *Contrib. Boyce Thompson Inst.* 7: 37–53 [54]

694. Zarafonetis, C. J. D. (1948) The serological reactions in the rickettsial diseases of man. In: *The Rickettsial Diseases of Man*, A.A.A.S., Washington [366]

695. Zinder, N. D., and Lederberg, J. (1952) Genetic exchange in *Salmonella*. *J. Bact.* 64: 679–699 [115, 206, 352]

696. Zinsser, H. (1935) *Rats, Lice, and History*, Boston, Little, Brown [368]

697. Zinsser, H., and Schoenbach, E. B. (1937) Studies on the physiological conditions prevailing in tissue cultures. *J. Exp. Med.* 66: 207–227 [229, 369]

Index

Viruses are listed under the name of the corresponding disease, except where omitting the word "virus" would create confusion.

Abutilon variegation, 14, 34
Acquired immunity, 229
  plant viruses, 275
Acriflavine, 357
Activation energy, 139, 141
Adaptation, 36, 290f
Adaptive enzymes, 179, 358
Adenine, 97
Aedes aegypti, 310f
Agallia constricta, 318
Age and virus susceptibility, 30, 305
Agglutination, 118
  virus-coated particles, 119
Alastrim, 11, 298
Alfalfa mosaic, 138
Allantoic fluid, normal components, 108, 248
Allantoic membrane, virus synthesis in, 263f
Allantois, 240
  inoculation, 241
Allele, 190
Alpha particles, 147
Amino acids, analogues, 146
  bacteriophage, 104
  inhibition by, 230
  tobacco mosaic, 102
Amnion, 240
  inoculation, 242
Anaphylactic reactions, 88
Animal viruses, composition, 105
  growth, 221f
  inclusions, 230f
  interference, 280f
  maturation, 235
  plaques, 42
  serology, 128f
  transmission, arthropods, 35, 310
    mechanical, 309

Animal viruses, variation, 298
  vectors, 310
Antibiotics, 145, 223
  against plant viruses, 219
Antibodies, definition, 116
  local, 282
  persistence, 30, 132
  plant, 279
Antigen-antibody reactions, 117
Antigens, bacterial, 167
  bacteriophage, 120
  complement-fixing, influenza, 263
  definition, 116
  host, 107, 260
  Paramecium aurelia, 357
  vaccinia, 120, 130
  See also Soluble antigens
Aphthous fever, *see* Foot-and-mouth
Aphthous stomatitis, 38
Arrhenius plot, 140
Arthropod vectors, 7, 310f
  rickettsiae, 364, 369
Aster yellows, 14, 27, 36
  heat inactivation, 138
  multiplication in vector, 318
  transmission, 317
Asymmetry coefficient, 76
Aucuba mosaic, 121, 277
Aureomycin, 145, 223, 369
Autosterilization, 280
Autotrophs, 346
Auxotrophs, 346

Bacillus megatherium, 206
Bacteria, genetic transfer, 351
  L forms, 4
  lysogenic, *see* Lysogenic bacteria
  phage-resistant mutants, 187, 303
Bacterial enzymes, 178

Bacterial virus, see Bacteriophage
Bacteriophage, adsorption, 164
  cations, 166
  cofactors, 166, 293
  amino acids, 104
  antigens, 120
  burst size, 168
  calcium requirement, 168
  classification, 18
  complement fixation, 126
  composition, 103
  depressor effect, 188
  desoxyribonucleic acid, 97, 105, 173, 174
  "doughnuts," 171
  eclipse period, 170
  ecology, 208
  genetic recombination, 189, 294, 350
  genetic transfer, 206, 353
  genetics, 183, 291
  ghost, 84, 104, 143, 173, 199
  heterozygotes, 193
  host nucleus, 180
  host syntheses, 177
  inactivation, bacterial extracts, 168
    formalin, 144
    heat, 138, 142
    radiation, 149, 151, 153, 165, 180, 194
    radioactive decay, 154
  infectious unit, 105
  interference, 188, 273f
  intracellular irradiation, 156, 195
  isotope transfer, 176
  latent period, 159, 168, 199
  linkage system, 191
  lysis, 199
    from without, 168, 179
    inhibition, 184, 292
    premature, 170
  lysogenic cycle, 158
  lytic cycle, 159
  maturation, 172
  mixed infection, 186, 274
  modification, 197
    host-induced, 197, 207, 295, 328
  morphology, 65f
  multiple infection, 186
  multiplicity of infection, 164

Bacteriophage, multiplicity reactivation, 156, 195
  mutants, 183, 203, 291, 292, 293
  mutation, 183
  mutual exclusion, 188, 202, 273
  neutralization, 123
    reversibility, 125
  one-step growth experiment, 159, 161
  origin of constituents, 175
  osmotic shock, 173
  phenotypic mixing, 295
  photoreactivation, 155, 194
  plaques, 21, 41, 184, 188, 200
  proflavine effect, 126, 170, 199
  prophage, 200f
    chromosomal location, 352
    in spores, 201
    loss, 205
  radiation, 149, 151, 153, 156, 165, 180, 194, 195
  receptors, 167
  replication, 194
  resistance, 9, 186, 187, 303
  Salmonella, 167
  sedimentation, 79
  serology, 122f
  single-burst experiment, 162, 192
  size, 57, 160
  skin (ghost), 84, 104, 143, 173, 199
  T group, 159, 160
  temperate, 159, 274
  titration, 41, 52
  typing, 167, 206
  ultrafiltrate factor, 111, 126, 131, 173
  variation, 291
  vegetative stage, 175, 185, 197
  virulent, 159, 273
  x-ray effects, 135
Bacteroids, 347, 370
Bartonella bacilliformis, 373
Bean mosaic, 14, 217
3,4-Benzopyrene, 323
Beta rays, 147
Biochemical evolution, 346
Biotin, 108, 348
Blue disease of Japanese beetle, 372
Blue tongue of sheep, 223
Bollinger bodies, 231
Bombyx mori (silkworm), 81

Borreliota, 18
Brill's disease, 372
Brown-Pearce carcinoma, 337
Burst size, bacteriophage, 168

Cacoecia murinana, 83
Canary pox, 331
Cancer, 321*f*
Capsular diseases of insects, *see* Granu-
    loses
Carcinoma, 322*f*
Carcinogenic agents, 323
Carp pox, 9
Cation exchange resins, 89, 166
Cattle plague, 12
Cell components, relation to viruses,
    272, 348, 359
Cell origin, 359*f*
Centrifugation, 73*f*
    density gradient, 89
Centrioles, 354
Centrosome, 354
Chemical agents, effects on viruses, 143
Chemical composition of viruses, 96*f*
Chemotherapy, 144, 223
Chick embryo, culture, 239*f*
    development, 239
    vaccines, 248
Chicken pox (varicella), 11, 24, 37
    inclusions, 237
    size, 57
Chlamydozoa, 231
Chlamydozoaceae, 18
Chloromycetin, 145, 223, 369
Chloroplasts, 213
Cholesterol, 107
Chorioallantoic membrane, develop-
    ment, 240
    grafts, 246
    inoculation, 242
    lesions (pocks), 25, 42, 129, 249
    titration, 42, 249
Chorion (serosa), 240
Choristoneura fumiferana, 80, 82
Chromosomes, 192, 272
Cicadulina mbila, 304, 315
Circulifer tenellus, 33, 279, 315
Classification, 16, 278
Clone, 185

Clover club-leaf, 317
Cocoa swollen shoot, 14
Colicines, 207, 353
Colorado fever, 311
Complement fixation, 119, 126, 134
    See also names of viruses
Condyloma acuminatum, 325
Contagium virum fluidum, 6
Copper, 108
Corn streak, 14, 304, 316
Corn stripe, 14
Corynebacterium diphtheriae, 206
Cowpox, *see* Vaccinia
Coxiella burneti, 365*f*
    popillia, 372
Coxsackie group, 10, 57
Crossing-over, 192
Cross-protection, 16, 18, 275, 276, 278
Crown gall, 216, 339
Crystallization of viruses, 90
Cucumber mosaic, 14, 215, 297
    composition, 101
    serology, 121
Culex tarsalis, 312
Cyanide, 170, 229, 369
Cytochrome oxidase, 258
Cytoplasmic inheritance, 354*f*
Cytosine, 97, 105

Dark-field microscope, 58
DDT, 371
Definition of viruses, 2
Dengue, 10, 245, 285, 305, 310, 312
Density, measurement, 76
Density gradient centrifugation, 89
Depressor effect, bacteriophage, 188
Dermacentor andersonii, 310
Dermacentroxenus akari, 365
Dermacentroxenus pediculi, 365
Dermacentroxenus rickettsi, 365*f*
Dermanyssus gallinae, 312
Desoxyribonuclease, 97, 143, 173, 179
Desoxyribonucleic acid (DNA), 97,
    238
    bacteriophage, 97, 105, 173, 174
    reduplication, 100
    structure, 100
    transforming principles, 351
Deuterons, 147

1,2,5,6-Dibenzanthracene, 323
Diffusion, 74
　measurement, 79
　nonspherical particles, 75
Diffusion constant, 75
Dinitrophenol, 229
Diplococcus pneumoniae, 351
Diploid number, 193
Distemper, 12, 288
DNA, *see* Desoxyribonucleic acid
Dodder, 34, 308, 309
"Doughnuts," bacteriophage, 171
Drosophila, CO_2 sensitivity, 357
　sigma factor, 359
Drying, 142
Dual infection, animal viruses, 238, 284
　plant viruses, 215, 279

Earthworm, 314
Eclipse period, 170, 212, 222, 263, 269
Ecology, of bacteriophage, 208
　of viruses, 312
Ectoderm, 239
Ectromelia, 301
　hemagglutination, 250
　morphology, 64
　titration, 249
Egg transmission, 312, 361
Egg-white inhibitor, 258
Electron microscope, particle count, 67
　techniques, 60
Electrophoresis, 79, 209
Elementary bodies, definition, 6, 58
Elm phloem necrosis, 14
Enation mosaic, 121
Enations, 28
Encephalitis, Russian type, 306
Encephalomyocarditis, 251
　Columbia MM, 285
　Columbia SK, 223, 285, 287
Entoderm, 239
Enzyme activity, MNI viruses, 253f,
　284
Enzymes, action on viruses, 143
　adaptive, 179, 358
　bacterial, 178 '
　in virus particles, 109
　receptor-destroying, 110, 256f

Equine encephalomyelitis, 10, 154, 230,
　234, 236
　antibodies, 282
　composition, 106
　egg culture, 244
　epidemiology, 312
　interference, 283, 285, 286, 287
　plaques, 26
　sedimentation, 78
　sensitivity, 305
　size, 57
　spread, 308
　tissue culture, 229
　vectors, 310
　　multiplication in, 312
Escherichia coli, 167, 202
　fertility agent, 352
　strain B, 22, 155, 295
　　mutants, 303
　strain K-12, 205, 303
DL-Ethionine, 230
Evolution, regressive, 4
　rickettsiae, 370
　sexual mechanisms, 361
　virus diseases, 301
　viruses, 318
Excitation by radiation, 147

False air space, chick embryo cultures,
　243
Feline infectious enteritis, 12
Feline pneumonitis, 62, 286
Feulgen reaction, 97, 233
Fibroma, 13, 14, 57, 228, 285, 325
　tarring, 338
Fibroma-myxoma group, 299
　transformation, 302
Fiji disease of sugar cane, 14, 216
Filtration end point, 72
Flow birefringence, 94
Fluorescence microscope, 60
Folic acid, 369
Foot-and-mouth (aphthous fever), 6,
　12, 324, 331
　growth, 228
　hemagglutination, 251
　interference, 285
　inactivation by x-rays, 151

Foot-and-mouth, size, 57
    tissue culture, 227
Fowl leukemia, 9, 13, 108, 324, 332,
    341
Fowl plague, 12, 227, 234, 251
Fowl pox, 13, 18, 246, 286, 331
Fowl sarcomas, 79
    See also Fujinami sarcoma, Rous sar-
    coma
Fowl tumors, 7, 15, 324f
Francis inhibitor, 258
Frei test, 134
Friction coefficient, 73
Frog, kidney carcinoma, 9, 325, 333
Fujinami sarcoma, 332, 336

Gamma globulin, 132
Gamma rays, 147
Generation time, influenza, 221
    tobacco mosaic, 212
Generalized reactions, 26f
Genes, 115
    naked, 350
    relation to viruses, 349
Genetic parasitism, 353
Genetic recombination, bacteriophage,
    189, 294, 350
    influenza, 267, 350
Genetic systems, merging, 361
Genetic transfer, 206, 351, 353
German measles, 11, 246
Glycerin, 144
"Gradocol" membranes, 71
Graft, transmission, 33, 308
    tumors, 322
    virus transmission by, 33, 115, 308
Granuloses (capsular diseases of in-
    sects), 13, 57, 82, 83, 272
Growth curve, animal viruses, 221f
    bacteriophage, 159
    plant viruses, 210f
Guarnieri bodies, 233, 234, 247, 298
Guanine, 97

Haploid number, 193
Haptens, 116
Heat inactivation, 138, 139, 141, 142
Heat therapy, plant viruses, 145
Helenine, 223
Hemagglutination, 70, 250f

Hemagglutination, cation effects, 260
    elution, 253
    inhibitors, 257
        egg-white, 257
        Francis, 258
    receptor gradient, 254
Hemolysis by viruses, 254
Hemophilus influenzae, 351
Hemophilus influenzae suis, 314
Herpes (Herpes simplex), 10, 35, 37,
    238, 343
    epidemiology, 320
    immunity, 280
    inclusions, 237
    interference, 285, 286
    latency, 271
    Magrassi phenomenon, 282
    neurotropism, 300
    titration, 249
Herpes zoster, 10, 57
Heterogenesis, 343
Heterotrophs, 346
History of virology, 5
Hit theory, 150
Hog cholera, 12
Host antigens, 107, 260
Host-induced modifications, bacterio-
    phage, 197, 207, 295, 328
Host specificity, 7, 227
Hydration, 76
5-Hydroxymethylcytosine, 97, 105, 174,
    180

Immunity, 131f, 280
    lysogenic bacteria, 30, 200f
    tissue, 280
Inclusion conjunctivitis, 10
Inclusions, 6
    animal viruses, 230f, 247, 298
        intranuclear, 237
    plant viruses, 214, 215
        intranuclear, 215
Incubation period, 220
    specificity, 29
    titration by, 45
    vectors, 311
Indole, 166
Induction, 201, 328
Infection, route of, 31

Infectious epithelioses, 324
Infectious hepatitis, 10
Infectious unit, 40f
  bacteriophage, 105
  relation to virus particle, 52, 54
  statistical interpretation, 48
Influenza, 11, 15
  adsorption and elution in lungs, 254
  antibodies, 132
  antigen, soluble, 110, 130, 263f
  composition, 106, 107
  generation time, 221
  genetic recombination, 267, 350
  growth, 221, 245, 261
    inhibition by polysaccharides, 146
  hemagglutination, 70, 250f
    electron microscopy, 67
  heat inactivation, 141, 142
  immature forms, 263, 288
  immunity, 281
  in mouse brain, 265
  interference, 261, 283f
  isolation, 248
  isotope labeling, 249
  morphology, 63, 64, 82, 267
  multiplicity reactivation, 268
  neurotropism, 246, 266, 267
  O–D variation, 253, 300
  one-step growth experiments, 261
  purification, 89
  radiation effects, 155
  serology, 129, 130
  size, 57
  swine, see Swine influenza
  tissue cultures, 227
  titration, 40, 45
  toxicity, 31, 223, 266, 271
  types, 299
  vaccines, 133
  Von Magnus phenomenon, 265, 288
  See also MNI viruses
Insect transmission, 314
  artificial, 33
Insect vectors, 310
  genetic factors, 316
  See also Arthropod vectors; Vectors
Insect viruses, 9, 19, 272
  composition, 110
  polyhedra, 237

Insect viruses, see also Granuloses; Polyhedral diseases
Interference, 261, 266, 273f
  animal viruses, 280f
    inactive, 284
  bacteriophages, 188, 273f
  mechanism, 287
  plant viruses, 275f
  tissue cultures, 283
Intracellular irradiation, 156, 195
  See also Radiation
Isotope tracers, 175, 210, 213, 249

Japanese (type B) encephalitis, 10, 57

Kappa factor, 356, 359
Kinetosomes, 355
King Edward potato, 359
Klebsiella pneumoniae, 222, 259
Koch's postulates, 32

Laryngotracheitis, 9, 13, 249, 286
Latency, 38, 340, 360
Latent dodder mosaic, 37
Latent viruses, 36, 271, 349
  and tumors, 340
Layering phenomenon, 94
Lettuce mosaic, 217
Levels of integration, 113
Liquid crystals, 94
Light absorption, 147
Light scattering, 79
Little peach, 278
Living organism, definition, 114
Local reactions, 21
Logarithms, 40
Louping ill, 12, 57, 129, 238, 285, 286,
  311
LS antigen, 130
Lungworm, 314
Lymphocytic choriomeningitis, 10, 131,
  285, 286, 309, 343
  latency, 38, 340, 361
Lymphogranuloma venereum, 11, 229,
  285, 286
  epidemiology, 309
  Frei test, 134
  growth, 247
Lysines, 199

Lysis, 199
   from without, 168, 179
   inhibition, 184, 292
   premature, 170
Lysogenesis, 200f
Lysogenic bacteria, 30, 200f
   immunity, 201, 202
   induction, 201, 328
   superinfection, 204
   toxicity, 206
Lysogenic cycle, bacteriophage, 158

Macrophages, 228
Macrosteles divisus, 318
Mad itch (pseudorabies), 12, 30, 305, 309, 320
Magrassi phenomenon, 282
Major host, 8
Malonate, 229
Mare abortion, 246
Masking, 296, 335f
   rabbit papilloma, 327, 361
   swine influenza, 314
Maternal inheritance, 355
Maturation, bacteriophage, 172
   viruses, 272
Measles, 11, 24, 25, 132, 309
   epidemiology, 320
   incubation period, 29
Melanophores, 359
Meningopneumonitis, 269
Mesoderm, 239
Metastases, 321
Methionine analogues, 230
Methylcholanthrene, 323
5-Methylcytosine, 97
5-Methyltryptophan, 166
Mh unit, 56
Microsomes, 105, 354
Milk factor, 57, 306, 328f, 340
Mites, 312
Mitochondria, 214, 237, 272, 354
MNI viruses (Mumps, Newcastle, influenza), 18, 251f, 284
Molecular distances, 56
Molecular weight, 56
Molecule, 112
Molluscum contagiosum, 11, 18, 231, 232, 238

Molluscum contagiosum, inclusions, 234, 236
   morphology, 59
   size, 57
Mosaic diseases, 218
   See also names of diseases
Mouse breast carcinoma, 328
Mouse encephalomyelitis (Theiler's), 37, 45
   growth, 269
   hemagglutination, 251
   interference, 285
   morphology, 62
   size, 57
Mouse leukemia, 330
Mucin, 258
Multiplicity reactivation, 156, 195, 268
Mumps, 11, 29, 245, 247, 285, 286, 287
   hemagglutination, 250f
   hemolysis, 254
   incubation period, 29
   reproduction, 269
   skin test, 134
   See also MNI viruses
Murray Valley encephalitis, 25
Mustard gas, 179
Mutability, 7, 290f, 345
   plastids, 356
Mutation rate, 291
Mutations, 291f
   and classification, 17
   bacteriophage, 183
   fluctuation test, 303
   host adaptation, 36
   in evolution, 319
   pleiotropic, 300
   reverse, 294
   somatic, 338
Mutual exclusion, bacteriophage, 188, 202, 273
Mycetomes, 370
Mycobacterium leprae, 3
Myxoma, 13, 25, 249, 298, 325
   rabbit control by, 320
   serology, 129
   size, 57
   transformation, 302
Myzus persicae, 315
Myzus pseudosolani, 316

Naked genes, 350
Nature of viruses, 112, 344f
Necrotic lesions, 22, 23, 47
    genetic influences, 22, 304
    morphology, 21
    titration by, 46
Negri bodies, 25, 230
Neoplasms, 321f
Nerve transport, 308
Newcastle disease, 9, 13, 244, 285, 286,
    287, 300
    hemagglutination, 250f
    hemolysis, 254
    morphology, 82
    toxicity, 223
    See also MNI viruses
Nicotiana, response to tobacco mosaic,
    22, 304, 319
Nicotiana digluta, 304
Nicotiana glutinosa, 23, 47, 304
Nicotiana silvestris, 277
Nicotiana tabacum, 23, 27, 304
    variety Ambalema, 304
Nitrogen mustard, 182
Nucleic acids, 97, 141
    ionizing radiations, 152
    ultraviolet absorption, 147
Nucleoproteins, 99
    and virus nature, 345
Numerical aperture, 58
Nutritional deficiencies, 31, 223

Obligate parasites, 3
Oncolysis, 306
One-step growth experiments, 159, 161,
    261
Oral papillomatosis, 326
Origin of cell, 359f
Origin of viruses, 344f
Ornithosis, 9
Orroya fever, 373

Panagglutinability, 253
Papain, 123
Papataci fever, 311
Papilloma, human, 24
    rabbit, see Rabbit papilloma
Paraminobenzoic acid, 145, 369
Paracrinkle, potato, 14, 34, 359

Paracrystals, 94
Paramecin, 356
Paramecium aurelia, antigens, 357
    kappa factor, 356, 359
    killer factor, 339
Parasites, obligate, 3
Parasitism, 182
    evolution, 347
    genetic, 353
Particles, counting, 67, 71
    density, 76
    enzymes in, 109
    nonspherical, 75
    size, 56
    spherical, diffusion, 74
    sedimentation, 73
    staining, 58
    visualization, 56
Passive immunization, 132
Pasteurella pestis, 366
Pasteurella tularensis, 366, 372
Pea mosaic, 14
Peach mosaic, 14
Peach rosette, 14
Peach viruses, temperature effect on, 31
Peach yellows (little peach), 14, 278
Penicillin, 145, 179, 223, 369
Percentage law, 122
pH effects, 142
Phagineae, 17
Phase-contrast microscope, 60
Phlebotomus papatasii, 311
Phloem necrosis, 217
Phony peach, 216
Photochemical reactions, 148
Photodynamic action of dyes, 154
Photoreactivation, bacteriophage, 155,
    194
Photosynthesis, 217, 219
Physical agents, effects on viruses, 138
Phytomonas tumefaciens, 339
Phytophagineae, 17
Pigmentation in guinea pig, 359
Pipettenfehler, 42
Plant antibodies, 279
Plant metabolism, 218
Plant viruses, acquired immunity, 275
    composition, 100
    cross-protection, 275, 278

Plant viruses, growth, 209f
    heat treatment, 145
    inclusions, 214, 215
    interference, 275f
    metabolism, 218
    multiplication in vectors, 317
    necrotic lesions, 21, 22, 46, 47, 304
    seed transmission, 217, 308
    serology, 127
    spread, 216
    symptoms, 26
    tissue cultures, 215
    titration, 46, 54
    transmission, dodder, 34, 308, 309
        graft, 33, 308
        insects, 33, 314
        mechanical, 32, 308
    variation, 296
Plaque count, 41, 52
    frequency distribution, 49
    proportionality to inoculum, 48
Plaques, animal viruses, 42
    bacteriophage, 21, 41, 184, 188, 200
    equine encephalomyelitis, 26
    tissue cultures, 25, 42, 226
Plasmadesmata, 216
Plasmagenes, 356f
Plastids, 214, 272, 354, 360
    mutability, 356
Pleuropneumonia, 4
Pneumococcus, type transformation, 351
Pneumonia virus of mice, 57, 87, 269,
        286, 340
    growth, 222
    hemagglutination, 251, 260
    latency, 37
Poisson distribution, 49, 165
Poliomyelitis, 11, 37, 82, 223, 238, 285,
        286, 287, 305
    antibodies, 282
    epidemiology, 310
    Lansing strain, 299
    localization, 25
    passive immunization, 132
    size, 57
    spread, 308
    tissue cultures, 227, 228
    transmission, 309
    vaccination, 133

Polyhedral diseases, 57, 80, 81, 83
Polyhedral protein, 110, 111
Polysaccharide inhibition, 259
    of influenza virus, 146
Polystyrene latex, 68
Porthetria dispar, 81
Potato leaf roll, 5, 14, 218
Potato paracrinkle, 14, 34, 359
Potato virus X, 14
    composition, 101
    cross-protection among strains, 276
    morphology, 63, 92
    necrotic response, 24
    size, 57
    synergism, 279
    top necrosis, 217
    transmission, 32
Potato virus Y, 14, 92, 278, 315
Potato witches' broom, 36
Potato yellow dwarf, 14, 57, 92
Precipitin reaction, 118, 127
Primary atypical pneumonia, 146
Prodenia praefica, 80
Proflavine, 126, 170, 199
Prophage, see Bacteriophage, prophage
Protamine, 88
Proteins, denaturation, 140
    noninfectious, 110
    protective effect, 142
    structure, 98
Proteus vulgaris, 368
Protons, 147
Protozoa, 347, 355
Provirus, 270, 277, 328, 337, 349, 351
Pseudorabies (mad itch), 12, 30, 305,
        309, 320
Psittacosis, 9, 13, 228
    ecology, 302
    inclusions, 232
    transmission, 309
Psittacosis-lymphogranuloma group, 15,
        18, 245, 298
    chemotherapy, 145, 223
    morphology, 64
    size, 57
    toxicity, 223
Purification methods, 88
Purine analogues, 210, 230

Purity, criteria, 85, 259
Pyrimidine analogues, 210, 223

Q fever, 365*f*
Quantum yield, 153

Rabbit papilloma, 14, 326, 335
  composition, 106
  irradiation, 151, 156, 328
  masking, 327, 361
  serology, 120
  size, 57
  titration, 45, 53
Rabies, 12, 57, 154, 223, 245, 246, 285,
    286, 299, 305, 308, 309
  fixed strains, 300
  Negri bodies, 25, 230
  street strains, 300
Radiation, 146
  bacteriophage inactivation, 149, 151,
    153, 156, 165, 180, 194, 195
  effects on influenza virus, 155
  excitation by, 147
  hit theory, 150
  ionizing, 147
    action volume, 150
    direct effect, 150
    indirect effect, 148
  kinetics, 150
  mutagenic effect, 297
  rabbit papilloma, 151, 156, 328
  target theory, 152
  ultraviolet, 152
    quantum yield, 153
    See also Ultraviolet
  visible, 154
Rail immunization, 280
Reactivation, 123, 194
  See also Multiplicity reactivation;
    Photoreactivation
Receptor-destroying enzyme (RDE),
    110, 256*f*
Receptor gradient, 254
Recombination, *see* Genetic recombination
Reed and Muench method, 43
Regressive evolution, 4
Replication, of bacteriophage, 194
  of genetic materials, 158

Reproduction, 269
Resistance to viruses, genetic factors,
    302
Resolving power, 3, 58
Reverse mutations, 294
Reversible neutralization, 137
Riboflavine, 108, 213, 348, 369
Ribonuclease, 97, 143
Ribonucleic acid (RNA), 97, 100, 238
Rice stunt, 14, 317
Rickettsiae, 3, 347, 364*f*
  chemotherapy, 369
  cultivation, 365
  evolution, 370
  in arthropods, 364, 369
  metabolism, 366
  pathogenic classification, 365
  reproduction, 368
  serology, 366
  soluble antigens, 366
  structure, 365
  toxins, 367
  Weil-Felix reaction, 368
Rickettsia orientalis, 365*f*
Rickettsia prowazeki, 365*f*
Rift Valley fever, 12, 283, 285
Rinderpest (cattle plague), 12
RNA, *see* Ribonucleic acid
Rocky Mountain spotted fever, 365*f*
Roentgen unit, 150
Roller tube, 225
Root infection, 217, 308
Rous sarcoma, 13, 31, 107, 246, 324*f*
  in ducks, 332
  size, 57
  tissue cultures, 227, 235
Rubella (German measles), 11, 246

Sacbrood of bees, 13
Salmonella, bacteriophages, 167
  genetic transfer, 206
  transduction, 352
Salmonella typhimurium, 206, 208
Salmonella typhosa, V*i*-phages, 167, 206
  V*i*-types, 296
Sandfly fever (papataci fever), 311
Sarcoma, 322
  See also Rous sarcoma
Schienenimmunisierung, 280

Sedimentation, 73*f*
Sedimentation constant, 74
Sedimentation equilibrium, 76
Seed transmission, 217, 308
Separation of virus properties, 120, 135, 154
Serological cross-reactions, 17, 121, 125
Serology, 116*f*
  rickettsiae, 366
  See also names of viruses
Semliki forest virus, 286
Severe etch, 278
Shaking, 142
Sheep dermatitis, 285
Shigella dysenteriae, 295
Sigma factor, 357
Silkworm, 81
Silkworm jaundice, 13, 320
  induction, 349
  tissue cultures, 237
Single-burst experiments, 162, 192
Size of virus particles, 57
Skin tests, 134
Smallpox (variola), 5, 24, 29, 230, 298
  vaccination, 132
  See also Vaccinia-smallpox group
Soluble antigen, influenza, 110, 130, 263*f*
  rickettsiae, 366
  vaccinia, 110, 130
Somatic mutations, 338
Southern bean mosaic, 57, 91, 101
Specific soluble substances (SSS), 110, 130
Spinal fluid, 308
Spread of viruses, 216, 307
Squash mosaic virus, 91
Starch-iodine lesions, 24, 31
St. Louis encephalitis, 57, 223, 285, 311
Stokes' law, 73
Storage, 55
Strawberry viruses, 87
Succinic dehydrogenase, 358
Sudan III, 331
Sugar beet curly top, 14, 216, 278, 316
  acquired immunity, 279
  spread, 217
  transmission, 33
  vector, 32, 279, 315

Sugar beet mosaic, 14
Sugar cane mosaic, 14
Sulfhydryl compounds, 144
Sulfonamides, 145, 223, 369
Swamp fever (equine infectious anemia), 12
Swine influenza, 12, 106, 258, 285, 287
  life cycle, 314
Swine-pox, 298
Symbionts, 347, 370
Synergism, 278, 279, 284

Tactoids, 94
Target theory, 152
Temperature effects, 31, 138
Teratomas, 334
Terramycin, 145
Theiler's virus, *see* Mouse encephalomyelitis
Thermal inactivation point, 139
Thymine, 97
Ticks, 311, 370
Tissue cultures, 7, 215, 224*f*
  interference, 283
  plaques, 25, 42, 226
  pure lines, 226
  techniques, 224*f*
Tissue specificity, 7, 227
Titer, 41
Titration, 39*f*
  bacteriophage, 41, 52
  end point, 43
  errors, 42
  50% infectious dose, 43
  herpes, 249
  incubation period, 45
  precision, 41
  necrotic lesions, 46
  plant viruses, 46, 54
  plaque count, 41*f*
  Reed and Muench method, 43
  vaccinia, 40, 51, 53, 249
Tobacco mosaic, 14, 15, 17, 67, 87, 90
  aucuba strain, 121, 277
  chemical changes, 103, 135, 144
  chemical composition, 101
  crystals, 93
  generation time, 212
  growth, 209*f*

Tobacco mosaic, inactivation, formalin, 144
heat, 138
x-rays, 151
inclusions, amorphous, 214
crystalline, iv, 96, 215
inhibition, 146, 210
internal structure, 95
isoelectric point, 88
layering phenomenon, 95
metabolic effects, 218
morphology, 63, 82, 92
necrotic lesions, 22, 23, 304
neutralization, 127
origin, 319
pepper response to, 22
ribgrass strain, 277
root infection, 217, 308
serological cross-reactions, 121
size, 57, 93
synergism, 279
tissue cultures, 216
titration, 54
transmission, 6, 33
variants, 31, 296
yellow strains, 27, 276, 278, 297
X-bodies, 214
Tobacco necrosis, 14, 17
composition, 101
crystals, 90, 92
growth, 212
heat inactivation, 138, 141
noninfectious protein, 110
root infection, 308
size, 57
x-ray effect, 151
Tobacco ringspot, 14, 23, 138, 276
Tomato bushy stunt, 14, 15
composition, 101
crystals, 86, 90
growth, 211
heat inactivation, 141
hydration, 91
morphology, 64
necrotic lesions, 23
size, 57, 79
x-ray effect, 151
Tomato mosaic, 23
Tomato spotted wilt, 14, 92

Top necrosis, 217
Toxicity, 31, 206, 223, 266, 271
rickettsiae, 367
Trachoma, 11, 245
Transaminase, 366
Transduction, 206, 352
Transforming principles, 115, 351
Transmissible mutagens, 325, 343
Transmission, artificial, 32f
natural, 307f
See also names of viruses and virus groups
Tricarboxylic acid cycle, 366
Tristeza of citrus, 14
Trychocyst, 355
Trypsin, 143
Tryptophan as cofactor, 166
Tulip break, 6, 14, 29
Tumors, 321f
grafting, 322
fowl, 7, 15, 324f
frog kidney, 9, 325, 333
virus affinity for, 306
wound, 14, 29, 216, 318, 330
Turnip yellow mosaic, 14
composition, 101
crystals, 91
noninfectious particles, 110
size, 57
structure, 101
vector, 315
Typhus, epidemic, 365f
murine (endemic), 365f
Tyrode's solution, 224

Ultracentrifugation, 6, 73f
Ultracentrifuges, 77
Ultrafiltrate factor, bacteriophage, 111, 126, 131, 173
Ultrafiltration, 6, 70
Ultraviolet, absorption, 97, 147
absorption spectra, 98
origin of life, 346
Ultraviolet microscope, 58
Uracil, 97
Urea, 144

Vaccination, 6, 132, 133, 248
Vaccines, 132, 133, 154, 248, 366

Vaccinia, 6, 11, 331
  antigens, 120, 130
    LS antigens, 110, 130
  chemotherapy, 223
  composition, 106
  elementary bodies, 58, 232
  enzymes, 109
  growth, 247, 270
    inhibition, 230
  hemagglutination, 259
  inclusions (Guarnieri bodies), 233, 234, 247, 298
  interference, 285, 286
  morphology, 59, 61, 64, 84
  neurotropic variant, 300
  origin, 348
  serology, 129
  size, 57
  tissue, 226, 228
  titration, 40, 51, 53, 249
  vaccination, 132
  x-ray effects, 151
Vaccinia-smallpox group, 251, 298, 301
Variation, 291f
  animal viruses, 298
  bacteriophage, 291
  plant viruses, 296
  See also names of viruses and virus groups
Varicella, see Chicken pox
Variegation, 14, 34, 214, 356
Variola, see Smallpox
Vectors, 310f, 369
Verruga peruana, 373
Vi-phages, 167, 206
Vibrio cholerae, 256
Virales, 17
Viroid theory, 361
Virus B, 320

Virus III, 13, 37, 227, 281, 285, 286, 340
Von Magnus phenomenon, 265, 288

Warts (verrucae), 11, 24, 105, 237, 238, 325, 331
Weil-Felix reaction, 368
West Nile fever, 251, 285, 305
Wheat mosaic, 14, 308
Wound tumor, 14, 29, 216, 318, 330

X-bodies, 214
X-rays, 147f, 156
  effects on bacteriophage, 135
  inactivation effects, 151

Yeast, 357
Yellow fever, 5, 11, 223
  epidemiology, 313
  immunity, 132
  inclusions, 237
  interference, 283, 285, 286
  jungle, 302, 313
  localization, 29
  multiplication in vectors, 311
  resistance in mice, 30, 305
  size, 57
  strain 17D, 133, 248, 300
  tissue culture, 227
  transmission, 35, 310
  vaccination, 248
Yellows diseases, 26, 214, 218
  See also names of viruses
Yolk sac, development, 241
  inoculation, 244

Zoochlorella, 347
Zoophagineae, 17